The UK Mathematics Trust

Yearbook

2012 – 2013

This book contains an account of UKMT activities from 1st September 2012 to 31st August 2013. It contains all question papers, solutions and results as well as a variety of other information.

Published by the United Kingdom Mathematics Trust.
School of Mathematics, The University of Leeds, Leeds LS2 9JT
Telephone: 0113 343 2339
E-mail: enquiry@ukmt.org.uk
Website: http://www.ukmt.org.uk

Cover design: – The backdrop is a Penrose tiling whose complexity
reflects the activities of the UKMT.

The photographs are

Front Cover:

National Mathematics Summer School 2013

Back Cover:
IMO 2013 Team in Colombia

TMC National Final Winners 2013
City of London School

© UKMT 2013

ISBN 978-1-906001-21-6

Printed and bound in Great Britain by
Charlesworth Press, Wakefield

Contents

Foreword

Once again it is time for me to introduce the UKMT Yearbook with heartfelt thanks to all the Trust's volunteers and staff, without whom none of the activities described in this Yearbook would have taken place.

As always, warm thanks go in particular to Bill Richardson for compiling the Yearbook, while this year I must pay a special tribute to Alan Slomson, who has retired this summer as UKMT Secretary after many years of providing wise and enormously helpful advice and support. Indeed, Alan has been closely involved with the Trust ever since its foundation in 1996, and I am extremely glad to say that the Trust will continue to benefit from his involvement as a volunteer, although no longer as Secretary.

We are very pleased to welcome another Alan as the new UKMT Secretary. Alan Eames-Jones is a recently retired maths teacher whose varied career started with a PhD in Engineering, leading to two decades in industry and then a small business, before a PGCE and thirteen years of teaching maths. He has a very hard act to follow as UKMT Secretary, but he is approaching the task with enthusiasm!

We were all delighted to see two UKMT volunteers honoured in the New Year Honours List; our congratulations go to Terry Heard and Jenny Ramsden who both received MBEs.

This year's IMO team also deserve many congratulations: they performed outstandingly well at the International Olympiad competition in Colombia in July. The UK finished ninth out of 97 participating countries with two gold medals, three silver medals and one bronze; this was its highest ranking since 1996, and of the European teams only Russia did better. Andrew Carlotti won gold, so that his IMO medal collection now consists of three gold medals and one bronze, giving him the best medal record at the IMO of any UK competitor ever. And of course congratulations and thanks are not only due to the students themselves, but also to Geoff Smith, Dominic Yeo, James Cranch, Joseph Myers, Jonathan Lee, Jack Shotton and the many other UKMT volunteers who have contributed directly and indirectly towards this excellent result.

Another regular UKMT activity is the organisation of the two National Mathematics Summer Schools for students mainly aged 15 and 16. These have been run with great success for the last few years by Vicky Neale and

James Gazet. In addition we were delighted to receive financial support this year from the Department for Education to organise two additional summer schools in August 2013 and again in 2014, as well as funding to expand the UKMT's recent development of two day, non-residential 'Maths Circles'. Following the successful launch of EGMO (the European Girls' Mathematical Olympiad) in Cambridge in April 2012, the Trust had already committed itself (with financial support from the Clay Mathematics Institute and others) to running an additional summer school for girls in August 2013 and again in 2014. So this summer, instead of just the two National Mathematics Summer Schools, there will be five summer schools run along similar lines with around 200 students able to participate.

However of course the Trust's core activities, in which hundreds of thousands of school students participate each year, are the Maths Challenges, and I am delighted that entry numbers for all the individual challenges rose this year. Entry numbers for the Junior Challenge rose from 280,860 in 2011/12 to 283,490 and the number of participating schools also increased from 3,798 to 3,841. For the Intermediate Challenge numbers of entries and participating schools increased to 245,740 entries and 3,096 schools from 237,480 entries and 3,022 schools in 2011/12. Likewise numbers for the Senior Challenge rose again to 98,560 entries and 2,037 schools in 2012/13 from 97,570 entries and 2,036 schools in 2011/12. In addition entries for the Team Challenge and for the Senior Team Challenge (the latter run in collaboration with the Further Maths Support Programme) both rose again this year to 1,647 and 1,100 teams respectively.

The Trust's activities in 2012/13 are described in much greater detail in this Yearbook; I am sure that you will enjoy reading it.

Frances Kirwan
Balliol College, Oxford
August 2013

Introduction

Foundation of the Trust

National mathematics competitions have existed in the UK for several decades. Up until 1987 the total annual participation was something like 8,000. Then there was an enormous growth, from 24,000 in 1988 to around a quarter of a million in 1995 – without doubt due to the drive, energy and leadership of Dr Tony Gardiner. By the end of this period there were some nine or ten competitions for United Kingdom schools and their students organised by three different bodies: the British Mathematical Olympiad Committee, the National Committee for Mathematical Contests and the UK Mathematics Foundation. During 1995 discussions took place between interested parties which led to agreement to seek a way of setting up a single body to continue and develop these competitions and related activities. This led to the formation of the United Kingdom Mathematics Trust, which was incorporated as a company limited by guarantee in October 1996 and registered with the Charity Commission.

Throughout its existence, the UKMT has continued to nurture and expand the number of competitions. As a result, over six hundred thousand students throughout the UK now participate in the challenges alone, and their teachers (as well as others) not only provide much valued help and encouragement, but also take advantage of the support offered to them by the Trust.

The Royal Institution of Great Britain is the Trust's Patron, and it and the Mathematical Association are Participating Bodies. The Association of Teachers of Mathematics, the Edinburgh Mathematical Society, the Institute of Mathematics and Its Applications, the London Mathematical Society and the Royal Society are all Supporting Bodies.

Aims and Activities of the Trust

According to its constitution, the Trust has a very wide brief, namely "to advance the education of children and young people in mathematics". To attain this, it is empowered to engage in activities ranging from teaching to publishing and lobbying. But its focal point is the organisation of mathematical competitions, from popular mass "challenges" to the selection and training of the British team for the annual International Mathematical Olympiad (IMO).

There are three main challenges, the UK Junior, Intermediate and Senior Mathematical Challenges. The number of challenge entries in 2012-2013 totalled 627,790, a slight increase compared to last year. The challenges were organised by the Challenges Subtrust (CS). The Challenges are open to all pupils of the appropriate age. Certificates are awarded for the best performances and the most successful participants are encouraged to enter follow-up competitions.

At the junior and intermediate levels, a total of around 8000 pupils enter the follow-up competitions. These consist of the Junior Mathematical Olympiad and a suite of papers forming the Intermediate Mathematical Olympiad and Kangaroo under the auspices of the Challenges Subtrust.

The British Mathematical Olympiad Committee Subtrust (BMOS) organises two rounds of the British Mathematical Olympiad. Usually about 800 students who have distinguished themselves in the Senior Mathematical Challenge are invited to enter Round 1, leading to about 100 in Round 2. From the latter, around twenty are invited to a training weekend at Trinity College, Cambridge. Additionally, an elite squad, identified largely by performances in the UKMT competitions, is trained at camps and by correspondence courses throughout the year. The UK team is then selected for the annual International Mathematical Olympiad (IMO) which usually takes place in July. Recent IMOs were held as follows: USA (2001); UK (2002), Japan (2003), Athens (2004), Mexico (2005), Slovenia (2006), Vietnam (2007), Madrid (2008), Bremen (2009), Kazakhstan (2010), Amsterdam (2011), Argentina (2012) and Colombia in 2013. The BMOS also runs a mentoring scheme for high achievers at senior, intermediate and junior levels.

Structure and Membership of the Trust

The governing body of the Trust is its Council. The events have been organised by three Subtrusts who report directly to the Council. The work of the Trust in setting question papers, marking scripts, monitoring competitions, mentoring students and helping in many other ways depends critically on a host of volunteers. A complete list of members of the Trust, its Subtrusts and other volunteers appears at the end of this publication.

Challenges Office Staff

Rachel Greenhalgh continues in her role as Director of the Trust, ably supported by the Maths Challenges Office staff of Nicky Bray, Janet Clark, Gerard Cummings, Heather Macklin, Shona Raffle and Jo Williams. Beverley Detoeuf continues as Packing Office Manager and leads the packing and processing team of Claire Hall, Gwyneth Hartley, Piatta Hellevaara, Rachael Raby-Cox, Stewart Ramsay and Alison Steggall, ably assisted by Mary Roberts, Packing Office Supervisor.

An outline of the events

A brief description of the challenges, their follow-up competitions and other activities is given here with much fuller information later in the book.

Junior competitions

The UK Junior Mathematical Challenge, typically held on the last Thursday in April, is a one hour, 25 question, multiple choice paper for pupils up to and including:

Y8 in England and Wales; S2 in Scotland, and Y9 in Northern Ireland.

Pupils enter their personal details and answers on a special answer sheet for machine reading. The questions are set so that the first 15 should be accessible to all participants whereas the remaining 10 are more testing.

Five marks are awarded for each correct answer to the first 15 questions and six marks are awarded for each correct answer to the rest. Each incorrect answer to questions 16–20 loses 1 mark and each incorrect answer to questions 21–25 loses 2 marks. Penalty marking is used to discourage guessing.

Certificates are awarded on a proportional basis:– Gold about 6%, Silver about 14% and Bronze about 20% of all entrants. Each centre also receives one 'Best in School Certificate'. A 'Best in Year Certificate' is awarded to the highest scoring candidate in each year group, in each school.

The Junior Mathematical Olympiad is the follow-up competition to the JMC. It is normally held six weeks after the JMC and between 1000 and 1200 high scorers in the JMC are invited to take part. It is a two-hour paper which has two sections. Section A contains ten questions and pupils are required to give the answer only. Section B contains six questions for which full written answers are required. It is made clear to candidates that they are not expected to complete all of Section B and that little credit will be given to fragmentary answers. Gold, silver and bronze medals are awarded to very good candidates. In 2013 a total of 255 medals was awarded. The top 25% candidates got Certificates of Distinction. Of the rest, those who had qualified for the JMO automatically via the JMC received a Certificate of Participation. In addition, the top 50 students were given book prizes.

Intermediate competitions

The UK Intermediate Mathematical Challenge is organised in a very similar way to the Junior Challenge. One difference is that the age range goes up to Y11 in England and Wales, to S4 in Scotland and Y12 in Northern Ireland. The other difference is the timing; the IMC is held on the first Thursday in February. All other arrangements are as in the JMC.

There are five follow-up competitions under the overall title 'Intermediate Mathematical Olympiad and Kangaroo' (IMOK). Between 400 and 550 in each of Years 9, 10 and 11 (English style) sit an Olympiad paper (Cayley, Hamilton and Maclaurin respectively). In 2013, each of these was a two-hour paper and contained six questions all requiring full written solutions. A total of around 5000 pupils from the three year groups took part in a Kangaroo paper. In the European Kangaroo papers, which last an hour, there are 25 multiple-choice questions. The last ten questions are more testing than the first fifteen and correct answers gain six marks as opposed to five. (Penalty marking is not applied.) The same Kangaroo paper (designated 'Pink') was taken by pupils in Years 10 and 11 and a different one, 'Grey', by pupils in Year 9. In 2013, the Olympiads were sat on Thursday 14th March and the Kangaroos on Thursday 21st March. In the Olympiads, the top 25% of candidates got Certificates of Distinction. Most of the rest receive a Merit and of the rest, those who had qualified for the Olympiad automatically via the IMC received a Certificate of Participation. In the Kangaroos, the top 25% got a Merit and the rest a Participation. All Olympiad and Kangaroo candidates received a 'Kangaroo gift'; a specially designed UKMT key fob. In addition, the top 50 students in each year group in the Olympiad papers were given a book. Performance in the Olympiad papers and the IMC was a major factor in determining pupils to be invited to one of the UKMT summer schools early in July.

Senior competitions

In 2012, the UK Senior Mathematical Challenge was held on Tuesday 6th November. Like the other Challenges, it is a 25 question, multiple choice paper marked in the same way as the Junior and Intermediate Challenges. However, it lasts 1½ hours. Certificates (including Best in School) are awarded as with the other Challenges. The follow-up competitions are organised by the British Mathematical Olympiad Subtrust.

The first is BMO1, which was held on Friday 30th November 2012. About 800 are usually invited to take part. The paper lasted 3½ hours and contained six questions to which full written solutions are required.

About 100 high scorers are then invited to sit BMO2, which was held on Thursday 31st January 2013. It also lasted 3½ hours but contained four, very demanding, questions.

The results of BMO2 are used to select a group of students to attend a Training Session at Trinity College, Cambridge at Easter. As well as being taught more mathematics and trying numerous challenging problems, this group sits a 4½ hour 'mock' Olympiad paper. On the basis of this and all other relevant information, a group of about eight is selected to take part in correspondence courses and assignments which eventually produce the UK Olympiad Team of six to go forward to the International Mathematical Olympiad in July. In 2012, the Senior Kangaroo paper, for pupils who were close to being eligible for BMO1, was held on the same day.

The growth of the Challenges

In the 2005 UKMT Yearbook, we showed the growth of the Challenges since UKMT was established and this has now been updated. The graphs below show two easily identifiable quantities, the number of schools and the number of entries. In each case, the lines, from top to bottom, represent the Junior, Intermediate and Senior Challenges. As those involved in the UKMT firmly believe that the Challenges are a very worthwhile endeavour, we hope that the upward trends are continued.

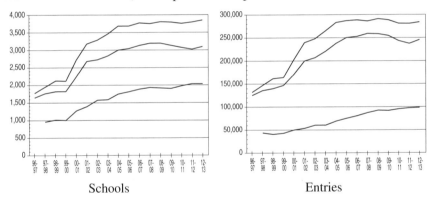

Schools   Entries

Team Maths Challenge

This event is the successor of the Enterprising Mathematics UK which was run in conjunction with the IMO in 2002. A team consists of four pupils who are in Year 9 (English style) or below with at most two members being in Year 9. In 2013, over 1500 schools took part in Regional Finals and 80 teams competed in the National Final held in the grand surroundings of the Lindley Hall, part of the prestigious Royal Horticultural Halls in Westminster, London on Monday 17th June.

In addition, 1110 schools took part in the Senior Team Maths Challenge which is aimed at pupils studying maths beyond GCSE. The final, which involved over 60 teams, was held in the Camden Centre on Tuesday 5th February.

Report from the Director

Another year comes to an end, and it is good to reflect on a successful and demanding past twelve months for the Trust.

Thank you to all who entered the Maths Challenges this year. It was fabulous to see increases in entries to the Junior, Intermediate and Senior Challenges, and to hear feedback about how participating students have been inspired and stretched mathematically by these. It was also pleasing to see a record number of participants to our Team Challenge events. I personally hope to continue to see an increase in entries to our Challenges, so that all students can benefit from these. Please do let us know if we can do anything more to support you to enter all your students in the future.

Following a successful trial of the UKMT Mathematical Circles last year, in which young mathematicians from a local area came together for two days to follow a mathematically demanding programme, we were particularly pleased to receive financial support from the Department for Education to expand our programme of these in 2013 and beyond. We ran seven Circles this year, and are planning for a further 20 or so in the coming two years.

Our thanks go to all our supporters and donors, in particular to the Institute of Actuaries who continue to support the Challenges. The economic climate is still uncertain, but we are very grateful to receive donations of any amount which can be made via www.donate.ukmt.org.uk, where you can also sign up to be a 'Friend of UKMT'.

I say it each year, but we could not run any of our events without the dedication and input of so many volunteers. Our volunteers do so much on our behalf, and I would personally like to thank this remarkable group of people for their commitment and enthusiasm throughout the year.

Finally, I would like to thank the schools who continue to participate in and support our work: from the teachers who organise the challenges, to the headteachers who allow and encourage them to do so. Mathematics is such an important subject and I appreciate all efforts in helping us to develop students' critical thinking, and for showing the usefulness, significance, and beauty of mathematics in our students' lives.

Rachel Greenhalgh

Institute
and Faculty
of Actuaries

Profile

The Institute and Faculty of Actuaries (IFoA) is the UK's only chartered professional body dedicated to educating, developing and regulating actuaries based both in the UK and internationally.

What is an actuary?

Actuaries are experts in risk management. They use their mathematical skills to help measure the probability and risk of future events. This information is useful to many industries, including healthcare, pensions, insurance, banking and investments, where a single decision can have a major financial impact.

It is a global profession with internationally-recognised qualifications. It is also very highly regarded, in the way that medicine and law are, and an actuarial career can be one of the most diverse, exciting and rewarding in the world. In fact, due to the difficult exams and the expertise required, being an actuary carries quite a reputation.

Training and development

To qualify as an actuary you need to complete the IFoA's exams. Most actuarial trainees take the exams whilst working for an actuarial employer. Exemptions from some of the exams may be awarded to students who have studied to an appropriate standard in a relevant degree, or have studied actuarial science at Postgraduate level. Qualification typically takes three to six years. Those on a graduate actuarial trainee programme can expect to earn £25,000-£35,000 a year. This increased to well over £100,000 as you gain more experience and seniority.

International outlook

The IFoA qualification is already highly valued throughout the world, with 40% of its members based overseas. Mutual recognition agreements with other international actuarial bodies facilitate the ability for actuaries to move and work in other parts of the world and create a truly global profession.

For more information on the qualifications and career path visit our website
http://www.actuaries.org.uk/becoming-actuary
or join us on Facebook
www.be-an-actuary.co.uk

The Junior Mathematical Challenge and Olympiad

The Junior Mathematical Challenge was held on Thursday 25th April 2013 and over 245,000 pupils took part. Approximately 1000 pupils were invited to take part in the Junior Mathematical Olympiad which was held on Tuesday 11th June. In the following pages, we shall show the question paper and solutions leaflet for both the JMC and JMO.

We start with the JMC paper, the front of which is shown below in a slightly reduced format.

UK JUNIOR MATHEMATICAL CHALLENGE

THURSDAY 25th APRIL 2013

Organised by the **United Kingdom Mathematics Trust**
from the School of Mathematics, University of Leeds

Institute
and Faculty
of Actuaries

RULES AND GUIDELINES (to be read before starting)

1. Do not open the paper until the Invigilator tells you to do so.

2. Time allowed: **1 hour**.
   No answers, or personal details, may be entered after the allowed hour is over.

3. The use of rough paper is allowed; **calculators** and measuring instruments are **forbidden**.

4. Candidates in England and Wales must be in School Year 8 or below.
   Candidates in Scotland must be in S2 or below.
   Candidates in Northern Ireland must be in School Year 9 or below.

5. **Use B or HB pencil only**. Mark *at most one* of the options A, B, C, D, E on the Answer Sheet for each question. Do not mark more than one option.

6. *Do not expect to finish the whole paper in 1 hour.* Concentrate first on Questions 1-15. When you have checked your answers to these, have a go at some of the later questions.

7. Five marks are awarded for each correct answer to Questions 1-15.
   Six marks are awarded for each correct answer to Questions 16-25.
   Each incorrect answer to Questions 16-20 loses 1 mark.
   Each incorrect answer to Questions 21-25 loses 2 marks.

8. Your Answer Sheet will be read only by a *dumb machine*. **Do not write or doodle on the sheet except to mark your chosen options**. The machine 'sees' all black pencil markings even if they are in the wrong places. If you mark the sheet in the wrong place, or leave bits of rubber stuck to the page, the machine will 'see' a mark and interpret this mark in its own way.

9. The questions on this paper challenge you to **think**, not to guess. You get more marks, and more satisfaction, by doing one question carefully than by guessing lots of answers.
   The UK JMC is about solving interesting problems, not about lucky guessing.

The UKMT is a registered charity
http://www.ukmt.org.uk

1. Which of the following has the largest value?

   A $1 - 0.1$ B $1 - 0.01$ C $1 - 0.001$ D $1 - 0.0001$ E $1 - 0.00001$

2. Heidi is 2.1 m tall, while Lola is only 1.4 m tall. What is their average height?

   A 1.525 m   B 1.6 m   C 1.7 m   D 1.725 m   E 1.75 m

3. What is the value of x?

   A 25   B 35   C 40   D 65   E 155

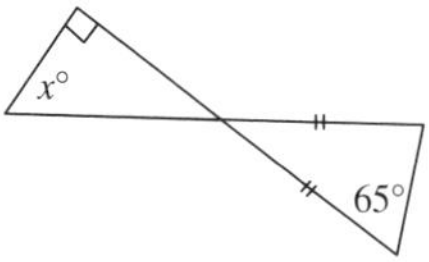

4. Gill went for a five-hour walk. Her average speed was between 3 km/h and 4 km/h. Which of the following could be the distance she walked?

   A 12 km   B 14 km   C 19 km   D 24 km   E 35 km

5. The diagram shows a weaver's design for a *rihlèlò*, a winnowing tray from Mozambique.
   How many lines of symmetry does the design have?

   A 0   B 1   C 2   D 4   E 8

6. What is the value of $\big((1 - 1) - 1\big) - \big(1 - (1 - 1)\big)$?

   A -2 B -1 C 0   D 1   E 2

7. After tennis training, Andy collects twice as many balls as Roger and five more than Maria. They collect 35 balls in total. How many balls does Andy collect?

   A 20   B 19   C 18   D 16   E 8

8. Two identical rulers are placed together, as shown (not to scale).
   Each ruler is exactly 10 cm long and is marked in centimetres from 0 to 10. The 3 cm mark on each ruler is aligned with the 4 cm mark on the other.

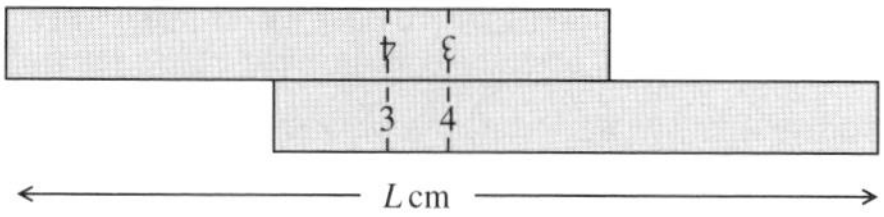

   The overall length is L cm. What is the value of L?

   A 13   B 14   C 15   D 16   E 17

9. Peter has three times as many sisters as brothers. His sister Louise has twice as many sisters as brothers. How many children are there in the family?

   A 15   B 13   C 11   D 9   E 5

10. On standard dice the total number of pips on each pair of opposite faces is 7. Two standard dice are placed in a stack, as shown, so that the total number of pips on the two touching faces is 5. What is the total number of pips on the top and bottom faces of the stack?

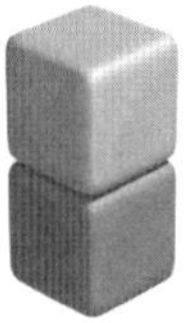

A 5   B 6   C 7   D 8   E 9

11. Usain runs twice as fast as his mum. His mum runs five times as fast as his pet tortoise, Turbo. They all set off together for a run down the same straight path. When Usain has run 100 m, how far apart are his mum and Turbo the tortoise?

A 5 m   B 10 m   C 40 m   D 50 m   E 55 m

12. How many hexagons are there in the diagram?

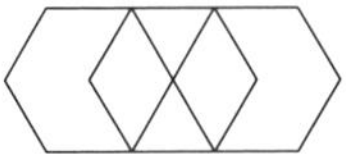

A 4   B 6   C 8   D 10   E 12

13. When painting the lounge, I used half of a 3 litre can to complete the first coat of paint. I then used two thirds of what was left to complete the second coat. How much paint was left after both coats were complete?

A 150 ml   B 200 ml   C 250 ml   D 500 ml   E 600 ml

14. Each side of an isosceles triangle is a whole number of centimetres. Its perimeter has length 20 cm. How many possibilities are there for the lengths of its sides?

A 3   B 4   C 5   D 6   E 7

15. The Grand Old Duke of York had 10 000 men. He lost 10% of them on the way to the top of the hill, and he lost 15% of the rest as he marched them back down the hill. What percentage of the 10 000 men were still there when they reached the bottom of the hill?

A $76\frac{1}{2}\%$ B 75%   C $73\frac{1}{2}\%$ D $66\frac{2}{3}\%$ E 25%

16. Ulysses, Kim, Mei and Tanika have their 12th, 14th, 15th and 15th birthdays today. In what year will their ages first total 100?

A 2023   B 2024   C 2025   D 2057   E 2113

17. A 5 cm × 5 cm square is cut into five pieces, as shown. Each cut is a sequence of identical copies of the same shape but pointing up, down, left or right. Which piece has the longest perimeter?

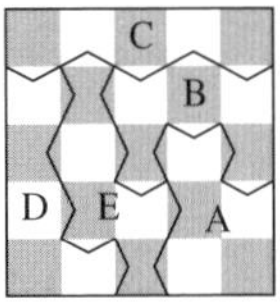

A   B   C   D   E

18. Weighing the baby at the clinic was a problem. The baby would not keep still and caused the scales to wobble. So I held the baby and stood on the scales while the nurse read off 78 kg. Then the nurse held the baby while I read off 69 kg. Finally I held the nurse while the baby read off 137 kg. What was the combined weight of all three ?

A 142 kg   B 147 kg   C 206 kg   D 215 kg   E 284 kg

(This problem appeared in the first Schools' Mathematical Challenge in 1988 − 25 years ago.)

19. A swimming club has three categories of members: junior, senior, veteran. The ratio of junior to senior members is 3 : 2 and the ratio of senior members to veterans is 5 : 2.

   Which of the following could be the total number of members in the swimming club?

   A 30 B 35 C 48 D 58 E 60

20. A 'long knight' moves on a square grid. A single move, as shown, consists of moving three squares in one direction (horizontally or vertically) and then one square at right angles to the first direction. What is the smallest number of moves a long knight requires to go from one corner of an 8 × 8 square board to the diagonally opposite corner?

   A 4 B 5 C 6 D 7 E 8

21. The 5 × 4 grid is divided into blocks. Each block is a square or a rectangle and contains the number of cells indicated by the integer within it.

   Which integer will be in the same block as the shaded cell?

   A 2 B 3 C 4 D 5 E 6

22. Two numbers in the 4 × 4 grid can be swapped to create a Magic Square (in which all rows, all columns and both main diagonals add to the same total).

   What is the sum of these two numbers?

   A 12 B 15 C 22 D 26 E 28

23. In our school netball league a team gains a certain whole number of points if it wins a game, a lower whole number of points if it draws a game and no points if it loses a game. After 10 games my team has won 7 games, drawn 3 and gained 44 points. My sister's team has won 5 games, drawn 2 and lost 3. How many points has her team gained?

   A 28 B 29 C 30 D 31 E 32

24. Three congruent squares overlap as shown. The areas of the three overlapping sections are 2 cm^2, 5 cm^2 and 8 cm^2 respectively. The total area of the non-overlapping parts of the squares is 117 cm^2.

   What is the side-length of each square?

   A 6 cm B 7 cm C 8 cm D 9 cm E 10 cm

25. For Beatrix's latest art installation, she has fixed a 2 × 2 square sheet of steel to a wall. She has two 1 × 2 magnetic tiles, both of which she attaches to the steel sheet, in any orientation, so that none of the sheet is visible and the line separating the two tiles cannot be seen. As shown alongside, one tile has one black cell and one grey cell; the other tile has one black cell and one spotted cell.

   How many different looking 2 × 2 installations can Beatrix obtain?

   A 4 B 8 C 12 D 14 E 24

The JMC solutions

The usual solutions leaflet was issued.

UK JUNIOR MATHEMATICAL CHALLENGE

THURSDAY 25th APRIL 2013

Organised by the **United Kingdom Mathematics Trust**
from the School of Mathematics, University of Leeds

http://www.ukmt.org.uk

Institute
and Faculty
of Actuaries

SOLUTIONS LEAFLET

This solutions leaflet for the JMC is sent in the hope that it might provide all concerned with some alternative solutions to the ones they have obtained. It is not intended to be definitive. The organisers would be very pleased to receive alternatives created by candidates.

The UKMT is a registered charity

14

1. **E** All of the alternatives involve subtracting a number from 1. The largest result, therefore, will correspond to the smallest number to be subtracted, i.e. 0.00001.

2. **E** Their average height is $\dfrac{2.1 + 1.4}{2}$ m $= 1.75$ m.

3. **C** Triangle BCD is isosceles, so $\angle BCD = \angle BDC = 65°$.
The sum of the interior angles of a triangle is $180°$ so
$\angle CBD = \left(180 - 2 \times 65\right)° = 50°$.
Therefore $\angle ABE = 50°$ (vertically opposite angles). So
$\angle AEB = \left(180 - 90 - 50\right)° = 40°$.

4. **C** Distance travelled = average speed × time of travel, so Gill travelled between 15 km and 20 km. Of the alternatives given, only 19 km lies in this interval.

5. **D** The diagram shows the four lines of symmetry.

6. **A** $\left((1 - 1) - 1\right) - \left(1 - (1 - 1)\right) = (0 - 1) - (1 - 0) = -1 - 1 = -2.$

7. **D** Let the number of balls collected by Roger be x. Then Andy collects $2x$ balls and Maria collects $(2x - 5)$ balls. So $x + 2x + 2x - 5 = 35$, i.e. $5x = 40$, i.e. $x = 8$. So Andy collected 16 balls.

8. **A** The number 3 on the top ruler (which is 7cm from the left-hand end) aligns with the 4 on the bottom one (which is 6cm from the right-hand end). Thus $L = 7 + 6 = 13$.

9. **B** Let there be b boys and g girls in the family. Then Peter has g sisters and $(b - 1)$ brothers. So $g = 3(b - 1)$. Louise has $(g - 1)$ sisters and b brothers. So $g - 1 = 2b$. Therefore $2b + 1 = 3b - 3$, i.e. $b = 4$. So $g = 9$.
Therefore there are 4 boys and 9 girls in the family, i.e. 13 children in total.

10. **E** The top and bottom faces of the stack and the two touching faces form two pairs of opposite faces.
So the total number of pips on these four faces is $2 \times 7 = 14$. Therefore the total number of pips on the top and bottom faces of the stack is $14 - 5 = 9$.

11. **C** After Usain has run 100 m, his mum has run 50 m and Turbo has 'run' 10 m. So the distance between Usain's mum and Turbo is 40 m.

12. **E** Figure $ABEFGJ$ itself is a hexagon. There are three hexagons congruent to $ABCLIJ$; two hexagons congruent to $ABDMHJ$; four hexagons congruent to $ABCKIJ$; two hexagons congruent to $ABDLHJ$. So in total there are twelve hexagons.

13. **D** After the first coat, half of the paint is left. So after the second coat, the volume of paint remaining is one third of half of the capacity of the tin, i.e. one sixth of three litres = 500 ml.

14. **B** Let the two equal sides of the isosceles triangle have length a and the other side have length b. Then $2a + b = 20$. Since the sum of the lengths of any two sides of a triangle is greater than the length of the third, $2a > b$. Hence $4a > 2a + b$. So $4a > 20$, i.e. $a > 5$. Also $a < 10$ since $2a + b = 20$. So the possibilities are $a = 6, b = 8$; $a = 7, b = 6$; $a = 8, b = 4$; and $a = 9, b = 2$.

15. **A** When he starts to come down the hill, the Grand Old Duke of York has 90% of his men left. He loses 15% of these, so at the bottom of the hill he has 85% of 90% of the original number left. As $\dfrac{85}{100} \times 90 = 76\dfrac{1}{2}$, this means that $76\frac{1}{2}$% of his men were still there when they reached the bottom of the hill.

16. **B** The sum of the ages of the four children is $12 + 14 + 15 + 15 = 56$. Each year on their birthday, this sum increases by 4. So the number of years before the sum reaches 100 is $(100 - 56) \div 4 = 11$. Therefore their ages will first total 100 in 2024.

17. **E** Let x cm be the length of the $\smile$ shape. Although x is not given, it is clear that $x > 1$. The lengths, in cm, of the perimeters of pieces A, B, C, D, E are $4 + 6x$, $2 + 10x, 7 + 5x, 6 + 6x, 1 + 11x$ respectively. As $4 + 6x < 6 + 6x$, the piece with the longest perimeter is B, C, D or E. As $x > 1$, it may be deduced that $7 + 5x < 6 + 6x < 2 + 10x < 1 + 11x$, so E has the longest perimeter.

18. **A** Let the weights, in kg, of baby, nurse and me be x, y, z respectively. Then $x + z = 78$; $x + y = 69$; $y + z = 137$. Adding all three equations gives $2x + 2y + 2z = 284$, so $x + y + z = 284 \div 2 = 142$.
(To find the combined weight, it is not necessary to find the individual weights, but baby weighs 5kg, nurse weighs 64 kg and I weigh 73 kg.)

19. **D** For every 2 senior members in the swimming club there are 3 junior members. For every 5 senior members there are 2 veteran members. The lowest common multiple of 2 and 5 is 10, so it may be deduced that the number of senior members is a multiple of 10. For every 10 senior members in the swimming club there are 15 junior members and 4 veteran members. So the total number of members is a multiple of 29. Of the alternatives given, the only multiple of 29 is 58.

20. **B** The 'long knight' needs to move exactly seven squares to the right and exactly seven squares upwards. Although it is possible to move seven squares to the right in three moves (1, 3 and 3), in doing so it could move upwards by a maximum of five squares (3, 1 and 1). Similarly, it could move seven squares upwards in three moves, but could then move a maximum of five squares to the right. In four moves, the number of squares moved to the right must be even, since it is the sum of four odd numbers. So at least five moves are required and the diagram shows one way in which the task may be achieved in five moves.

21. **C** As 5 is a prime number, it must lie in a 5×1 rectangle. So the only possibility is the rectangle which covers the top row of the grid. Now consider 6: there is insufficient room for a 6×1 rectangle so it must lie in a 3×2 rectangle. There are only two such rectangles which include 6 but do not include either 4 or 3. If 6 comes in the middle of the top row of a 2×3 rectangle then there is space for a 3×1 rectangle including 3. But then there is not enough space for a rectangle including 4. So 6 must be placed in the rectangle shown. There is now insufficient room to place 4 in a 4×1 rectangle so it must lie in the 2×2 square shown, which includes the shaded square. This leaves the grid to be completed as shown.

22. **E** The diagram shows the totals of the rows and columns. The circled numbers are the total of the numbers in the two main diagonals. Note, by considering the average values of the rows and columns, that each should total 34. Row 2 and column 2 are both 2 short. So their common entry, 13, needs to increase by 2. So 13 must be interchanged with 15. (This change also reduces row 4 and column 3 by 2 and increases the main diagonal by 2, thus making all the sums equal 34 as desired.) So the sum of the numbers to be swapped is 28.

9	6	3	16	34
4	13	10	5	32
14	1	8	11	34
7	12	15	2	36
(34) 34	32	36	34	(32)

23. **D** Let the points awarded for a win and a draw be w and d respectively. Then $7w + 3d = 44$. The only positive integer solutions of this equation are $w = 2$, $d = 10$ and $w = 5, d = 3$. However, more points are awarded for a win than for a draw so we deduce that 5 points are awarded for a win and 3 points for a draw. So the number of points gained by my sister's team is $5 \times 5 + 2 \times 3 = 31$.

24. **B** Each of the overlapping areas contributes to the area of exactly two squares. So the total area of the three squares is equal to the area of the non-overlapping parts of the squares plus twice the total of the three overlapping areas i.e. $(117 + 2(2 + 5 + 8))\ \text{cm}^2 = (117 + 30)\ \text{cm}^2 = 147\ \text{cm}^2$. So the area of each square is $(147 \div 3)\ \text{cm}^2 = 49\ \text{cm}^2$. Therefore the length of the side of each square is 7 cm.

25. **C** By arranging the tiles in suitable positions it is possible to place the 1×1 spotted square in any one of four corners of the steel sheet and then to place the grey square in any one of the other three corners. The other two corners will then be occupied by black squares. So, in total, there are $4 \times 3 = 12$ different looking installations.)

The JMC answers

The table below shows the proportion of pupils' choices. The correct answer is shown in bold. [The percentages are rounded to the nearest whole number.]

Qn	A	B	C	D	E	Blank
1	45	1	0	0	**52**	1
2	4	4	13	5	**71**	2
3	7	5	**42**	42	2	3
4	6	12	**71**	4	4	2
5	0	0	3	**87**	8	1
6	**52**	12	25	4	6	2
7	24	4	5	**61**	3	3
8	**28**	39	12	12	6	3
9	8	**27**	13	24	21	7
10	8	10	17	10	**48**	7
11	2	14	**66**	12	4	2
12	41	34	14	5	**3**	2
13	8	5	8	**72**	3	3
14	24	**20**	17	12	20	7
15	**23**	58	4	5	5	3
16	9	**53**	9	9	5	15
17	4	11	16	6	**31**	32
18	**21**	14	4	3	35	23
19	6	9	14	**20**	7	44
20	19	**17**	9	6	5	43
21	5	6	**16**	7	4	61
22	5	6	9	6	**18**	56
23	4	5	4	**34**	4	49
24	5	**10**	7	7	5	68
25	11	13	**8**	4	3	62

JMC 2013: Some comments on the pupils' choices of answers as expressed in the feedback letter to schools

As usual, the results sheet includes a table showing the distribution of answers from your own school, and from all the entrants. We hope that you will find the comparison interesting. The following comments are based on the overall distribution of answers.

The overall average score of 45 is significantly lower than last year, but comparable to 2010 and 2011. There were a number of 'easy' questions which candidates seem not to have engaged with, but their performance on some of the 'hard' questions was better than might have been expected.

At first sight it is alarming that in Question 1, 45% of the candidates seemed to think that $1 - 0.1$ is larger than $1 - 0.00001$. Did they fail to read or understand the question? Or was this just a 'warming up' effect with brains not yet fully booted-up? If your pupils did as badly as the national average, please discuss this with them and try and work out why. We would be pleased to receive your comments about this.

The response to Question 3 was another disappointment. A three-step argument is required, involving what should be well-known properties of isosceles triangles, vertically opposite angles, and the angle sum of a triangle. Was this too much for the 42% of the pupils who rather than think it through, seem to have just chosen the only number they could see in the diagram?

However, the biggest surprise came in Question 12, where only 3% of all candidates nationally found all 12 of the hexagons in the diagram. By not giving 3 as an option, we hoped that pupils would realize that a hexagon need not be regular. It was not a surprise that 34% of pupils said there were 6 hexagons and so seem not to have realized that a hexagon need not be convex, but why was option A (4 hexagons) the most popular response? The 12 hexagons in the diagram are shown explicitly in the extended solutions which you can find on our web site. We hope you will show these to your pupils.

In contrast, the responses to Questions 7, 11 and 13 are good to see. The biggest pleasant surprise came with the 'hard' Question 23. Just over half the candidates tried this question, and over 70% of those who attempted got it right. Many of these may have used a 'trial and error' approach rather than the more systematic algebraic method. If so, please show your pupils the algebraic solution, as this shows that there is just one solution.

We cannot see any pattern in the varied results on the questions in this year's JMC. We would welcome receiving your ideas about this.

The profile of marks obtained is shown below.

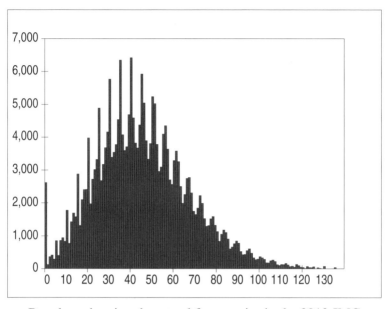

Bar chart showing the actual frequencies in the 2013 JMC

On the basis of the standard proportions used by the UKMT, the cut-off marks were set at

GOLD – 82 or over   SILVER – 63 to 81   BRONZE – 49 to 62

A sample of one of the certificates is shown on the next page.

The Junior Mathematical Olympiad is the follow-up competition to the Challenge. It was decided that candidates who obtained a JMC score of 113 or over were eligible to take part in the JMO. This resulted in 1019 candidates being invited. In line with other follow-on events, schools were allowed to enter 'unqualified' candidates on payment of an appropriate fee. The number who were entered by this route was 182.

20

UK JUNIOR MATHEMATICAL CHALLENGE
2013

of

received a

GOLD CERTIFICATE

The Actuarial Profession
making financial sense of the future

Chairman, United Kingdom Mathematics Trust

THE UNITED KINGDOM JUNIOR MATHEMATICAL CHALLENGE

The Junior Mathematical Challenge (JMC) is run by the UK Mathematics Trust. The JMC encourages mathematical reasoning, precision of thought, and fluency in using basic mathematical techniques to solve interesting problems. It is aimed at pupils in years 7 and 8 in England and Wales, S1 and S2 in Scotland and years 8 and 9 in Northern Ireland. The problems on the JMC are designed to make students think. Most are accessible, yet challenge those with more experience; they are also meant to be memorable and enjoyable.

Mathematics controls more aspects of the modern world than most people realise – from iPods, cash machines, telecommunications and airline booking systems to production processes in engineering, efficient distribution and stock-holding, investment strategies and 'whispering' jet engines. The scientific and industrial revolutions flowed from the realisation that mathematics was both the language of nature, and also a way of analysing – and hence controlling – our environment. In the last fifty years, old and new applications of mathematical ideas have transformed the way we live.

All of these developments depend on mathematical thinking – a mode of thought whose essential style is far more permanent than the wave of technological change which it has made possible. The problems on the JMC reflect this style, which pervades all mathematics, by encouraging students to think clearly about challenging problems.

The UK JMC has grown out of a national challenge first run in 1988. In recent years over 250,000 pupils have taken part from around 3,700 schools. Certificates are awarded to the highest scoring 40% of candidates (Gold:Silver:Bronze 1:2:3).

There are Intermediate and Senior versions for older pupils. All three events are organised by the United Kingdom Mathematics Trust and are administered from the School of Mathematics at the University of Leeds.

The UKMT is a registered charity. Please see our website www.ukmt.org.uk for more information. Donations to support our work would be gratefully received; a link for on-line donations is below.

www.donate.ukmt.org.uk

The Junior Mathematical Olympiad

UK Junior Mathematical Olympiad 2013

Organised by The United Kingdom Mathematics Trust

Tuesday 11th June 2013

RULES AND GUIDELINES :
READ THESE INSTRUCTIONS CAREFULLY BEFORE STARTING

1. Time allowed: 2 hours.

2. **The use of calculators, measuring instruments and squared paper is forbidden.**

3. All candidates must be in *School Year 8 or below* (England and Wales), *S2 or below* (Scotland), *School Year 9 or below* (Northern Ireland).

4. For questions in Section A *only the answer is required*. Enter each answer neatly in the relevant box on the Front Sheet. Do not hand in rough work. Write in blue or black pen or pencil.

   For questions in Section B you must give *full written solutions*, including clear mathematical explanations as to why your method is correct.

   Solutions must be written neatly on A4 paper. Sheets must be STAPLED together in the top left corner with the Front Sheet on top.

   Do not hand in rough work.

5. Questions A1-A10 are relatively short questions. Try to complete Section A within the first 45 minutes so as to allow well over an hour for Section B.

6. Questions B1-B6 are longer questions requiring *full written solutions*.
   This means that each answer must be accompanied by clear explanations and proofs.
   Work in rough first, then set out your final solution with clear explanations of each step.

7. These problems are meant to be challenging! Do not hurry. Try the earlier questions in each section first (they tend to be easier). Try to finish whole questions even if you are not able to do many. A good candidate will have done most of Section A and given solutions to at least two questions in Section B.

8. Answers must be FULLY SIMPLIFIED, and EXACT using symbols like π, fractions, or square roots if appropriate, but NOT decimal approximations.

DO NOT OPEN THE PAPER UNTIL INSTRUCTED BY THE INVIGILATOR TO DO SO!

Section A

A1 What is the value of $\sqrt{3102 - 2013}$?

A2 For how many three-digit positive integers does the product of the digits equal 20?

A3 The solid shown is made by gluing together
four 1 cm × 1 cm × 1 cm cubes.

What is the total surface area of the solid?

A4 What percentage of $\frac{1}{4}$ is $\frac{1}{5}$?

A5 Sue has a rectangular sheet of paper measuring 40 cm × 30 cm. She
cuts out ten squares each measuring 5 cm × 5 cm, as shown. In each
case, exactly one side of the square lies along a side of the rectangle
and none of the cut-out squares overlap.

What is the perimeter of the resulting shape?

A6 I want to write a list of integers containing two square numbers, two prime numbers, and two
cube numbers. What is the smallest number of integers that could be in my list?

A7 Calculate the value of x in the diagram shown.

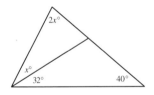

A8 The area of a square is 0.25 m². What is the perimeter of the square, in metres?

A9 Each interior angle of a quadrilateral, apart from the smallest, is twice the next smaller one.
What is the size of the smallest interior angle?

A10 A cube is made by gluing together a number of unit cubes face-to-face.
The number of unit cubes that are glued to exactly four other unit cubes is 96.

How many unit cubes are glued to exactly five other unit cubes?

Section B

Your solutions to Section B will have a major effect on your JMO results. Concentrate on one or two questions first and then **write out full solutions** (not just brief 'answers').

B1 How many numbers less than 2013 are both:
  (i) the sum of two consecutive positive integers; **and**
  (ii) the sum of five consecutive positive integers?

B2 Pippa thinks of a number. She adds 1 to it to get a second number. She then adds 2 to the second number to get a third number, adds 3 to the third to get a fourth, and finally adds 4 to the fourth to get a fifth number.

Pippa's brother Ben also thinks of a number but he subtracts 1 to get a second. He then subtracts 2 from the second to get a third, and so on until he too has five numbers.

They discover that the sum of Pippa's five numbers is the same as the sum of Ben's five numbers. What is the difference between the two numbers of which they first thought ?

B3 Two squares *BAXY* and *CBZT* are drawn on the outside of a regular hexagon *ABCDEF*, and two squares *CDPQ* and *DERS* are drawn on the inside, as shown.

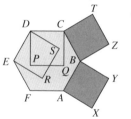

Prove that $PS = YZ$.

B4 A regular polygon P with n sides is divided into two pieces by a single straight cut. One piece is a triangle T, the other is a polygon Q with m sides.

How are m and n related?

B5 Consider three-digit integers N with the two properties:
  (a) N is not exactly divisible by 2, 3 or 5;
  (b) no digit of N is exactly divisible by 2, 3 or 5.
How many such integers N are there?

B6 On the 4 × 5 grid shown, I am only allowed to move from one square to a neighbouring square by crossing an edge. So the squares I visit alternate between black and white. I have to start on a black square and visit each black square exactly once. What is the smallest number of white squares that I have to visit? Prove that your answer is indeed the smallest.

(If I visit a white square more than once, I only count it as one white square visited).

UK Junior Mathematical Olympiad 2013 Solutions

A1 **33** $3102 - 2013 = 1089 = 9 \times 121 = 3^2 \times 11^2 = 33^2$. Therefore $\sqrt{3102 - 2013} = \sqrt{33^2} = 33$.

A2 **9** First, we need to find triples of digits whose product is $20 = 2^2 \times 5$.
The only possible triples are $\{1, 4, 5\}$ and $\{2, 2, 5\}$.
There are 6 possible ways of ordering the digits: $\{1, 4, 5\}$.
There are 3 possible ways of ordering the digits: $\{2, 2, 5\}$.
Therefore the total number of 3-digit numbers for which the product of the digits is equal to 20 is 9.

A3 **18 cm²** The surface area of four such cubes arranged separately is 4×6 cm² $= 24$ cm².
However, in this solid, there are three pairs of faces that overlap and so do not contribute to the surface area of the solid.
Therefore, the total surface area is $(24 - 3 \times 2 \times 1)$ cm² $= 18$ cm².

Alternatively, a bird's eye view from each of six directions has surface area 3 cm². So the total surface area is $6 \times 3 = 18$ cm².

A4 **80%** Note that $\frac{1}{5} : \frac{1}{4} = \frac{4}{20} : \frac{5}{20} = 4 : 5 = 80 : 100$. Hence $\frac{1}{5}$ is 80% of $\frac{1}{4}$.
Alternatively $\frac{1}{5} \div \frac{1}{4} = \frac{4}{5}$; and $\frac{4}{5} \times 100 = 80$. Therefore $\frac{1}{5}$ is 80% of $\frac{1}{4}$.

A5 **240 cm** The perimeter of the original paper is $40 + 40 + 30 + 30 = 140$ cm.
Each cut-out square adds 10 cm to the perimeter.
So the final perimeter is $140 + 10 \times 10 = 240$ cm.

A6 **4** A prime number cannot be a square or cube.
Hence there must be at least 4 numbers in the list.
We can find a list with two sixth powers (i.e. both squares and cubes) and two prime numbers e.g. $1^6, 2, 3, 2^6$ or $2^6, 3^6, 5, 7$ (where 2, 3, 5, 7 are all prime).
So the smallest number of integers in my list is 4.

A7 **36** Since the angles in a triangle add up to $180°$, we have $2x + (x + 32) + 40 = 180$.
This simplifies to $3x + 72 = 180$, which has the solution $x = 36$.

A8 **2 m** The length of each side equals 0.5 m since $0.5^2 = 0.25$.
Hence the perimeter is $4 \times 0.5 = 2$ m.

A9 **24°** Let the angles of the quadrilateral be $x°$, $2x°$, $4x°$ and $8x°$.

The sum of angles in a quadrilateral is $360°$.

Thus $15x = 360$ which gives $x = 24$.

A10 **384** Let the side length of the large cube be n.

On each edge of the large cube, there are $n - 2$ cubes glued to exactly 4 other cubes, shown shaded grey.

So in total there are $12(n - 2)$ cubes glued to exactly 4 other cubes.

Therefore $12(n - 2) = 96$ which gives $n = 10$.

On each face of the large cube, there are 8^2 cubes glued to exactly 5 other cubes, which are unshaded.

So in total, there are $6 \times 64 = 384$ cubes glued to exactly five other unit cubes.

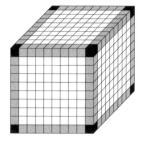

26

B1   How many numbers less than 2013 are both:

    (i) the sum of two consecutive positive integers; **and**

    (ii) the sum of five consecutive positive integers?

Solution

A number satisfies condition (i) if and only if it is of the form

$$n + (n + 1) = 2n + 1$$

for $n \geqslant 1$, i.e. it is an odd number greater than or equal to 3.

A number satisfies condition (ii) if and only if it is of the form

$$(m - 2) + (m - 1) + m + (m + 1) + (m + 2) = 5m$$

for some $m \geqslant 3$, i.e. it is a multiple of 5 greater than or equal to 15.

So a number satisfies both conditions if and only if it is of the form $5p$ with p an odd number and $p \geqslant 3$; i.e. $p = 2q + 1$ for $q \geqslant 1$.

Now $5(2q + 1) \leqslant 2013$ implies that $q \leqslant 200$. So there are 200 such numbers. satisfying both conditions.

B2   Pippa thinks of a number. She adds 1 to it to get a second number. She then adds 2 to the second number to get a third number, adds 3 to the third to get a fourth, and finally adds 4 to the fourth to get a fifth number.

Pippa's brother Ben also thinks of a number but he subtracts 1 to get a second. He then subtracts 2 from the second to get a third, and so on until he too has five numbers.

They discover that the sum of Pippa's five numbers is the same as the sum of Ben's five numbers. What is the difference between the two numbers of which they first thought ?

Solution

Let Pippa's original number be p and Ben's be b.

Then $p + (p + 1) + (p + 1 + 2) + (p + 1 + 2 + 3) + (p + 1 + 2 + 3 + 4)$
$= b + (b - 1) + (b - 1 - 2) + (b - 1 - 2 - 3) + (b - 1 - 2 - 3 - 4)$.

This simplifies first to $5p + 20 = 5b - 20$ and then to $8 = b - p$.

Hence the difference between the original numbers is 8.

B3   Two squares *BAXY* and *CBZT* are drawn on the outside of a regular hexagon
ABCDEF, and two squares *CDPQ* and *DERS* are drawn on the inside, as shown.

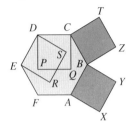

Prove that $PS = YZ$.

Solution 1

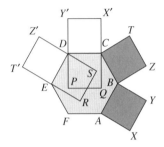

Draw squares *EDZ'T'* and *DCX'Y'* on the outside of the hexagon.

Since *ABCDEF* is regular, angles *EDC* and *ABC* are both 120° and also angles *EDZ'*,
CDY', *CBZ* and *ABY* are all right angles so $\angle Y'DZ' = \angle YBZ = 60°$. Also the
lengths of the sides of the four squares are all equal as they are equal to the sides of the
regular hexagon. Thus triangles *DY'Z'* and *BYZ* are congruent (SAS) and hence
$Z'Y' = ZY$.

Now compare triangles *Y'DZ'* and *PDS*.

$Y'D = PD$ and $Z'D = DS$. (These are the same length as the sides of the hexagon.)

Angle $Y'DZ'$ = Angle *PDS* as they are vertically opposite angles.

So triangle *Y'DZ'* is congruent to triangle *PDS*.

So $PS = Z'Y' = ZY$.

28

Solution 2

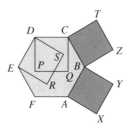

In a regular hexagon, an interior angle is 120°. In a square an interior angle is 90°.

Consider $\triangle BZY$. $BZ = CB$ as both are sides of the square $BZTC$. $CB = AB$ as both are sides of the regular hexagon. $AB = BY$ as both are sides of the square $BAXY$. Therefore $BZ = BY$.

Since angles at a point total 360°, it follows that $90° + 120° + 90° + \angle ZBY = 360°$ and so $\angle ZBY = 60°$.

Therefore $\triangle BZY$ is an isosceles triangle with an angle of 60° between the equal sides and so is an equilateral triangle.

In a similar way, consider $\triangle DPS$. $DP = DC$ as both are sides of the square $DPQC$; $DC = DE$ as both are sides of the regular hexagon and $DE = DS$ as both are sides of the square $DERS$. Hence $DP = DS$.

$\angle EDC = 120°$ and $\angle PDC = 90°$ hence $\angle EDP = 30°$. $\angle EDC = 120°$ and $\angle EDS = 90°$ hence $\angle SDC = 30°$. $\angle EDC = \angle EDP = \angle PDS = \angle SDC$ so $\angle PDS = 60°$.

Therefore $\triangle PDS$ is an isosceles triangle with an angle of 60° between the equal sides and so is an equilateral triangle.

Also $DP = DC = CB = BZ$ so the sides of the two equilateral triangles are the same length.

Therefore $\triangle DPS$ and $\triangle BYZ$ are exactly the same size (*called congruent triangles*). Therefore $PS = YZ$.

B4
A regular polygon P with n sides is divided into two pieces by a single straight cut. One piece is a triangle T, the other is a polygon Q with m sides.

How are m and n related?

Solution
There are three possible ways in which one straight cut can create a triangle.

Case 1: The straight cut goes through two vertices of the polygon.
Then $m = n - 1$.

Case 2: The straight cut goes through exactly one vertex of the polygon.

Then $m = n$.

Case 3: The straight cut goes through no vertices of the polygon.

Then $m = n + 1$.

B5
Consider three-digit integers N with the two properties:
    (a) N is not exactly divisible by 2, 3 or 5;
    (b) no digit of N is exactly divisible by 2, 3 or 5.
How many such integers N are there?

Solution
Condition (b) means that each digit of N must be either 1 or 7 (since 0, 2, 4, 6, 8 are divisible by 2; 0, 5 are divisible by 5 and 3, 6, 9 are divisible by 3).

A number is divisible by 3 if and only if the sum of its digits is divisible by 3.

But

$1 + 1 + 1 = 3$ $1 + 1 + 7 = 9$ $1 + 7 + 7 = 15$ $7 + 7 + 7 = 21$

which are all divisible by 3.

Hence there are no 3-digit numbers N satisfying both these conditions.

B6   On the 4 × 5 grid shown, I am only allowed to move from one square to a neighbouring square by crossing an edge. So the squares I visit alternate between black and white. I have to start on a black square and visit each black square exactly once. What is the smallest number of white squares that I have to visit? Prove that your answer is indeed the smallest.

(If I visit a white square more than once, I only count it as one white square visited).

Solution

It is possible to visit each black square exactly once by travelling through 4 white squares (as shown in this diagram).

Suppose there is a route using only three white squares. The maximum number of black squares adjacent to the first white square on the route is 4. To reach the second white square on the route, the route must pass via one of those black squares – and so there are no more than 3 additional black squares adjacent to the second white square. Likewise, when the third white square is reached there are at most 3 additional black squares adjacent to it. This means that with 3 white squares we can reach at most 10 black squares and, moreover, we can only reach 10 if each of the three white squares is adjacent to 4 black squares. However, in the given diagram, there are only three such white squares – and none of them is adjacent to the black squares in the bottom corners. Hence three white squares is not enough. This means that the smallest number of white squares I have to visit is four.

The marking and results

The pupils' scripts began arriving very rapidly and the marking took place in Leeds on the weekend of 22nd and 23rd June. The discussions as to how marks should be given and for what were ably led by Jo Harbour. A full list of markers appears in the Volunteers section.

As has been stated, the object of the JMO is for pupils to be *challenged*, possibly in ways they have not been before. Some participants may find all of Section B rather beyond them, but it is hoped that they achieve a degree of satisfaction from Section A. Satisfaction is an important aspect of this level of paper; nevertheless, those who do succeed in tackling Section B deserve credit for that and such credit is mainly dependent on getting solutions to questions in Section B which are 'perfect' or very nearly so. The awarding process is somewhat complicated, some might say bizarre. Firstly there are certificates which come in two versions, Participation and Distinction. The top 25% of scorers receive a Certificate of Distinction; candidates who score below this and who qualified automatically for the JMO via the JMC receive a Certificate of Participation. There were book prizes for the top fifty. The book prize for 2013 was *The Penguin Dictionary of Curious and Interesting Numbers* by David Wells. Finally, there were medals of the traditional Gold, Silver, Bronze varieties of design introduced in 2004.

The paper drew a stronger performance from candidates in Section A compared to 2012, but the spread of results was otherwise similar. The numbers of medals awarded were: 39 Gold, 86 Silver and 130 Bronze.

The list below includes all the medal winners in the 2013 JMO. Within each category, the names are in alphabetical order.

Special mention should be made of Luke Barratt, James Sun, Dmitry Lubyako and Harvey Yau who now have two JMO Gold Medals.

The results and all the extras (books, book plates, certificates and medals) were posted to schools by the middle of July. Where appropriate, some materials were e-mailed to schools.

GOLD MEDALS

Luke Barratt	Backwell School, North Somerset
Jonathan Bostock	Eltham College, London
Theo Breeze	Manchester Grammar School
Alex Chen	Westminster Under School
Jessamyn Chiu	German Swiss International School, Hong Kong
Alexander Darby	Sutton Grammar School for Boys, Surrey
Keir Degg	Meole Brace Science College, Shrewsbury
Mila Feldman	The Stephen Perse Foundation, Cambridge
Sam Ferguson	King's College School, London
Alexander Fruh	St Aloysius College, Glasgow
Theo Gillis	Sussex House School, London
Alice Harray	St Paul's Girls' School, Hammersmith
Thomas Hillman	Beechwood Park, St Albans
Samuel Howard	Stockport Grammar School
Charlie Hu	City of London School
Timothy Lavy	Cherwell School, Oxford
Dong Chan Lee	Magdalen College School, Oxford
Ryan Leung	Renaissance College, Hong Kong
Ricky Li	Fulford School, York
William Li	Beijing Dulwich International School
Dmitry Lubyako	Summer Fields School, Oxford
Chandra Lyengar	St Paul's Cathedral School, London
George Merryweather	Magdalen College School, Oxford
Ewan Murphy	King Edward VI School, Southampton
Yuji Okitani	Tapton School, Sheffield
Zacharie Sciamma	Devonshire House Prep School, Hampstead
Alexander Song	St Olave's Grammar School, Kent
Daniel Starkey	Judd School, Tonbridge, Kent
Pasa Suksmith	Harrow International School, Bangkok
Emma Sun	Henrietta Barnett School, London
James Sun	Reading School

Samuel Sutherland	Wells Cathedral School, Somerset
Arjun Tapasvi	Yarm School, nr Stockton-on-Tees
Yuriy Tumarkin	Durham Johnston School
Naomi Wei	City of London Girls' School
Sean White	City of London School
Ryan Wong	Reading School
Harvey Yau	Ysgol Dyffryn Taf, Carmarthenshire
Danlei Zhu	Bristol Grammar School

SILVER MEDALS

Pok Aramthanapon	Shrewsbury International School, Thailand
Iman Awan	St Paul's Girls' School, Hammersmith
Connie Bambridge Sutton	Reigate Grammar School, Surrey
Naomi Bazlov	EHSG Prep School, Birmingham
Sam Bealing	Bridgewater High School, Warrington
Emily Beatty	King Edward VII School, Sheffield
Matthew Bullock	Heckmondwike Grammar School, West Yorkshire
Yifei Chen	Cardiff High School
Yan Yau Cheng	Discovery College, Hong Kong
Samuel Clarke	Comberton Village College, Cambridgeshire
Henry Colbert	Haberdashers' Aske's School for Boys, Herts
John Conacher	Furze Platt Senior School, Maidenhead
Alex Cooke	Farlingaye High School, Suffolk
Nathan Creighton	Mossbourne Community Academy, Hackney
Louisa Cullen	Pocklington School, near York
Thomas Edmiston	Magdalen College School, Oxford
Andrew Ejemai	Brentwood School
Jun Eshima	Dragon School, Oxford
Joel Fair	Bethany School, Sheffield
Chris Finn	Royal Grammar School, High Wycombe
Max French	Millfield Preparatory School, Somerset
Daniel Gore	Northwood Prep School, Herts
Sara Ha	Mountbatten School, Hampshire
Freddie Hand	Judd School, Tonbridge, Kent

Jacob Hands	Dragon School, Oxford
John Hayton	King Edward VI Camp Hill Boys' S., Birmingham
Ruiyang He	Glasgow Academy
Connor Headen	Beechen Cliff School, Bath
Aaron Heighton	Aylesbury Grammar School
Alec Hong	St Olave's Grammar School, Kent
Billy Howard	Colet Court School, London
Yang Hsu	Colet Court School, London
Dion Huang	Westminster Under School
Philip Jackson	Perse School, Cambridge
Jessie Jiang	Tiffin Girls' School, Kingston-upon-Thames
Rachel Jones	Tiffin Girls' School, Kingston-upon-Thames
Ryan Kang	Westminster Under School
Yash Kewalramani	BD Somani Int. School, Mumbai, India
Chanho Kim	British School of Paris
Brian Kim	British Int. School of Shanghai (Puxi)
Alex Kim	Seoul Foreign School
Trung Le Quang	BVIS Ho Chi Minh City
Shri Lekkala	Westminster Under School
Angus Macleod	Dollar Academy, Clackmannanshire
Fraser Mason	George Heriot's School, Edinburgh
Sophie McInerney	Tonbridge Grammar School, Kent
Liam McKnight	Magdalen College School, Oxford
George Mercieca	Homefield School, Surrey
Toby Mills	Trinity School, Croydon
Alex Moen	Dulwich Prep School (Cranbrook), Kent
Ritobrata Mukhopadhyay	Glasgow Academy
Joseph Nash	Abingdon School
Karthik Neelamegam	Reading School
Sam Oldham	Christ Church Academy, Staffs
Sooyong Park	North London Collegiate S. Jeju, South Korea
Tanish Patil	Institut International de Lancy, Switzerland
Fred Phillips	Aylesbury Grammar School

Elijah Price	Reading School
Alex Radcliffe	Stewart's Melville College, Edinburgh
Benedict Randall Shaw	Betty Layward Primary School, London
Alex Root	Immanuel College, Bushey, Herts
Noah Roper	Newton Prep School, London
Joshua Rowe	St John Fisher High School, Harrogate
Mayuka Saegusa	Mount School, London
Jeremy Salkeld	German Swiss Int. School, Hong Kong
Oliver Schonle	City of London School
Andrea Sendula	Kenilworth School, Warks
Harjivan Singh	Haberdashers' Aske's School for Boys, Herts
Anna Soligo	Lady Margaret School, Fulham
Robert Thomson	Perse School, Cambridge
Daniel Townsend	Colchester Royal Grammar School
Vincent Trieu	Tiffin School, Kingston-upon-Thames
Arthur Ushenin	Summer Fields School, Oxford
Mathilda Vere	Chenderit School, Northants
Tommy Walker Mackay	William Hulme's Grammar S., Manchester
Benjamin Wang	Harrow International School, Hong Kong
Andrew Wei	Sha Tin College, Hong Kong
Nicholas West	Alleyn's School, Dulwich
Nicholas Wiseman	City of London School
Charlie Worsley	Dollar Academy, Clackmannanshire
Christopher Yacoumatos	Westminster Under School
Miyu Yamaguchi	Henrietta Barnett School, London
Tony Yang	North London Collegiate S. Jeju, South Korea
Sebastian Hong Hui Yap	Alice Smith School, Malaysia
James Zhang	Hutchesons' Grammar School, Glasgow
Jeremy Zolnai Lucas	Watford Grammar School for Boys

BRONZE MEDALS

Julie Ahn	South Island School, Hong Kong
Daniel Amdurer	The Crossley Heath School, Halifax
Michael Arnold	Chetham's School of Music, Manchester

Mateo Attanasio	Dame Alice Owen's School, Herts
Joshua Attwell	Chatham House Grammar S., Ramsgate
Armaan Bajaj	Haberdashers' Aske's School for Boys, Herts
Emily Beckford	Lancaster Girls' Grammar School
Oliver Beken	Horndean Technology Coll., Hampshire
Oliver Bennett	St Olave's Grammar School, Kent
Juliet Biard	Stroud High School
Isaac Brown	Kingsdale School, Dulwich
Sam Brown	Jews' Free School, London
Luke Butcher	City of London Freemen's School, Surrey
Alex Byrne	King Edward VI Camp Hill Boys' S., Birmingham
Jonathan Cain	Frederick Bremer School, Walthamstow
Gabriel Cairns	Wilson's School, Surrey
Emma Campbell	Newstead Wood School, Kent
Claire Carlotti	Castle Community College, Kent
Hazel Cartwright	George Spencer Academy, Notts
Jeewoong Chang	Yew Chung International School of Beijing
Jun Wen Chen	High School of Glasgow
Ryan Choi	South Island School, Hong Kong
Anurag Choksey	Warwick School
Aneesh Chopada	Queen Elizabeth's School, Barnet
Rishabh Chugh	King Edward VI School, Southampton
Jongihn Chung	Perse School, Cambridge
George Clements	Taverham Hall, near Norwich
Chelsea Crawford	Norwich High School
Rivkah Damon	Royal Latin School, Buckingham
Ayman Dsouza	Dulwich College
Jonathan Durston	Kesgrave High School, Ipswich
David Evans	St Dunstan's College, London
Xincan Fan	Harrow International School, Beijing
Adam Fidler	Judd School, Tonbridge, Kent
Christopher Flach	Bishop Ramsey CE School, Middlesex
Lucy Flint	Aylesbury High School
Kitty Foster	King's School Ely, Cambridgeshire

Daniel Gallagher	King Edward VI Grammar S., Chelmsford
George Garber	Old Buckenham Hall School, Suffolk
Aaron Gilchrist	Reigate Grammar School, Surrey
Segev Gonen Cohen	Jews' Free School, London
Richard Gooch	Tapton School, Sheffield
James Greatrex	St Ivo School, St Ives, Cambs
Callum Gunning	Chorister School, Durham
Cameron Hardman	Lewes Old Grammar School, East Sussex
Thomas Haslam	Dr Challoner's Grammar School, Amersham
Alexander Haydn Williams	Colet Court School, London
Peter Hedges	Ashton Middle School, Dunstable
Nicholas Heymann	Colet Court School, London
Kohki Horie	International School of Luxembourg
Nathan Huntington	Aylesbury Grammar School
Jacob Intrater	UWCSEA Dover Campus, Singapore
Takao Ito	Manchester Grammar School
Arthur James	Dragon School, Oxford
Stella Johnson	School of St Helen and St Katharine, Abingdon
Matthew Jolly	St Laurence School, Wiltshire
George Jose	Tiffin School, Kingston-upon-Thames
Seo Rin Kang	British International School Vietnam
Minseong Kang	Danes Hill School, Surrey
Basim Khajwal	Heckmondwike Grammar S., West Yorkshire
Zion Kim	Hampton School, Middlesex
Minji Kim	Dulwich College Suzhou, China
Elliot Klyne	Royal Grammar School, High Wycombe
Souhardh Kotakadi	Queen Elizabeth's School, Barnet
Shikhar Kumar	Birkenhead School
Devya Kumaresan	Tiffin Girls' School, Kingston-upon-Thames
Samuel Kwiatkowski	St George's School, Harpenden
Rose Laurie	Church Stretton School, Shropshire
Dylan Lea	Winterbourne International Academy, Bristol
Aidan Lee	New Hall School, Chelmsford
Sean Lennard Barney	Highgate School, London

Sarah Li	North London Collegiate School
Stephen Lidbetter	Judd School, Tonbridge, Kent
Bruno Lindan	Simon Langton Boys' Grammar S., Canterbury
Aloysius Lip	King Edward's School, Birmingham
Tom Liu	Colet Court School, London
Rachel Lu	George Watson's College, Edinburgh
Lucy Mackie	Nottingham High School for Girls
Daniel Maghsoudi	St Olave's Grammar School, Kent
Shaun Marshall	Scissett Middle School, Huddersfield
Laurence Mayther	John Roan School, London
Callum McDougall	Newton Prep School, London
Grace Molloy	Mary Erskine School, Edinburgh
Kieran Moore	German Swiss Int. School, Hong Kong
Aru Mukherjea	Island School, Hong Kong
Anna Mullock	St John's College School, Cambridge
Andy Nam	North London Collegiate S. Jeju, South Korea
James Nelson	Holmfirth High School, Huddersfield
Jasper Newbold	St George's School, Windsor
Euan Ong	Magdalen College School, Oxford
Rachel Orrell	Bancroft's School, Essex
Akane Ota	Hall School Wimbledon
David Packer	Dr Challoner's Grammar School, Amersham
Juneyong Park	North London Collegiate S. Jeju, South Korea
Luke Patel	Wilson's School, Surrey
Tobias Patten	King Edward VI School, Stratford-upon-Avon
Jed Preist	Cotham School, Bristol
Owen Purnell	Christ's Hospital, Horsham
Daniel Quigley	Belfast Royal Academy
James Redford	St Edward's Royal Free Middle S., Windsor
Niels Rupf	Westminster Under School
Manu Rutherford	Burnham Grammar School, Slough
Marie Sato	Henrietta Barnett School, London
Yasith Senanayake	Sutton Grammar School for Boys, Surrey
Min Seok Seo	North London Collegiate S. Jeju, South Korea

Amri Shakir	Dr Challoner's Grammar School, Amersham
Andrew Shaw	Verulam School, St Albans
Rebecca Siddall	Oundle School, Northants
Toby Sinclair	Kings' School, Winchester
Arinjay Singhai	UWCSEA Dover Campus, Singapore
Raam Songara	Westminster Under School
Phillip Sosnin	Perse School, Cambridge
Oliver Stubbs	Bristol Grammar School
Gabriel Swallow	Judd School, Tonbridge, Kent
Jake Swann	Mall School, Twickenham
Alexander Thomson	King Alfred Academy, Oxon
Angus Turnor	City of London School
Joseph Tyler	Dame Alice Owen's School, Herts
Thien Udomsrirungruaang	Shrewsbury International School, Thailand
Laurence Van Someren	Kings College School, Cambridge
William Vinnicombe	Perse School, Cambridge
Alex Wallace	Cargilfield Preparatory, Edinburgh
Anyi Wang	King Edward's School, Birmingham
Joseph Wang	New Beacon School, Sevenoaks
Lauren Weaver	St Paul's Girls' School, Hammersmith
Jahkaan Wray	Alleyn's School, Dulwich
Seung Jin Yang	Frankfurt International School
Amy You	Bangkok International School
Daniel Yue	King Edward's School, Birmingham
Angela Zhao	Harrow International School, Beijing

The Intermediate Mathematical Challenge and its follow-up events

The Intermediate Mathematical Challenge was held on Thursday 7th February 2013. Entries numbered 244,010 and 198,550 pupils took part. There were several different IMOK follow-up competitions and pupils were invited to the one appropriate to their school year and mark in the IMC. Around 500 candidates in each of Years 9, 10 and 11 sat the Olympiad papers (Cayley, Hamilton and Maclaurin respectively) and approximately 1700 more in each year group took a Kangaroo paper. We start with the IMC paper.

UK INTERMEDIATE MATHEMATICAL CHALLENGE

THURSDAY 7TH FEBRUARY 2013

Organised by the **United Kingdom Mathematics Trust**

and supported by

The Actuarial Profession

making financial sense of the future

RULES AND GUIDELINES (to be read before starting)

1. Do not open the paper until the Invigilator tells you to do so.

2. Time allowed: **1 hour**.
   No answers, or personal details, may be entered after the allowed hour is over.

3. The use of rough paper is allowed; **calculators** and measuring instruments are **forbidden**.

4. Candidates in England and Wales must be in School Year 11 or below.
   Candidates in Scotland must be in S4 or below.
   Candidates in Northern Ireland must be in School Year 12 or below.

5. **Use B or HB pencil only**. Mark *at most one* of the options A, B, C, D, E on the Answer Sheet for each question. Do not mark more than one option.

6. *Do not expect to finish the whole paper in 1 hour.* Concentrate first on Questions 1-15. When you have checked your answers to these, have a go at some of the later questions.

7. Five marks are awarded for each correct answer to Questions 1-15.
   Six marks are awarded for each correct answer to Questions 16-25.
   Each incorrect answer to Questions 16-20 loses 1 mark.
   Each incorrect answer to Questions 21-25 loses 2 marks.

8. Your Answer Sheet will be read only by a *dumb machine*. **Do not write or doodle on the sheet except to mark your chosen options.** The machine 'sees' all black pencil markings even if they are in the wrong places. If you mark the sheet in the wrong place, or leave bits of rubber stuck to the page, the machine will 'see' a mark and interpret this mark in its own way.

9. The questions on this paper challenge you to **think**, not to guess. You get more marks, and more satisfaction, by doing one question carefully than by guessing lots of answers.
   The UK IMC is about solving interesting problems, not about lucky guessing.

The UKMT is a registered charity

http://www.ukmt.org.uk

1. Which of the following is divisible by 6?

   A one million minus one   B one million minus two   C one million minus three
           D one million minus four   E one million minus five

2. A machine cracks open 180 000 eggs per hour. How many eggs is that per second?

   A 5   B 50   C 500   D 5000   E 50 000

3. How many quadrilaterals are there in this diagram, which is constructed using 6 straight lines ?

   A 4   B 5   C 7   D 8   E 9

4. A standard pack of pumpkin seeds contains 40 seeds. A special pack contains 25% more seeds. Rachel bought a special pack and 70% of the seeds germinated. How many pumpkin plants did Rachel have?

   A 20   B 25   C 28   D 35   E 50

5. The northern wheatear is a small bird weighing less than an ounce. Some northern wheatears migrate from sub-Saharan Africa to their Arctic breeding grounds, travelling almost 15 000 km. The journey takes just over 7 weeks. Roughly how far do they travel each day, on average?

   A 1 km   B 9 km   C 30 km   D 90 km   E 300 km

6. Which of the following has the least value?

   A $1^0 - 0^1$ B $2^1 - 1^2$ C $3^2 - 2^3$ D $4^3 - 3^4$ E $5^4 - 4^5$

7. The faces of a regular octahedron are to be painted so that no two faces which have an edge in common are painted in the same colour. What is the smallest number of colours required?

   A 2   B 3   C 4   D 6   E 8

8. Jim rolled some dice and was surprised that the sum of the scores on the dice was equal to the product of the scores on the dice. One of the dice showed a score of 2, one showed 3 and one showed 5. The rest showed a score of 1. How many dice did Jim roll?

   A 10   B 13   C 17   D 23   E 30

9. Jane has 20 identical cards in the shape of an isosceles right-angled triangle. She uses the cards to make the five shapes below. Which of the shapes has the shortest perimeter?

   A   B   C   D   E

10. *ABCDE* is a regular pentagon and *BCF* is an equilateral triangle such that *F* is inside *ABCDE*. What is the size of $\angle FAB$?

    A 48°   B 63°   C 66°   D 69°   E 72°

11. For which of the following numbers is the sum of all its factors *not* equal to a square number?

    A 3   B 22   C 40   D 66   E 70

12. The sum

one + four = seventy

becomes correct if we replace each word by the number of letters in it to give $3 + 4 = 7$. Using the same convention, which of these words could be substituted for x to make the sum

three + five = x true?

A eight   B nine   C twelve   D seventeen   E eighteen

13. Four congruent isosceles trapeziums are placed so that their longer parallel sides form the diagonals of a square $PQRS$, as shown. The point X divides PQ in the ratio 3:1. What fraction of the square is shaded?

A $\dfrac{5}{16}$ B $\dfrac{3}{8}$ C $\dfrac{7}{16}$ D $\dfrac{5}{12}$ E $\dfrac{1}{2}$

14. Which of the following has the greatest value?

A $\left(\dfrac{11}{7}\right)^3$ B $\left(\dfrac{5}{3}\right)^3$ C $\left(\dfrac{7}{4}\right)^3$ D $\left(\dfrac{9}{5}\right)^3$ E $\left(\dfrac{3}{2}\right)^3$

15. I have a bag of coins. In it, one third of the coins are gold, one fifth of them are silver, two sevenths are bronze and the rest are copper. My bag can hold a maximum of 200 coins. How many coins are in my bag?

A 101   B 105   C 153   D 195   E more information is needed

16. Which diagram shows the graph of $y = x$ after it has been rotated 90° clockwise about the point $(1, 1)$?

A   B   C   D   E

17. The diagram shows four equal discs and a square. Each disc touches its two neighbouring discs. Each corner of the square is positioned at the centre of a disc. The side length of the square is $2/\pi$. What is the length of the perimeter of the figure?

A 3   B 4   C $\dfrac{3\pi}{2}$ D 6   E 2π

18. The triangle T has sides of length 6, 5, 5. The triangle U has sides of length 8, 5, 5.

What is the ratio area T : area U?

A 9 : 16   B 3 : 4   C 1 : 1   D 4 : 3   E 16 : 9

19. Which of the expressions below is equivalent to $(x \div (y \div z)) \div ((x \div y) \div z)$?

A 1   B $\dfrac{1}{xyz}$ C x^2 D y^2 E z^2

20. Jack's teacher asked him to draw a triangle of area 7cm^2. Two sides are to be of length 6cm and 8cm. How many possibilities are there for the length of the third side of the triangle?

A 1   B 2   C 3   D 4   E more than 4

21. The square *ABCD* has an area of 196. It contains two overlapping squares; the larger of these squares has an area 4 times that of the smaller and the area of their overlap is 1. What is the total area of the shaded regions?

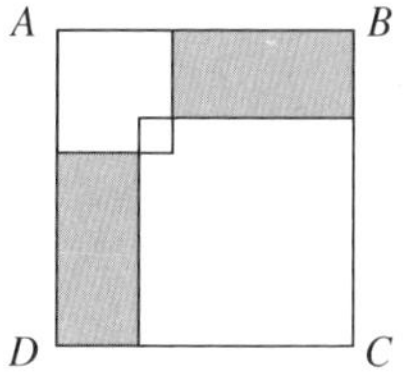

A 44   B 72   C 80   D 152

E more information is needed

22. The diagrams show squares placed inside two identical semicircles. In the lower diagram the two squares are identical.

What is the ratio of the areas of the two shaded regions?

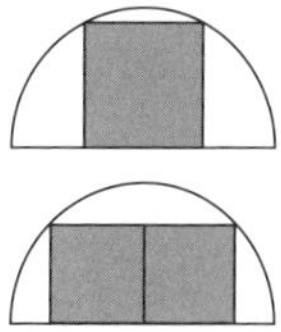

A 1 : 2   B 2 : 3   C 3 : 4   D 4 : 5   E 5 : 6

23. Four brothers are discussing the order in which they were born. Two are lying and two are telling the truth. Which two are telling the truth?

Alfred: "Bernard is the youngest."   Horatio: "Bernard is the oldest and I am the youngest."
Inigo: "I was born last."   Bernard: "I'm neither the youngest nor the oldest."

A Bernard and Inigo   B Horatio and Bernard   C Alfred and Horatio
          D Alfred and Bernard   E Inigo and Horatio

24. The diagram shows a shaded shape bounded by circular arcs with the same radius. The centres of three arcs are the vertices of an equilateral triangle; the other three centres are the midpoints of the sides of the triangle. The sides of the triangle have length 2.

What is the difference between the area of the shaded shape and the area of the triangle?

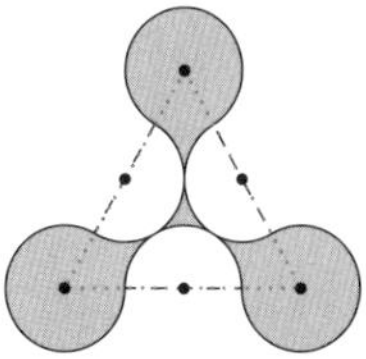

A $\dfrac{\pi}{6}$ B $\dfrac{\pi}{4}$ C $\dfrac{\pi}{3}$ D $\dfrac{\pi}{2}$ E π

25. In 1984 the engineer and prolific prime-finder Harvey Dubner found the biggest known prime each of whose digits is either a one or a zero. The prime can be expressed as $\dfrac{10^{641} \times \left(10^{640} - 1\right)}{9} + 1$. How many digits does this prime have?

A 640   B 641   C 1280   D 1281   E 640 × 641

44

The IMC solutions

As with the Junior Challenge, a solutions leaflet was sent out.

The Actuarial Profession
making financial sense of the future

UK INTERMEDIATE MATHEMATICAL CHALLENGE

THURSDAY 7TH FEBRUARY 2013

Organised by the **United Kingdom Mathematics Trust**
from the School of Mathematics, University of Leeds

http://www.ukmt.org.uk

SOLUTIONS LEAFLET

This solutions leaflet for the IMC is sent in the hope that it might provide all concerned with some alternative solutions to the ones they have obtained. It is not intended to be definitive. The organisers would be very pleased to receive alternatives created by candidates. More comprehensive solutions are on the website.

The UKMT is a registered charity

1. **D**   In order to be a multiple of 6, a number must be both even and a multiple of 3. Of the numbers given, only B 999 998 and D 999 996 are even. Using the rule for division by 3, we see that, of these two, only 999 996 is a multiple of 3.

2. **B**   180 000 eggs per hour is equivalent to 3000 eggs per minute, i.e. to 50 eggs per second.

3. **E**   The figure is itself a quadrilateral. It can be divided into four small quadrilaterals labelled A, B, C, D. There are also four quadrilaterals formed in each case by joining together two of the smaller quadrilaterals: A and B; B and C; C and D; D and A.

4. **D**   The number of seeds in a special packet is $1.25 \times 40 = 50$. So the number of seeds which germinate is $0.7 \times 50 = 35$.

5. **E**   A wheatear travels the distance of almost 15 000 km in approximately 50 days. This is on average roughly 300 km per day.

6. **E**   In order, the values of the expressions given are: $1 - 0 = 1; 2 - 1 = 1; 9 - 8 = 1;$ $64 - 81 = -17; 625 - 1024 = -399.$

7. A Only two colours are needed for the upper four faces of the octahedron. If, for example, blue and red are used then these four faces may be painted alternately red and blue. Consider now the lower four faces: every face adjacent to an upper blue face may be painted red and every face adjacent to an upper red face may be painted blue. So only two colours are required for the whole octahedron.

8. D Let the number of scores of 1 be n. Then the product of the scores is $1^n \times 2 \times 3 \times 5 = 30$. Therefore $1 \times n + 2 + 3 + 5 = 30$, i.e. $n = 20$. So Jim threw 23 dice.

9. A Let the length of the shorter sides of the cards be 1 unit. Then, by Pythagoras' Theorem, the length of the hypotenuse of each card is $\sqrt{1^2 + 1^2} = \sqrt{2}$.

So the lengths of the perimeters of the five figures in order are: $4\sqrt{2}$; $4 + 2\sqrt{2}$; $4 + 2\sqrt{2}$; 6; $4 + 2\sqrt{2}$. Also, as $\left(\frac{3}{2}\right)^2 = \frac{9}{4} = 2\frac{1}{4} > 2$ we see that $\frac{3}{2} > \sqrt{2}$. Therefore, $4\sqrt{2} < 6 < 4 + 2\sqrt{2}$. So figure A has the shortest perimeter.

10. C The sum of the interior angles of a pentagon is 540° so $\angle ABC = 540° \div 5 = 108°$. Each interior angle of an equilateral triangle is 60°, so $\angle FBC = 60°$. Therefore $\angle ABF = 108° - 60° = 48°$. As $ABCDE$ is a regular pentagon, $BC = AB$. However, $BC = FB$ since triangle BFC is equilateral.

So triangle ABF is isosceles with $FB = AB$. Therefore $\angle FAB = \angle AFB = \left(180° - 48°\right) \div 2 = 66°$.

11. C We first look at $66 = 2 \times 3 \times 11$. Its factors involve none, one, two or all three of these primes. So the factors are 1, 2, 3, 11, 6, 22, 33, 66; and their sum is $144 = 12^2$. Similarly, we can check that the sum of the factors of 3, 22, 40 and 70 is, respectively, $4 = 2^2$, $36 = 6^2$, 90 and $144 = 12^2$. So 40 is the only alternative for which the sum of the factors is not a square number.

12. D As the words 'three' and 'five' contain 5 and 4 letters respectively, their 'sum' will be a 9-letter word. Of the alternatives given, only 'seventeen' contains 9 letters.

13. B The diagram shows the top-right-hand portion of the square. The shaded trapezium is labelled $QXYZ$ and W is the point at which ZY produced meets PQ.

As $QXYZ$ is an isosceles trapezium, $\angle QZY = \angle ZQX = 45°$. Also, as YX is parallel to ZQ, $\angle XYW = \angle WXY = 45°$. So WYX and WZQ are both isosceles right-angled triangles. As $\angle ZWQ = 90°$ and Z is at the centre of square $PQRS$, we deduce that W is the midpoint of PQ. Hence $WX = XQ = \frac{1}{4}PQ$. So the ratio of the side-lengths of similar triangles WYX and WZQ is $1 : 2$ and hence the ratio of their areas is $1 : 4$.

Therefore the area of trapezium $QXYZ = \frac{3}{4} \times$ area of triangle $ZWQ = \frac{3}{32} \times$ area $PQRS$ since triangle ZWQ is one-eighth of $PQRS$. So the fraction of the square which is shaded is $4 \times \frac{3}{32} = \frac{3}{8}$.

14. D As all the fractions are raised to the power 3, the expression which has the largest value is that with the largest fraction in the brackets.

Each of these fractions is a little larger than $1\frac{1}{2}$. Subtracting $1\frac{1}{2}$ from each in turn, we get the fractions $\frac{1}{14}, \frac{1}{6}, \frac{1}{4}, \frac{3}{10}, 0$, the largest of which is $\frac{3}{10}$ (because $0 < \frac{1}{14} < \frac{1}{6} < \frac{1}{4} = \frac{2\frac{1}{2}}{10} < \frac{3}{10}$). Hence $\left(\frac{9}{5}\right)^3$ is the largest.

15. B From the information given, we may deduce that the number of coins is a multiple of each of 3, 5, 7. Since these are distinct primes, their lowest common multiple is $3 \times 5 \times 7 = 105$. So the number of coins in the bag is a multiple of 105. So there are 105 coins in the bag since 105 is the only positive multiple of 105 less than or equal to 200.

16. A The image of a straight line under a rotation is also a straight line. The centre of rotation, the point $(1, 1)$, lies on the given line and so also lies on the image. The given line has slope 1 and so its image will have slope -1. Hence graph A shows the image.

17. D The radius of each disc in the figure is equal to half the side-length of the square, i.e. $\frac{1}{\pi}$. Because the corners of a square are right-angled, the square hides exactly one quarter of each disc.
So three-quarters of the perimeter of each disc lies on the perimeter of the figure. Therefore the length of the perimeter is $4 \times \frac{3}{4} \times 2\pi \times \frac{1}{\pi} = 6$.

18. C The diagrams show isosceles triangles T and U. The perpendicular from the top vertex to the base divides an isosceles triangle into two congruent right-angled triangles as shown in both T and U. Evidently, by Pythagoras' Theorem, $h_1 = 4$ and $h_2 = 3$. So both triangles T and U consist of two '3, 4, 5' triangles and therefore have equal areas.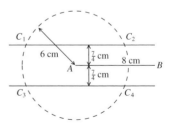

19. E $(x \div (y \div z)) \div ((x \div y) \div z) = \left(x \div \frac{y}{z}\right) \div \left(\left(\frac{x}{y}\right) \div z\right) = \left(x \times \frac{z}{y}\right) \div \left(\frac{x}{y} \times \frac{1}{z}\right)$
$= \frac{xz}{y} \div \frac{x}{yz} = \frac{xz}{y} \times \frac{yz}{x} = z^2$.

20. B Let the base AB of the triangle be the side of length 8 cm and let AC be the side of length 6 cm. So C must lie on the circle with centre A and radius 6 cm as shown. The area of the triangle is to be 7 cm², so the perpendicular from C to AB (or to BA produced) must be of length $\frac{7}{4}$ cm.

The diagram shows the four possible positions of C. However, since $\angle BAC_1 = \angle BAC_3$ and $\angle BAC_2 = \angle BAC_4$, these correspond to exactly two possibilities for the length of the third side AC. The diagrams below show the two possibilities.

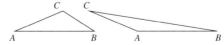

21. B The large square has area $196 = 14^2$. So it has side-length 14. The ratio of the areas of the inner squares is 4 : 1, so the ratio of their side-lengths is 2 : 1. Let the side-length of the larger inner square be $2x$, so that of the smaller is x. The figure is symmetric about the diagonal AC and so the overlap of the two inner squares is also a square which therefore has side-length 1. Thus the vertical height can be written as $x + 2x - 1$. Hence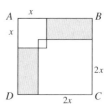
$3x - 1 = 14$ and so $x = 5$. Also, the two shaded rectangles both have side-lengths $2x - 1$ and $x - 1$; that is 9 and 4. So the total shaded area is 72.

22. D Let the radius of each semicircle be r. In the left-hand diagram, let the side-length of the square be $2x$. By Pythagoras' Theorem, $x^2 + (2x)^2 = r^2$ and so $5x^2 = r^2$. So this shaded area is $4x^2 = \frac{4r^2}{5}$. In the right-hand diagram, let the side-length of each square be y. Then by Pythagoras' Theorem, $y^2 + y^2 = r^2$ and so this shaded area is r^2. Therefore the ratio of the two shaded areas is $\frac{4}{5} : 1 = 4 : 5$.

23. A If Alfred is telling the truth, the other three lying (as their statements would then be false) and we know this is not the case. Hence Alfred is lying. Similarly, if Horatio is telling the truth, the other three are lying which again cannot be the case. So Horatio is lying. Hence the two who are telling the truth are Bernard and Inigo. (A case where this situation would be realised would be if the brothers in descending order of age were Alfred , Bernard, Horatio and Inigo.)

24. B The length of the side of the triangle is equal to four times the radius of the arcs. So the arcs have radius $2 \div 4 = \frac{1}{2}$. In the first diagram, three semicircles have been shaded dark grey. The second diagram shows how these semicircles may be placed inside the triangle so that the whole triangle is shaded. Therefore the difference between the area of the shaded shape and the area of the triangle is the sum of the areas of three sectors of a circle. The interior angle of an equilateral triangle is 60°, so the angle at the centre of each sector is $180° - 60° = 120°$. Therefore each sector is equal in area to one-third of the area of a circle. Their combined area is equal to the area of a circle of radius $\frac{1}{2}$. So the required area is $\pi \times \left(\frac{1}{2}\right)^2 = \frac{\pi}{4}$.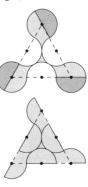

25. D $\left(10^{640} - 1\right)$ is a 640-digit number consisting entirely of nines. So $\dfrac{\left(10^{640} - 1\right)}{9}$ is a 640-digit number consisting entirely of ones. Therefore $\dfrac{10^{641} \times \left(10^{640} - 1\right)}{9}$ consists of 640 ones followed by 641 zeros. So $\dfrac{10^{641} \times \left(10^{640} - 1\right)}{9} + 1$ consists of 640 ones followed by 640 zeros followed by a single one. Therefore it has 1281 digits.

The answers

The table below shows the proportion of pupils' choices. The correct answer is shown in bold. [The percentages are rounded to the nearest whole number.]

Qn	A	B	C	D	E	Blank
1	10	12	6	**69**	1	2
2	5	**57**	20	13	2	2
3	8	16	4	3	**67**	1
4	2	2	4	**85**	5	1
5	1	2	17	6	**72**	2
6	18	4	3	16	**56**	2
7	**44**	9	33	4	8	1
8	8	17	10	**46**	12	5
9	**51**	5	4	34	3	2
10	18	16	**17**	12	27	10
11	15	18	**43**	10	8	5
12	6	19	2	**63**	7	2
13	16	**31**	16	16	10	9
14	15	7	10	**43**	17	7
15	2	**24**	8	4	57	4
16	**20**	13	13	4	26	24
17	3	5	11	**15**	7	59
18	5	36	**11**	5	2	41
19	15	13	3	4	**8**	57
20	14	**8**	6	3	6	62
21	6	**11**	4	3	11	65
22	7	8	5	**5**	2	73
23	**46**	2	9	2	3	38
24	3	**4**	6	5	3	79
25	2	3	8	**10**	8	69

IMC 2013: Some comments on the pupils' choice of answers as sent to schools in the letter with the results

The mean score this year of 42.9 is a little lower than last year. Most of the early questions were answered correctly by more than half the pupils, but only one question, Question 4, was answered correctly by more than 80% of the pupils. We hope that you will look at the table comparing the answers given by your pupils with the national distribution, and that you will find this informative. For example, in Question 1 did 10% of your pupils say that one million minus one is divisible by 6? If so, were they just slow starters?

It is always interesting to look at questions where the pupils did much less well than we expected. The outcome on Question 7 was disappointing, and seems to indicate a lack of visual imagination. If you look at the solutions on our web page (www.ukmt.org.uk) you will find some extension questions related to Question 7 which will enable you to explore the corresponding problem for other polyhedrons.

The most disappointing outcome was on Question 10. Angle-chasing questions of this type are often answered correctly by more than half the pupils. However, only 17% of the pupils answered the question correctly, with 9% leaving the answer blank. This is an unusually high proportion of blank answers for a question so early on the paper. This poor result was not anticipated but, in retrospect, it is not difficult to understand. Question 10 is a geometry question *without a diagram*. We guess that many pupils tried to answer the question without drawing their own diagram. If this was the case, and we suggest that you check this with your own pupils, the outcome is not so surprising. The question was set in the expectation that pupils would, quite easily, be able to produce their own diagram. Were we wrong? If you think that it is not reasonable to expect today's pupils to supply missing diagrams for geometry problems, please let us know.

The later questions are intended to be harder, and are used to help us select the pupils who are invited to take the Cayley, Hamilton and Maclaurin papers. Not surprisingly many of them proved to be very challenging, and most students did not attempt them. So the number of correct answers to Question 23 seems to be very encouraging. It is a question that requires careful logical thinking, but not ability in using any mathematical techniques. Therefore, the success of pupils with this question conveys, perhaps, another uncomfortable message. As ever, pupils who did well enough on the later, harder questions to qualify for one of the follow-on events should be congratulated on their excellent achievement.

The profile of marks obtained is shown below.

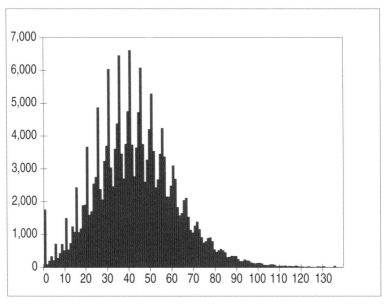

Bar chart showing the actual frequencies in the 2013 IMC

On the basis of the standard proportions used by the UKMT, the cut-off marks were set at

GOLD – 74 or over   SILVER – 59 to 73   BRONZE – 47 to 58

The certificates were virtually identical in design to those used for the JMC.

The cut-off scores for the follow-up competitions were

Year (E&W)	Minimum mark	Event	Minimum mark	Event
11	104	Maclaurin	84	Kangaroo Pink
10	96	Hamilton	84	Kangaroo Pink
9	88	Cayley	73	Kangaroo Grey

The Intermediate Mathematical Olympiad and Kangaroo

(a) *Kangaroo*

The 2013 European Kangaroo (a multiple choice paper with 25 questions) took place on Thursday 21st March. It was also held in many other countries across Europe and beyond with over five million candidates. As in previous years, the UKMT constructed two Kangaroo papers.

EUROPEAN 'KANGAROO' MATHEMATICAL CHALLENGE
'GREY'
Thursday 21st March 2013

**Organised by the United Kingdom Mathematics Trust and the
Association Kangourou Sans Frontières**

This competition is being taken by 6 million students in over 50 countries worldwide.

RULES AND GUIDELINES (to be read before starting):

1. Do not open the paper until the Invigilator tells you to do so.

2. Time allowed: **1 hour**.
   No answers, or personal details, may be entered after the allowed hour is over.

3. The use of rough paper is allowed; **calculators** and measuring instruments are **forbidden**.

4. Candidates in England and Wales must be in School Year 9 or below.
   Candidates in Scotland must be in S2 or below.
   Candidates in Northern Ireland must be in School Year 10 or below.

5. **Use B or HB pencil only**. For each question mark *at most one* of the options A, B, C, D, E on the Answer Sheet. Do not mark more than one option.

6. Five marks will be awarded for each correct answer to Questions 1 - 15.
   Six marks will be awarded for each correct answer to Questions 16 - 25.

7. *Do not expect to finish the whole paper in 1 hour*. Concentrate first on Questions 1-15. When you have checked your answers to these, have a go at some of the later questions.

8. The questions on this paper challenge you **to think**, not to guess. Though you will not lose marks for getting answers wrong, you will undoubtedly get more marks, and more satisfaction, by doing a few questions carefully than by guessing lots of answers.

*Enquiries about the European Kangaroo should be sent to: Maths Challenges Office,
School of Mathematics, University of Leeds, Leeds, LS2 9JT.*
(Tel. 0113 343 2339)
http://www.ukmt.org.uk

2013 European Grey Kangaroo

1. It is true that $\dfrac{1111}{101} = 11$. What is the value of $\dfrac{3333}{101} + \dfrac{6666}{303}$?

    A 5　　　　B 9　　　　C 11　　　　D 55　　　　E 99

2. Ann has the square sheet of paper shown in the left-hand diagram. By cutting along lines of the square, she produces copies of the shape shown in the right-hand diagram. What is the smallest possible number of cells she can leave unused?

    A 0　　　B 2 ⁱ　　　C 4　　　D 6　　　E 8

    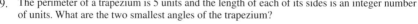

3. Roo wants to tell Kanga a number whose digits have a product of 24. What is the sum of the digits of the smallest number Roo could choose?

    A 6　　　　B 8　　　　C 9　　　　D 10　　　　E 11

4. There are five families living in my road. Which of the following could not be the mean number of children per family that live there?

    A 0.2　　　B 1.2　　　C 2.2　　　D 2.4　　　E 2.5

5. Nicky and Rachel stand on opposite sides of a circular fountain. They then start to run at a constant speed clockwise round the fountain. Nicky's speed is $\frac{9}{8}$ of Rachel's speed. How many circuits has Rachel completed when Nicky catches up with her for the first time?

    A 2　　　　B 4　　　　C 8　　　　D 9　　　　E 72

6. The positive integers x, y and z satisfy $xy = 14$, $yz = 10$ and $xz = 35$. What is the value of $x + y + z$?

    A 10　　　　B 12　　　　C 14　　　　D 16　　　　E 18

7. Olivia and a friend are playing a game of 'battleships' on a 5×5 board. Olivia has already placed two ships as shown. She still has to place a 3×1 ship so that it covers exactly three cells. No two ships can have a boundary point in common. How many positions are there for her 3×1 ship?

    A 4　　　B 5　　　C 6　　　D 7　　　E 8

8. In the diagram, $\alpha = 55°$, $\beta = 40°$ and $\gamma = 35°$. What is the value of δ?

    A 100°　　B 105°　　C 120°　　D 125°　　E 130°

9. The perimeter of a trapezium is 5 units and the length of each of its sides is an integer number of units. What are the two smallest angles of the trapezium?

    A 30° and 30°　　B 60° and 60°　　C 45° and 45°　　D 30° and 60°　　E 45° and 90°

10. Carl wrote down several consecutive integers. Which of the following could not be the percentage of odd numbers among them?

    A 40　　　　B 45　　　　C 48　　　　D 50　　　　E 60

11. All the 4-digit positive integers with the same digits as the number 2013 are written in increasing order. What is the largest difference between two adjacent numbers?

    A 702　　　　B 703　　　　C 693　　　　D 793　　　　E 198

12. The edges of rectangle *PQRS* are parallel to the coordinate axes. *PQRS* lies below the *x*-axis and to the right of the *y*-axis as shown in the diagram. The coordinates of *P*, *Q*, *R* and *S* are all integers. For each point, we calculate the value (*y*-coordinate) ÷ (*x*-coordinate). Which of the four points gives the least value?

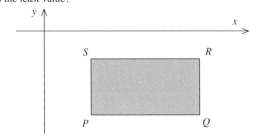

   A P   B Q   C R   D S   E It depends on the rectangle.

13. In the 6 × 8 grid shown, 24 cells are not intersected by either diagonal. When the diagonals of a 6 × 10 grid are drawn, how many cells are not intersected by either diagonal?

   A 28   B 29   C 30   D 31   E 32

14. John has made a building of unit cubes standing on a 4 × 4 grid. The diagram shows the number of cubes standing on each cell. When John looks horizontally at the building from behind, what does he see?

BEHIND

4	2	3	2
3	3	1	2
2	1	3	1
1	2	1	2

FRONT

   A   B   C   D   E

15. The diagram shows a shaded quadrilateral *PQRS* drawn on a grid. Each cell of the grid has sides of length 2 cm. What is the area of quadrilateral *PQRS*?

   A 96 cm^2 B 84 cm^2 C 76 cm^2 D 88 cm^2 E 104 cm^2

16. Let *S* be the number of square numbers among the integers from 1 to 2013^6 inclusive. Let *Q* be the number of cube numbers among the same integers. Which of the following relationships between *S* and *Q* is true?

   A $S = Q$ B $2S = 3Q$ C $3S = 2Q$ D $S = 2013Q$ E $S^3 = Q^2$

17. Adam chooses a 5-digit positive integer and deletes one of its digits to form a 4-digit integer. The sum of this 4-digit integer and the original 5-digit integer is 52713. What is the sum of the digits of the original 5-digit integer?

   A 17   B 19   C 20   D 23   E 26

18. A gardener wants to plant 20 trees along one side of an avenue. He decides to use a mixture of maple trees and linden trees. The number of trees between any two maple trees must not be equal to three. What is the largest number of maple trees that the gardener can plant?

   A 8   B 10   C 12   D 14   E 16

19. Andrew and Dean recently took part in a marathon. After they had finished, they noticed that Andrew had finished ahead of twice as many runners as finished ahead of Dean and that Dean had finished ahead of $1\frac{1}{2}$ times as many runners as finished ahead of Andrew. Andrew finished in 21st place. How many runners took part in the marathon?

A 31   B 41   C 51   D 61   E 81

20. One of the following nets cannot be folded along the dashed lines shown to form a cube. Which one?

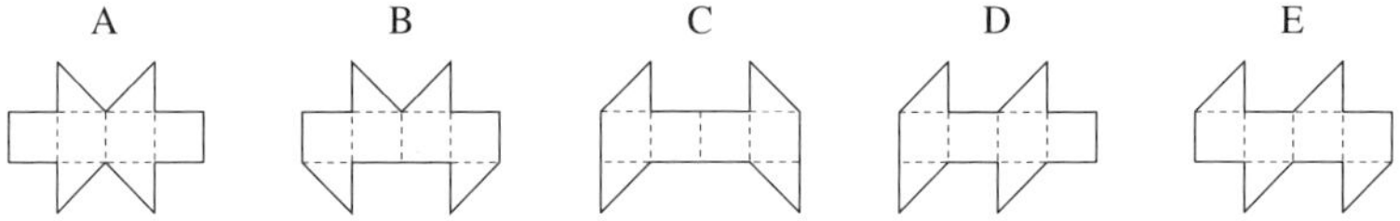

21. Four cars enter a roundabout at the same time, each one from a different direction, as shown in the diagram. Each car drives in a clockwise direction and leaves the roundabout before making a complete circuit. No two cars leave the roundabout by the same exit. How many different ways are there for the cars to leave the roundabout?

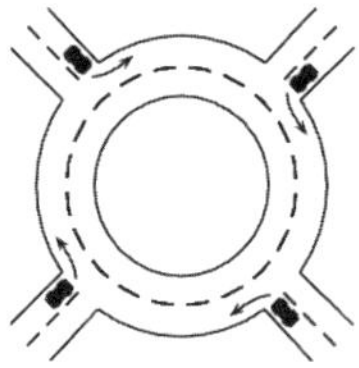

A 9   B 12   C 15   D 24   E 81

22. The first five terms of a sequence are $1, -1, -1, 1, -1$. After the fifth term, every term is equal to the product of the two preceding terms. For example, the sixth term is equal to the product of the fourth term and the fifth term. What is the sum of the first 2013 terms of the sequence?

A −1006   B −671   C 0   D 671   E 1007

23. Ria bakes six raspberry pies one after the other, numbering them 1 to 6 in order, with the first being number 1. Whilst she is doing this, her children occasionally run into the kitchen and eat the hottest pie. Which of the following could not be the order in which the pies are eaten?

A 123456   B 125436   C 325461   D 456231   E 654321

24. Each of the four vertices and six edges of the tetrahedron $PQRS$ is marked with one of the numbers 1, 2, 3, 4, 5, 6, 7, 8, 9 and 11; so the number 10 is not used. Each number is used exactly once. Each edge is marked with the sum of the numbers at the two vertices connected by that edge. Edge PQ is marked with number 9. Which number is used to mark edge RS?

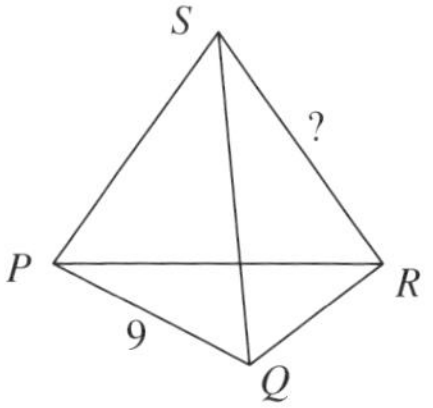

A 4   B 5   C 6   D 8   E 11

25. A positive integer N is smaller than the sum of its three greatest divisors (naturally, excluding N itself). Which of the following statements is true?

A All such N are divisible by 4.   B All such N are divisible by 5.

C All such N are divisible by 6.   D All such N are divisible by 7.

E There is no such N.

Solutions to the 2013 European Grey Kangaroo

1. D $\dfrac{3333}{101} = 3 \times \dfrac{1111}{101} = 33$ and $\dfrac{6666}{303} = 6 \times \dfrac{1}{3} \times \dfrac{1111}{101} = 22$.

Therefore the original sum is 55.

2. C Ann is cutting out shapes made up of four cells from an original square of 16 cells. It is possible to cut out three shapes in a number of different ways, one of which is shown in the diagram. However, it is not possible to cut out four such shapes. To cut out four such shapes, Anne would need to use all 16 cells. Consider the bottom left corner cell. The only possibilities for this cell to be used are in the lightest shaded shape as shown or in the darkest shaded shape moved down one cell. In the first case, the bottom right corner cell could not be used while in the second case, the top left corner cell could not be used. Hence it is impossible to use all 16 cells. So the largest number of shapes Anne can cut out is three and so the smallest number of cells she can leave unused is $16 - 3 \times 4 = 4$.

3. E No 1-digit number has a digital product of 24. However, $24 = 3 \times 8$ and $24 = 4 \times 6$ and these are the only ways to write 24 as the product of two single digit numbers. Hence there are precisely four 2-digit numbers (38, 83, 46 and 64) with digital product 24. The smallest of these is 38, which has a digital sum of 11.

4. E The total number of children in five families is equal to five times the mean. Of the options given, only $2.5 \times 5 = 12.5$ does not give a whole number. Therefore, the mean number of children cannot be 2.5.

5. B Nicky's speed is $\frac{9}{8}$ of Rachel's speed so, for each lap of the fountain Rachel completes, Nicky gains $\frac{1}{8}$ of a lap. To catch Rachel, Nicky has to gain $\frac{1}{2}$ a lap. This will take $\frac{1}{2} \div \frac{1}{8} = 4$ laps.

6. C We observe that x divides both 14 and 35, so $x = 1$ or 7. If $x = 1$, then from $xz = 35$, we deduce that $z = 35$. But this is impossible as y is an integer and $yz = 10$. Therefore $x = 7$. Hence as $xy = 14$, we have $y = 2$ and as $xz = 35$, $z = 5$. So $x + y + z = 7 + 2 + 5 = 14$.

7. E The 3×1 ship can be placed in two positions horizontally and six positions vertically as shown making a total of eight positions.

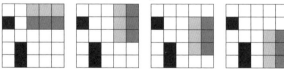

8. E Let θ be the angle as shown in the diagram.

As the exterior angle of a triangle is equal to the sum of the two interior opposite angles, we have $\theta = \alpha + \beta$ and $\delta = \gamma + \theta$.

This gives $\delta = \alpha + \beta + \gamma = 55° + 40° + 35° = 130°$.

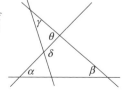

9. **B** The situation as described must refer to an isosceles trapezium with three sides of length one unit and one side of length two units. Extend the two non-parallel sides of the trapezium to form a triangle as shown.

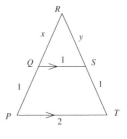

Lines PT and QS are parallel. Hence, using corresponding angles, we know that $\angle TPR = \angle SQR$ and also that $\angle PTR = \angle QSR$. This shows that the two triangles PRT and QRS have equal angles and so are similar. Therefore $\dfrac{x}{x+1} = \dfrac{1}{2}$ which has solution $x = 1$ and $\dfrac{y}{y+1} = \dfrac{1}{2}$ which has solution $y = 1$. Hence triangle QRS is equilateral and so its angles are all $60°$. This means that the base angles of the trapezium are also both $60°$.

Alternative solution:

The only way we can have four positive integers that add up to 5 is $1 + 1 + 1 + 2 = 5$. So the trapezium must be as shown in the diagram on the left. Let this trapezium be $WXYZ$ as shown. Let U and V be the points where the perpendiculars from X and Y meet WZ. Since $WZ = 2$ and $UV = XY = 1$, we have $WU + VZ = 1$. Therefore, if we put together the two right-angled triangles XUW and YVZ, we obtain the equilateral triangle MZW shown on the right. As this is an equilateral triangle, $\angle XWZ = \angle YZW = 60°$.

10. **B** In any set of consecutive integers, there will either be the same number of odd and even numbers, one more odd number or one more even number. Hence the fraction of odd numbers in a set of consecutive integers will either be $\frac{1}{2}$ or be of the form $\dfrac{n}{2n-1}$ or of the form $\dfrac{n}{2n+1}$. The given percentages can be reduced to fractions as follows: $40\% = \frac{2}{5}$, $45\% = \frac{9}{20}$, $48\% = \frac{12}{25}$, $50\% = \frac{1}{2}$ and $60\% = \frac{3}{5}$. Of these, the only one not in an acceptable form is 45%.

11. **A** As the digits involved are 0, 1, 2 and 3, the largest difference will occur when the first digit changes. Hence the only cases that need considering are the change from 1320 to 2013 (difference 693) and the change from 2310 to 3012 (difference 702). This means the largest difference is 702.

12. **A** The value calculated for all four points will be negative. The least value will be obtained by calculating the most negative y-coordinate $\div$ least positive x-coordinate. The most negative y-coordinates are at P and Q while the least positive x-coordinates are at P and S. Hence the point that will give the least value is P.

13. **E** The 6×10 grid can be divided into four 3×5 grids, each intersected by only one diagonal line as shown.

Each time the diagonal crosses a grid line, it enters a new cell.

From a start point in the top left corner of the grid, the line crosses two horizontal grid lines and four vertical grid lines to reach the bottom right corner. On the 3×5 grid, the line does not pass through any points at which the grid lines intersect. The number of cells in the 3×5 grid that the line intersects is $1 + 2 + 4 = 7$. Hence the total number of cells that are *not* intersected is $6 \times 10 - 4 \times 7 = 32$.

14. C Looking horizontally from behind, John will see the largest number of cubes in each column in the table. This means that, from his left, he will see 2, 3, 3 and 4 cubes. Therefore, the shape he will see is C.

15. B Surround the quadrilateral *PQRS* by a rectangle with sides parallel to the grid lines as shown. The area of the rectangle is $14 \times 10 = 140\,\text{cm}^2$. The area of quadrilateral *PQRS* can be calculated by subtracting from this the sum of the areas of the four triangles and one square that lie outside *PQRS* but inside the rectangle from the area of the rectangle. This gives the area of *PQRS* as

$$140 - \tfrac{1}{2} \times 14 \times 2 - \tfrac{1}{2} \times 8 \times 6 - \tfrac{1}{2} \times 6 \times 2 - 2 \times 2 - \tfrac{1}{2} \times 8 \times 2 = 140 - 14 - 24 - 6 - 4 - 8$$
$$= 84 \text{ cm}^2.$$

16. D The expression 2013^6 can also be written as $\left(2013^3\right)^2$. So $1^2, 2^2, \ldots, \left(2013^3\right)^2$ is the list of squares and hence $S = 2013^3$. Similarly $2013^6 = \left(2013^2\right)^3$ and so $Q = 2013^2$. Hence $S = 2013Q$.

17. D Adam must have removed the final digit of his number before adding or the final digit of the sum would have been an even number. If his original number was *ABCDE* then, using this, we have
$52713 = ABCDE + ABCD = 11 \times ABCD + E$. However
$52713 \div 11 = 4792$ remainder 1 so Adam's original number was 47921 which has a digit sum of 23.

18. C The question states that the number of trees between any two maple trees must not equal three. Hence, in any block of eight trees, wherever a maple tree is placed, there must be a corresponding linden tree either four places in front of it or four places behind it. This means that the number of maple trees in any row of eight trees cannot exceed the number of linden trees. This means that in a row of 20 trees, no more than eight of the first 16 trees can be maples and so no more than 12 of the 20 can be maples. This can be achieved as shown below:
$$\text{M M M M L L L L M M M M L L L L M M M M}$$

19. B Andrew finished 21st so 20 runners finished in front of Andrew. This means that Dean finished ahead of $1\tfrac{1}{2} \times 20 = 30$ runners. Let x be the number of runners who finished ahead of Dean. This means that the number of runners who finished after Andrew was $2x$. By considering the total number of runners in the race in two different ways, we obtain the equation $x + 1 + 30 = 20 + 1 + 2x$. This has solution $x = 10$. Therefore, the number of runners in the race is $10 + 1 + 30 = 41$.

20. C In each net, the central 4×1 rectangle can be folded round to form the front, the sides and the back of a cube. The remaining triangles, if correctly positioned, will then fold to form the top and the bottom of the cube. To complete the cube, the triangles must fold down so that the shorter sides of each triangle are aligned with different edges of the top (or bottom) of the cube. It can be checked that this is the case in nets A, B, D and E. However, in net C, the two shorter sides of the lower two triangles would, when folded, align with the same two edges and so could not form a complete face of the cube.

21. A Label the cars 1, 2, 3 and 4 and their original junctions P, Q, R and S respectively. Whichever junction car 1 leaves by, any of the other three cars could leave by junction P. Once car 1 and the car leaving by junction P have been assigned their junctions, we have to consider the other two cars and the other two junctions. However, at least one of these remaining junctions will be the original junction of one of these two cars. Therefore there will be exactly one way in which the two remaining cars can leave by the two remaining junctions. So car 1 can leave by one of three junctions and, for each of these, the remaining cars can leave the roundabout in three different ways. Hence the total number of ways the cars can leave the roundabout is $3 \times 3 = 9$.

22. B From the definition of the sequence, it can be seen that the terms repeat in blocks of three. The sum of the first three terms is -1. In a sequence of 2013 terms, there will be $2013 \div 3 = 671$ sets of three terms. Hence, the sum of 2013 terms of the sequence is $671 \times (-1) = -671$.

23. D In the orderings, the only way it is possible for a smaller number to occur before a larger number would be if the pie corresponding to that larger number has not yet finished baking. In option D, 2 occurs before 3 but as pies 4, 5 and 6 have already been eaten, pie 3 would also have been baked. This means that option D is not possible. (It can easily be checked that all the other options do give possible orderings.)

24. B Let the values at the vertices P, Q, R and S be p, q, r and s respectively. The values on the edges are equal to the sum of the values at the vertices connected by that edge. Each vertex is at the end of three edges. Also, the sum of the values on all the edges and the values on all the vertices must be the same as the sum of the numbers 1 to 11 (excluding 10). Therefore $3(p + q + r + s) + p + q + r + s = 1 + 2 + 3 + 4 + 5 + 6 + 7 + 8 + 9 + 11$. This simplifies to $4(p + q + r + s) = 56$ or $p + q + r + s = 14$. Edge PQ is marked with 9 so that $p + q = 9$. This leaves $r + s = 5$ so edge RS will be marked with 5.

Alternative solution:

Labels 1 and 2 must be placed on vertices as it is impossible to find two numbers from the list that will add to give either 1 or 2. This implies that 3 must be placed on an edge between 1 and 2. Once 3 has been placed on an edge, 4 must be placed on a vertex as the only two numbers in the list that add to give 4 are 1 and 3 and 3 is not on a vertex. Then 11 must be placed on an edge as it is the largest number and so could not be part of any sum. Since the two largest vertex numbers must add to give the largest edge number, the remaining vertex has a value of 7. Hence the numbers on the vertices are 1, 2, 4 and 7. Edge PQ is marked with $9 (= 2 + 7)$ so edge RS must be marked with $5 (= 1 + 4)$.

25. C The three greatest divisors of N are the values obtained by dividing N by its three smallest divisors. To discover when it is possible to have the three greatest divisors of N adding to a value greater than N, it is only necessary to consider the cases when N is divisible by small integers. If N is divisible by 2, 3 and 4 then the sum of the three greatest divisors will be $\dfrac{N}{2} + \dfrac{N}{3} + \dfrac{N}{4} = \dfrac{13}{12}N > N$. Similarly, if N is divisible by 2, 3 and 5 then the sum of the three greatest divisors will be $\dfrac{N}{2} + \dfrac{N}{3} + \dfrac{N}{5} = \dfrac{31}{30}N > N$.

We then note that $N\left(\dfrac{1}{2} + \dfrac{1}{3} + \dfrac{1}{6}\right) = N$ and that $N\left(\dfrac{1}{2} + \dfrac{1}{4} + \dfrac{1}{5}\right) < N$ so that no further cases need to be considered. In both cases where the sum of the divisors is greater than N, N is divisible by 2 and 3. Hence all such N with the desired property are divisible by 6.

2013 European Pink Kangaroo

1. Which of the following is *not* a factor of $200013 - 2013$?

   A 2   B 3   C 5   D 7   E 11

2. The diagram shows six identical squares, each containing a shaded region.

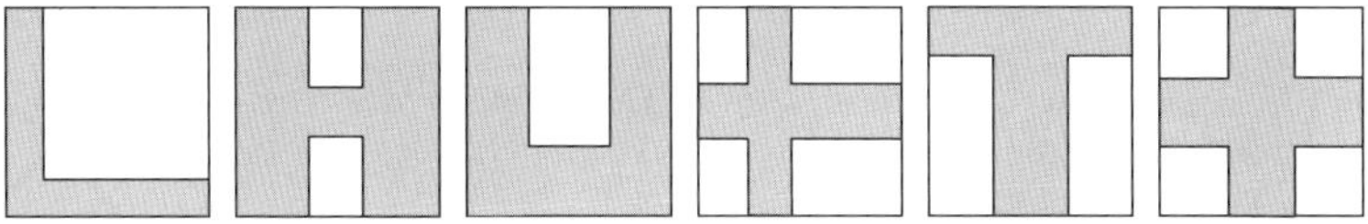

   How many of the regions have perimeter equal in length to the perimeter of one of the squares?

   A 2   B 3   C 4   D 5   E 6

3. Three of the numbers 2, 4, 16, 25, 50, 125 have product 1000. What is the sum of those three numbers?

   A 70   B 77   C 131   D 143   E 145

4. Which of the following is equal to $4^{15} + 8^{10}$?

   A 2^{10} B 2^{15} C 2^{20} D 2^{30} E 2^{31}

5. The outside of a $2 \times 2 \times 2$ cube is painted with black and white squares in such a way that it appears as if it was built using alternate black cubes and white cubes, as shown. Which of the following is a net of the painted cube?

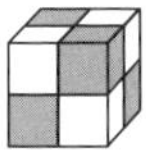

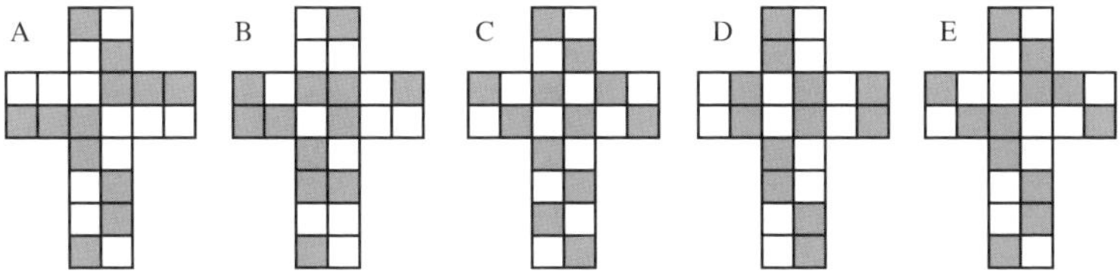

6. The number n is the largest positive integer for which $4n$ is a 3-digit number, and m is the smallest positive integer for which $4m$ is a 3-digit number. What is the value of $4n - 4m$?

   A 900   B 899   C 896   D 225   E 224

7. The trapezium shown in the diagram is rotated anti-clockwise by $90°$ around the origin O, and then reflected in the x-axis. Which of the following shows the end result of these transformations?

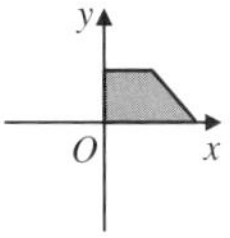

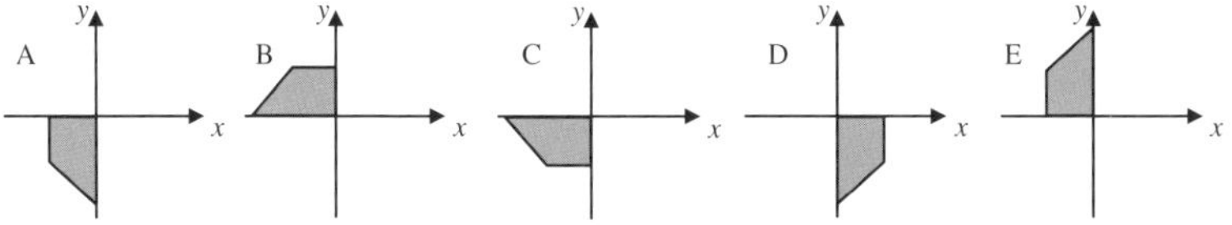

8. Which of the following has the largest value?

   A $20\sqrt{13}$ B $\sqrt{20} \times \sqrt{13}$ C $\sqrt{20} \times 13$ D $\sqrt{201} \times 3$ E $\sqrt{2013}$

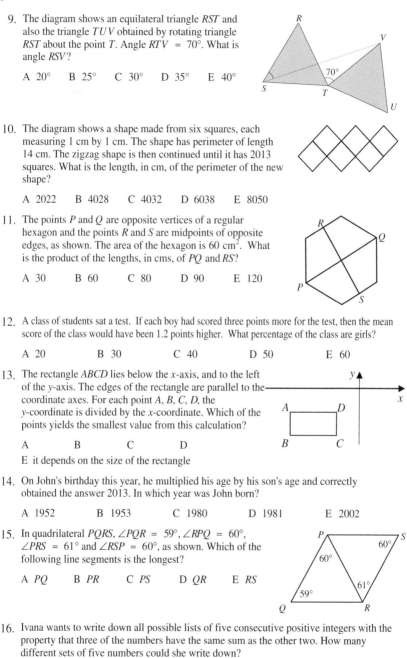

9. The diagram shows an equilateral triangle *RST* and also the triangle *TUV* obtained by rotating triangle *RST* about the point *T*. Angle *RTV* = 70°. What is angle *RSV*?

   A 20°   B 25°   C 30°   D 35°   E 40°

10. The diagram shows a shape made from six squares, each measuring 1 cm by 1 cm. The shape has perimeter of length 14 cm. The zigzag shape is then continued until it has 2013 squares. What is the length, in cm, of the perimeter of the new shape?

    A 2022   B 4028   C 4032   D 6038   E 8050

11. The points *P* and *Q* are opposite vertices of a regular hexagon and the points *R* and *S* are midpoints of opposite edges, as shown. The area of the hexagon is 60 cm². What is the product of the lengths, in cms, of *PQ* and *RS*?

    A 30   B 60   C 80   D 90   E 120

12. A class of students sat a test. If each boy had scored three points more for the test, then the mean score of the class would have been 1.2 points higher. What percentage of the class are girls?

    A 20   B 30   C 40   D 50   E 60

13. The rectangle *ABCD* lies below the *x*-axis, and to the left of the *y*-axis. The edges of the rectangle are parallel to the coordinate axes. For each point *A*, *B*, *C*, *D*, the *y*-coordinate is divided by the *x*-coordinate. Which of the points yields the smallest value from this calculation?

    A   B   C   D
    E it depends on the size of the rectangle

14. On John's birthday this year, he multiplied his age by his son's age and correctly obtained the answer 2013. In which year was John born?

    A 1952   B 1953   C 1980   D 1981   E 2002

15. In quadrilateral *PQRS*, ∠*PQR* = 59°, ∠*RPQ* = 60°, ∠*PRS* = 61° and ∠*RSP* = 60°, as shown. Which of the following line segments is the longest?

    A *PQ*   B *PR*   C *PS*   D *QR*   E *RS*

16. Ivana wants to write down all possible lists of five consecutive positive integers with the property that three of the numbers have the same sum as the other two. How many different sets of five numbers could she write down?

    A 1   B 2   C 3   D 4   E 5

17. How many different paths are there between points P and Q, only travelling along the edges in the direction of the arrows shown?

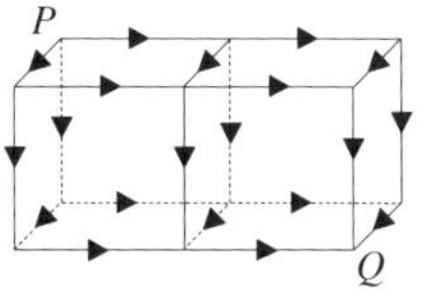

    A 6   B 8   C 9   D 12   E 15

18. How many decimal places are needed after the decimal point to write the fraction $\dfrac{1}{1024000}$ as a decimal, using the smallest possible number of digits?

    A 10   B 11   C 12   D 13   E 14

19. How many positive integers are multiples of 2013 and have exactly 2013 factors (including 1 and the number itself)?

    A none   B 1   C 2   D 3   E 6

20. Using the whole numbers from 1 to 22 inclusive, Sylvie wants to form eleven fractions by choosing one number as the numerator, and one number as the denominator. Every number will be used exactly once. What is the maximum number of Sylvie's fractions that could have an integer value?

    A 11   B 10   C 9   D 8   E 7

21. Julio creates a procedure for turning a set of three numbers into a new set of three numbers: each number is replaced by the sum of the other two. For example, $\{3, 4, 6\}$ becomes $\{10, 9, 7\}$. How many times must Julio apply this procedure to the set $\{1, 2, 3\}$ before he first obtains a set containing the number 2013?

    A 8   B 9   C 10   D more than 10 times   E 2013 will never appear

22. The numbers 1, 2, 3, 4, 5, 6, 7, 8, 9, 10 are to be written around a circle in some order. Then each number will be added to its immediate neighbours to obtain ten new numbers. What is the largest possible value of the smallest of these new numbers?

    A 14   B 15   C 16   D 17   E 18

23. Several non-overlapping isosceles triangles have vertex O in common. Every triangle shares an edge with each immediate neighbour. The smallest of the angles at O has size $m°$, where m is a positive integer and the other triangles have angles at O of size $2m°$, $3m°$, $4m°$, and so on. The diagram shows an arrangement of five such triangles. What is the smallest value of m for which such a set of triangles exists?

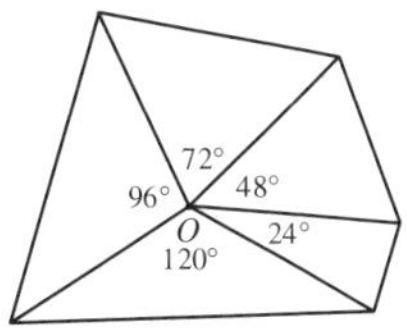

    A 2   B 3   C 4   D 5   E 6

24. A regular 13-sided polygon is inscribed in a circle with centre O. Triangles can be formed by choosing three vertices of this polygon to be the vertices of a triangle. For how many of the triangles formed in this way is the point O inside the triangle?

    A 39   B 72   C 78   D 91   E 260

25. Yurko saw a tractor slowly pulling a long pipe down the road. Yurko walked along beside the pipe in the same direction as the tractor, and counted 140 paces to get from one end to the other. He then turned around and walked back to the other end, taking only 20 paces. The tractor and Yurko kept to a uniform speed, and Yurko's paces were all 1 m long. How long was the pipe?

    A 35 m   B 40 m   C $46\frac{2}{3}$ m   D 80 m   E 120 m

Solutions to the 2013 European Pink Kangaroo

1. D We first find the prime factorisation of $200013 - 2013$. We have $200013 - 2013 = 199000 = 198 \times 1000 = \left(2 \times 3^2 \times 11\right) \times \left(2^3 \times 5^3\right) = 2^4 \times 3^2 \times 5^3 \times 11$. From this we see that 2, 3, 5 and 11 are factors of $200013 - 2013$, but that 7 is not a factor.

2. C Each of the shaded regions is made by cutting rectangles out of the squares. When a rectangle is cut out of a corner it doesn't change the perimeter, but when a rectangle is cut out of an edge then the perimeter of the shaded region is greater than the original perimeter. Hence the perimeters of the first, fourth, fifth and sixth shapes are all equal in length to that of one of the squares, and those of the other two are greater.

3. C The prime factor decomposition of 1000 is $2^3 \times 5^3$ so the three numbers from the list must contain three factors of 2 and three factors of 5 between them. The only factors of 5 appear in $25 = 5^2$, $50 = 2 \times 5^2$ and $125 = 5^3$. The only way to obtain 5^3 from these is to use 125. This leaves 2^3 to be obtained from two other numbers, which can only be done using 2×4.
The sum of these numbers is $2 + 4 + 125 = 131$.

4. E Rewriting each number as a power of two, we get: $4^{15} = \left(2^2\right)^{15} = 2^{30}$ and $8^{10} = \left(2^3\right)^{10} = 2^{30}$. So the sum becomes $2^{30} + 2^{30} = 2 \times 2^{30} = 2^{31}$.

5. E The net of the cube consists of six large squares, each of which is split into four 2×2 squares. Each of these large squares must have 2 black squares and 2 white squares in alternating colours. This eliminates nets A, B, D.
Around each of the 8 vertices of the cube, there are either 3 black squares or 3 white squares. These squares must appear around the vertices in the net of the cube. This eliminates net C which has 2 squares of one colour, and one of the other colour around its vertices. And net E does indeed fold up to make the cube as required.

6. C The largest 3-digit multiple of 4 is 996, and the smallest is 100, so $4n - 4m = 996 - 100 = 896$.

7. A After rotation 90° anticlockwise, we obtain shape E. When reflected in the x-axis this gives shape A.

8. A The expressions can be rewritten as single square roots as follows:
A $20\sqrt{13} = \sqrt{400} \times \sqrt{13} = \sqrt{5200}$
B $\sqrt{20} \times \sqrt{13} = \sqrt{20 \times 13} = \sqrt{260}$
C $\sqrt{20} \times 13 = \sqrt{20} \times \sqrt{169} = \sqrt{3380}$
D $\sqrt{201} \times 3 = \sqrt{201} \times \sqrt{9} = \sqrt{201 \times 9} = \sqrt{1809}$
E $\sqrt{2013}$
It is then easy to see that A is the largest.

9. D Since triangle STR is equilateral, $\angle STR = 60°$. Hence $\angle STV = 130°$. Triangle STV is isosceles (since $ST = TV$), so $\angle TSV = \frac{1}{2}\left(180° - 130°\right) = 25°$. Thus $\angle RSV = 60° - 25° = 35°$.

10. B The two squares at either end of the shape contribute 3 cm towards the total perimeter of the zigzag. Each of the other 2011 squares contribute 2 cm towards the perimeter of the overall shape. Thus the perimeter of the zigzag is $2 \times 3 + 2011 \times 2 = 4028\,\text{cm}$.

11. C   The hexagon can be split into six congruent equilateral triangles. Each triangle has base of length $\frac{1}{2}PQ$ and height $\frac{1}{2}RS$, so the total area is

$$6 \times \tfrac{1}{2} \times \left(\tfrac{1}{2}PQ\right) \times \left(\tfrac{1}{2}RS\right) = \tfrac{3}{4} \times PQ \times RS = 60 \text{ cm}^2.$$

Hence $PQ \times RS = \frac{4}{3} \times 60 = 80$.

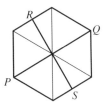

12. E   Let T be the total number of points scored by the class, and let N be the number of students in the class. Let B be the number of boys.

Then the mean is $\dfrac{T}{N}$. If each boy scored an extra 3 points, this would increase T by $3B$, so the mean would be $\dfrac{T + 3B}{N} = \dfrac{T}{N} + \dfrac{3B}{N}$. This new mean would be 1.2 points higher than the original mean, so $\dfrac{3B}{N} = 1.2$, giving $\dfrac{B}{N} = 0.4$. But $\dfrac{B}{N}$ is the proportion of boys in the whole class, so the percentage of boys is 40%, leaving 60% girls.

13. A   Since all the coordinates are negative, each of the calculations will yield a positive value. The smallest value will come from the least negative y-coordinate divided by the most negative x-coordinate; this comes from point A.

14. A   The prime factorisation of 2013 is $3 \times 11 \times 61$. The factor pairs of 2013 are (1, 2013), (3, 671), (11, 183), and (33, 61). The only pair that could realistically be ages is 33 and 61. Hence John is 61 and was born in 1952.

15. A   The triangles are similar because they both contain angles of $59°$, $60°$, $61°$. The smallest side of a triangle is always opposite the smallest angle, so line segment PR is the smallest edge of triangle PQR, though it is not the smallest edge of triangle PRS; hence triangle PQR is larger than triangle PRS and must contain the longest line segment. The longest side in a triangle is opposite the largest angle, so side PQ is the longest (opposite to $\angle PRQ$ which is $61°$).

16. B   Let the five consecutive integers be $n, n + 1, n + 2, n + 3, n + 4$. Ivana wants to split them into a pair and a triple with the same sum. First we show that $n + 4$ cannot be part of the triple. For if it were, then the triple would have a sum of at least $(n + 4) + n + (n + 1) = 3n + 5$, and the pair would have a sum at most $(n + 3) + (n + 2) = 2n + 5$. However, this is impossible since, if n is a positive integer, $2n + 5$ is less than $3n + 5$. Therefore the largest integer $n + 4$ must be in the pair. This gives four possible pairs.

Pair	Triple	Sums equal	Value of n
$(n + 4) + n = 2n + 4$	$(n + 1) + (n + 2) + (n + 3) = 3n + 6$	$2n + 4 = 3n + 6$	-2 (not positive)
$(n + 4) + (n + 1) = 2n + 5$	$n + (n + 2) + (n + 3) = 3n + 5$	$2n + 5 = 3n + 5$	0 (not positive)
$(n + 4) + (n + 2) = 2n + 6$	$n + (n + 1) + (n + 3) = 3n + 4$	$2n + 6 = 3n + 4$	2
$(n + 4) + (n + 3) = 2n + 7$	$n + (n + 1) + (n + 2) = 3n + 3$	$2n + 7 = 3n + 3$	4

There are only two sets of consecutive integers that can work, starting either with 2 or with 4.

17. D The arrows prevent any path from returning to a vertex already visited, so we can enumerate the number of different paths available to each vertex, beginning with the vertices nearest to P and working through to the vertex Q (shown on diagram). The number of paths to a particular vertex accumulate. In particular, Q can be reached from 3 vertices, which themselves can be reached in 3, 3, and 6 ways, so Q can be reached in $3 + 3 + 6 = 12$ ways.

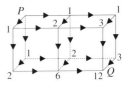

18. D To turn the fraction into a decimal, we need to rewrite it with a denominator that is a power of ten: $\dfrac{1}{1024000} = \dfrac{1}{2^{10} \times 10^3} = \dfrac{5^{10}}{5^{10} \times 2^{10} \times 10^3} = \dfrac{5^{10}}{10^{10} \times 10^3} = 5^{10} \times 10^{-13}$ which has 13 decimal places. This is the least number of decimal places possible because 5^{10} is not divisible by 10.

19. E Let N be a number which is a multiple of 2013 and has exactly 2013 factors. We will show that N must have exactly three distinct prime factors. The prime factor decomposition of 2013 is $3 \times 11 \times 61$ so the prime factor decomposition of N must include powers of 3, 11, and 61; hence N certainly has at least three distinct primes in its prime factor decomposition.

Moreover, N cannot have more than three primes in its prime factorisation. To show this, it is useful to know that the number of factors of a number with prime factor decomposition $p_1^{r_1} \times p_2^{r_2} \times \dots \times p_n^{r_n}$ is $(r_1 + 1)(r_2 + 1)\dots(r_n + 1)$, where each $r_i \geqslant 1$, so each $(r_i + 1) > 1$. So for N to have 2013 factors, it is necessary for the product of these terms to be 2013. But the largest number of integers (greater than 1) that can multiply to make 2013 is three ($3 \times 11 \times 61$). Hence N can have at most three prime factors (3, 11, 61) and, as $(r_1 + 1)(r_2 + 1)(r_3 + 1) = 2013$, they appear with powers 2, 10, 60 in the prime factorisation of N.

Since the powers 2, 10, 60 can be assigned to the primes 3, 11 and 61 in six different ways, and each order yields a different integer N, there are 6 such possible values for N.

20. B Each fraction that Sylvie forms will have integer value if the denominator is a factor of the numerator. It is possible to find ten fractions that have integer values:

$$\frac{13}{1}, \frac{4}{2}, \frac{21}{3}, \frac{15}{5}, \frac{12}{6}, \frac{14}{7}, \frac{16}{8}, \frac{18}{9}, \frac{20}{10}, \frac{22}{11}.$$

It is not possible to make eleven integers. Since 13, 17, 19 are prime but do not have multiples on the list, they can appear only if they are on the numerator with 1 as the denominator. This can happen in only one of them, so the other two must form fractions without integer value (putting them together in the same fraction allows the ten integers listed above).

21. E If Julio starts with a set of three consecutive integers, $\{n - 1, n, n + 1\}$, then applying his procedure gives him $\{2n + 1, 2n, 2n - 1\}$ which, when put in order, is $\{2n - 1, 2n, 2n + 1\}$. That is, he obtains another set of three consecutive integers but with the middle number double that of the original set. Thus when he starts with $\{1, 2, 3\}$, the middle numbers that result from repeatedly applying his procedure are 2, 4, 8, 16, ... , i.e. the powers of two. Since 2013 is not a power of two, nor is it one more or one less than a power of two, it will not appear in any set produced by Julio.

22. B It is possible for the ten new numbers to all be at least 15, and the diagram shows one way of achieving this (a little trial and improvement is required to obtain an example that works).

However, it is not possible for all the new numbers to be at least 16. For if it were possible, then we could split the original numbers 1, 2, …, 10 as follows:

Going clockwise from the number 10, the next three numbers must add to at least 16. The three numbers after that must add to at least 16, and the three numbers after that must add to at least 16.

When we add in the number 10 itself, we have a sum that must be at least $16 + 16 + 16 + 10 = 58$, but we know that the numbers 1, 2, …, 10 add to 55. Hence it is not possible to achieve at least 16.

23. B Let n be the number of triangles with vertex O. Then the sum of the angles at the vertex O is $m + 2m + 3m + … + nm = (1 + 2 + 3 + … + n)m$ and must equal 360 (angles around a point). To minimise m we should find the largest value of n for which $(1 + 2 + 3 + … + n)$ is a factor of 360. Starting with $n = 1$, and increasing n by one each time until the sum exceeds 360, we get 1, 3, 6, 10, 15, 21, 28, 36, 45, 55, 66, 78, 91, 105, 120, 136, 153, 171, 190, 210, 231, 253, 276, 300, 325, 351, 378. The largest one of these that is a factor of 360 is 120, which gives $m = 360 \div 120 = 3$ when $n = 15$.

24. D First consider the triangles that use vertex A. If the second vertex is B, then the only triangle that contains point O must use vertex H.

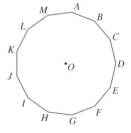

If the second vertex is C, then the third vertex could be H or I (2 triangles).

If the second vertex is D, then the third vertex could be H, I or J (3 triangles).

If the second vertex is E, then the third vertex could be H, I, J or K (4 triangles).

If the second vertex is F, then the third vertex could be H, I, J, K or L (5 triangles).

If the second vertex is G, then the third vertex could be H, I, J, K, L or M (6 triangles).

If the second vertex is H, I, J, K, L, M, then the third vertex would have to be one of B, C, D, E, F, G so these triangles would have been already counted above.

Hence the number of triangles which use vertex A are $1 + 2 + 3 + 4 + 5 + 6 = 21$. Since there are thirteen possible vertices that we could have started with, we might expect 21×13 triangles. But each triangle uses three vertices so we have counted each triangle three times. Hence the number of triangles is $21 \times 13 \div 3 = 91$.

25. A Let d metres be the distance travelled by the tractor in the time it takes Yurko to walk a pace of one metre. When Yurko was walking in the same direction as the tractor, he moved a distance of $1 - d$ metres along the pipe with each pace. It took him 140 paces, so the length of the pipe is $140(1 - d)$ metres. When he is walking in the opposite direction, each pace moves him a distance of $1 + d$ metres along the pipe. It takes 20 paces, so the length of the pipe is $20(1 + d)$ metres. Hence we have $140(1 - d) = 20(1 + d)$, which gives $140 - 140d = 20 + 20d$, leading to $160d = 120$. Then $d = \frac{3}{4}$ so the length is $20\left(1 + \frac{3}{4}\right) = 35$ metres.

(b) *The IMOK Olympiad*

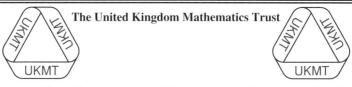

The United Kingdom Mathematics Trust

Intermediate Mathematical Olympiad and Kangaroo (IMOK)

Olympiad Cayley/Hamilton/Maclaurin Papers

Thursday 14th March 2013

READ THESE INSTRUCTIONS CAREFULLY BEFORE STARTING

1. Time allowed: 2 hours.

2. **The use of calculators, protractors and squared paper is forbidden.**
    Rulers and compasses may be used.

3. Solutions must be written neatly on A4 paper. Sheets must be STAPLED together in the top left corner with the Cover Sheet on top.

4. Start each question on a fresh A4 sheet.
    You may wish to work in rough first, then set out your final solution with clear explanations and proofs. *Do not hand in rough work.*

5. Answers must be FULLY SIMPLIFIED, and EXACT. They may contain symbols such as π, fractions, or square roots, if appropriate, but NOT decimal approximations.

6. Give full written solutions, including mathematical reasons as to why your method is correct.
    Just stating an answer, even a correct one, will earn you very few marks; also, incomplete or poorly presented solutions will not receive full marks.

7. **These problems are meant to be challenging!** The earlier questions tend to be easier; the last two questions are the most demanding.
    Do not hurry, but spend time working carefully on one question before attempting another. Try to finish whole questions even if you cannot do many: you will have done well if you hand in full solutions to two or more questions.

DO NOT OPEN THE PAPER UNTIL INSTRUCTED BY THE INVIGILATOR TO DO SO!

The United Kingdom Mathematics Trust is a Registered Charity.
Enquiries should be sent to: Maths Challenges Office,
School of Mathematics, University of Leeds, Leeds, LS2 9JT.
(Tel. 0113 343 2339)
http://www.ukmt.org.uk

2013 Olympiad Cayley Paper

> All candidates must be in *School Year 9 or below* (England and Wales), *S2 or below* (Scotland), or *School Year 10 or below* (Northern Ireland).

1. What is the smallest non-zero multiple of 2, 4, 7 and 8 which is a square?

2. The diagram shows a pentagon $ABCDE$.
   Prove that $a + b + c + d = 180 + e$.

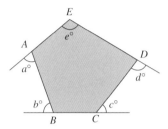

3. Consider sequences of positive integers for which both the following conditions are true:

   (a) each term after the second term is the sum of the two preceding terms;
   (b) the eighth term is 260.

   How many such sequences are there?

4. The positive integer m has leading digit 1. When this digit is moved to the other end, the result is $3m$. What is the smallest such m?

5. Pablo plans to take several unit cubes and arrange them to form a larger cube. He will then paint some of the faces of the larger cube. When the paint has dried, he will split the larger cube into unit cubes again.

   Suppose that Pablo wants exactly 150 of the unit cubes to have no paint on them at all. How many faces of the larger cube should he paint?

6. The diagram shows an *annulus*, which is the region between two circles with the same centre. Twelve equal touching semicircles are placed inside the annulus. The diameters of the semicircles lie along diameters of the outer circle.

   What fraction of the annulus is shaded?

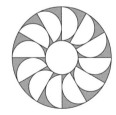

2013 Olympiad Hamilton Paper

> All candidates must be in *School Year 10* (England and Wales), *S3* (Scotland), or *School Year 11* (Northern Ireland).

1. If $xy = 10$ and $(x + 1)(y + 1) = 20$, what is the value of $(x + 2)(y + 2)$?

2. The sides of an equilateral triangle $\mathscr{T}$ are three tangents of a circle $\mathscr{C}$, as shown. Prove that

   $$\frac{\text{area of }\mathscr{C}}{\text{area of }\mathscr{T}} = \frac{\text{circumference of }\mathscr{C}}{\text{perimeter length of }\mathscr{T}}.$$

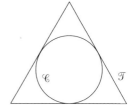

3. Pablo plans to take several unit cubes and arrange them to form a larger cube. He will then paint some of the faces of the larger cube. When the paint has dried, he will split the larger cube into unit cubes again.

   Suppose that Pablo wants exactly 150 of the unit cubes to have no paint on them at all. How many faces of the larger cube should he paint?

4. The vertices of a square have coordinates $(p, 0)$, (a, b), (c, d) and $(0, q)$, where a, b, c, d, p and q are all positive.

   Prove that $p + q = \frac{1}{3}(a + b + c + d)$.

5. When Anne entered the room, the mean age increased by 4 years. When Beth then entered the room, the mean age increased by a further 3 years. Anne and Beth were the same age.

   How many people were in the room before Anne entered?

6. Two snails slither at the same speed around the perimeter of triangle XYZ, in which $\angle Y$ is a right angle. They start together at X, one travelling clockwise, the other anticlockwise, until they meet at the point P on YZ.

   Prove that

   $$\frac{2}{XY} + \frac{1}{YP} = \frac{1}{PZ}.$$

2013 Olympiad Maclaurin Paper

All candidates must be in *School Year 11* (England and Wales), *S4* (Scotland), or *School Year 12* (Northern Ireland).

---

1. Positive integers a, b, c and d are such that

$$a + \cfrac{1}{b + \cfrac{1}{c + \cfrac{1}{d}}} = \frac{20}{13}.$$

   What are the values of a, b, c and d?

2. The positive integer n is such that $n^2 + 20$ is exactly divisible by $n + 2$.

   What are the possible values of n?

3. A circle has centre O and diameter AB. The points C and D lie on the arc $ACDB$ so that AD bisects $\angle BAC$. The line AC is extended to E so that $DE = DA$.

   Prove that $\angle CDE$ is a right angle.

4. Two coins are biased in such a way that, when they are both tossed once:

   (i) the probability of getting two heads is the same as the probability of getting two tails;

   (ii) the probability of getting one head and one tail is $\frac{5}{8}$.

   For each coin, what is the probability of getting a head?

5. Three squares are drawn on the outside of a right-angled triangle, whose shorter sides have lengths a and $2a$. The whole figure is then surrounded by a rectangle, as shown.

   What is the ratio of the area of the shaded region to the area of the rectangle?

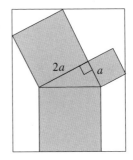

6. All the faces of three identical cubes are to be painted so that 9 faces are green and 9 are yellow. After the paint has dried, the cubes are going to be placed in a velvet bag and given as a gift. So only the colouring can be used to tell two cubes apart.

   How many different gifts are possible?

Solutions to the 2013 Olympiad Cayley Paper

1. What is the smallest non-zero multiple of 2, 4, 7 and 8 which is a square?

   Solution

   The conditions state that the required number is a multiple of 2^1, of 2^2, of 7^1 and of 2^3, respectively. This means that it is a multiple of $2^3 \times 7^1$. Therefore we need to find the smallest non-zero multiple of $2^3 \times 7^1$ which is a square.

   In the prime factorisation of a square number, each prime can only occur an even number of times. Thus the smallest non-zero multiple of $2^3 \times 7^1$ that is also a square is $2^4 \times 7^2$, which is 784.

2. The diagram shows a pentagon $ABCDE$.
   Prove that $a + b + c + d = 180 + e$.

   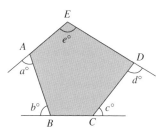

   Solution
   Many different solutions are possible; we give just one.

   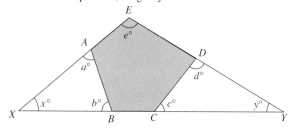

   We extend sides, as shown in the figure: let lines EA, CB meet at X, lines ED, BC meet at Y and let $x°$, $y°$ be the angles of triangle EXY at X and Y respectively.

   Applying 'angles in a triangle add to 180°' to the triangles AXB, CYD and XYE, we get the equations

   $$x + a + b = 180,$$

   $$y + c + d = 180,$$

   and $\quad x + y + e = 180.$

   Adding the first two equations and subtracting the third, we obtain

   $$a + b + c + d - e = 180.$$

   Therefore

   $$a + b + c + d = 180 + e$$

   as required.

3. Consider sequences of positive integers for which both the following conditions are true:

(a) each term after the second term is the sum of the two preceding terms;
(b) the eighth term is 260.

How many such sequences are there?

Solution
Let a and b be the first and second terms respectively. Then the first eight terms are

$$a, b, a + b, a + 2b, 2a + 3b, 3a + 5b, 5a + 8b, 8a + 13b.$$

Hence we seek solutions to the equation

$$8a + 13b = 260, \tag{1}$$

where a and b are positive integers, since any such solution will generate a sequence of positive integers of the required sort.

Now $8a = 260 - 13b = 13(20 - b)$, which is a multiple of 13. Therefore $8a$ is a multiple of 13, so that a is a multiple of 13.

Let $a = 13k$, where k is a positive integer. Then equation (1) becomes

$$8 \times 13k + 13b = 260,$$

so that

$$8k + b = 20.$$

Since b and k are positive integers there are therefore only two possible values for k, namely 1 and 2. When $k = 1$, we have $a = 13$ and $b = 12$. When $k = 2$, we have $a = 26$ and $b = 4$. Hence there are two possible sequences.

4. The positive integer m has leading digit 1. When this digit is moved to the other end, the result is $3m$. What is the smallest such m?

Solution

Method 1

It is useful to find what happens when the digits from 0 to 9 are multiplied by 3. The tables show the resulting last digits.

Digit d	Last digit of $3 \times d$	Digit d	Last digit of $3 \times d$
0	0	5	5
1	3	6	8
2	6	7	1
3	9	8	4
4	2	9	7

We know that $3m$ ends in a 1. From the table, the only digit that can be multiplied by 3 to give a units digit of 1 is 7. Thus m ends in 7 and so $3m$ ends in 71.

Hence we now wish to find a two-digit number '$a7$' which can be multiplied by 3 to give something ending in 71. Since $3 \times 7 = 21$ and $71 - 21 = 50$, we require $3 \times a$ to end in 5, and from the table we deduce that $a = 5$. Thus m ends in 57, and $3 \times 57 = 171$.

Continuing, we wish to find a three-digit number ending in '$b57$' which can be multiplied by 3 to give something ending in 571. In a similar way, we deduce that the only answer is 857, and $3 \times 857 = 2571$.

Similarly, when we look for a four-digit number ending in 857 which can be multiplied by 3 to give something ending in 8571, we find only 2857, and $3 \times 2857 = 8571$.

When we look for a five-digit number ending in 2857 which can be multiplied by 3 to give something ending in 28571, we find $3 \times 42\,857 = 428\,571$.

So m is 142 857, and indeed when we move the 1 to the end we get $428\,571 = 3 \times 142\,857$.

Method 2

The integer m clearly has more than one digit.

Suppose that m has two digits, so that $m = $ '$1a$' and $3m = $ '$a1$'. But '$1a$' $= 10 + a$ and '$a1$' $= 10a + 1$. Therefore we have

$$3(10 + a) = 10a + 1,$$

that is

$$29 = 7a$$

which has no solutions since a is an integer.

Suppose that m has three digits, so that $m = $ '$1ab$'. In a similar way, we obtain

$$3(100 + \text{'}ab\text{'}) = 10 \times \text{'}ab\text{'} + 1,$$

that is

$$299 = 7 \times \text{'}ab\text{'},$$

which also has no solutions since 'ab' is an integer.

Similarly, we find that m cannot have four digits, because $2999 = 7 \times \text{'}abc\text{'}$ has no solutions. Five digits also fails, because 29 999 is not a multiple of 7. But 299 999 is $7 \times 42\,857$. Thus the smallest such m has six digits and is 142 857.

5. Pablo plans to take several unit cubes and arrange them to form a larger cube. He will then paint some of the faces of the larger cube. When the paint has dried, he will split the larger cube into unit cubes again.

Suppose that Pablo wants exactly 150 of the unit cubes to have no paint on them at all. How many faces of the larger cube should he paint?

Solution

Suppose that the larger cube is made up of $n \times n \times n$ smaller cubes.

Now the unpainted smaller cubes form a cuboid, and we can work out the number of unpainted smaller cubes in the form abc. Here a is n (if neither the left nor the right face is painted), or $n - 1$ (if exactly one of the two faces is painted), or $n - 2$ (if both are). Similarly, b is n, $n - 1$ or $n - 2$ depending on which of the front and back faces is painted, and c is n, $n - 1$ or $n - 2$ depending on which of the top and bottom faces are painted.

So we are trying to express 150 as a product of three numbers that differ by at most 2. Now the prime factorisation of 150 is $2 \times 3 \times 5 \times 5$. Combining the 2 and 3 gives $150 = 5 \times 5 \times 6$, which is of the desired form. Any other option has the form $150 = 1 \times r \times s$, or $150 = 2 \times r \times s$ or $150 = 3 \times r \times s$, and none of these is possible since one of r and s will differ from the first factor by more than 2 (indeed, one of r and s will be greater than 7, because $3 \times 7 \times 7 < 150$). Thus $5 \times 5 \times 6$ is the only way of writing 150 in the required form.

Finally, $abc = 5 \times 5 \times 6$ corresponds to either

$$abc = (n - 1) \times (n - 1) \times n \text{ with } n = 6,$$

or

$$abc = (n - 2) \times (n - 2) \times (n - 1) \text{ with } n = 7.$$

These in turn correspond to either two or five faces being painted: if he has made a $6 \times 6 \times 6$ cube he should paint two (adjacent) faces; if he has made a $7 \times 7 \times 7$ cube he should paint five of the six faces.

6. The diagram shows an *annulus*, which is the region between two circles with the same centre. Twelve equal touching semicircles are placed inside the annulus. The diameters of the semicircles lie along diameters of the outer circle.

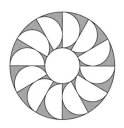

What fraction of the annulus is shaded?

Solution

The twelve diameters of the semicircles are regularly spaced: each is 30° from the next. Consider two adjacent semicircles (see the figure). Let A be the centre of the first, and let B be the point of tangency of the first semicircle with the diameter of the second. Finally, let O be the centre of the annulus.

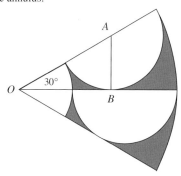

Angle ABO is a right angle, since OB is a tangent and AB is a radius. Thus angle OAB is 60°, because the angles in triangle OAB sum to 180°.

If we let $AB = 1$, then $OA = 2$ (this is a famous property of a 30°, 60°, 90° triangle, coming from considering it as half of an equilateral triangle).

This means that the outer radius of the annulus is 3 and the inner radius is 1, so the annulus has area $\pi \times 3^2 - \pi \times 1^2 = 8\pi$. The semicircles have radius 1, so twelve of them have total area $12 \times \frac{1}{2} \times \pi \times 1^2 = 6\pi$. Therefore the shaded area in the given diagram is $8\pi - 6\pi = 2\pi$.

Hence $\frac{1}{4}$ of the annulus is shaded.

Solutions to the 2013 Olympiad Hamilton Paper

1. If $xy = 10$ and $(x + 1)(y + 1) = 20$, what is the value of $(x + 2)(y + 2)$?

Solution

We are given two equations

$$xy = 10 \tag{1}$$

and

$$(x + 1)(y + 1) = 20. \tag{2}$$

After expanding the left-hand side of equation (2), we obtain

$$xy + x + y + 1 = 20,$$

from which we get, substituting from equation (1),

$$10 + x + y + 1 = 20.$$

Hence

$$x + y = 9. \tag{3}$$

Now we are asked to find the value of

$$(x + 2)(y + 2),$$

which we may expand to obtain

$$xy + 2x + 2y + 4.$$

Rewriting this in the form

$$xy + 2(x + y) + 4$$

we may substitute from equations (1) and (3) to get $10 + 2 \times 9 + 4 = 32$. Hence the value of $(x + 2)(y + 2)$ is 32.

2. The sides of an equilateral triangle $\mathcal{T}$ are three tangents of a circle $\mathcal{C}$, as shown. Prove that

$$\frac{\text{area of } \mathcal{C}}{\text{area of } \mathcal{T}} = \frac{\text{circumference of } \mathcal{C}}{\text{perimeter length of } \mathcal{T}}.$$

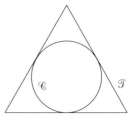

Solution

Let the radius of the circle be r. Hence the circumference of the circle is $2\pi r$ and the area of the circle is πr^2.

The angles in an equilateral triangle are all $60°$.

Join the centre of the circle, a vertex of the triangle, and a point of contact of the triangle and circle, to form the shaded triangle shown in the following figure. Note that the interior of $\mathcal{T}$ may be divided into 6 such triangles.

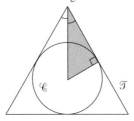

Since the tangent to a circle is perpendicular to the radius, the shaded triangle is right-angled. Also, the line joining the centre of the circle to a vertex of $\mathcal{T}$ bisects the interior angle of $\mathcal{T}$, since the sides of $\mathcal{T}$ are tangents to the circle.

Hence the shaded triangle has angles of $30°$, $60°$ and $90°$, so that it is half an equilateral triangle and therefore its sides are in the ratio $1 : \sqrt{3} : 2$. But one side has length r, so the other two sides have lengths $\sqrt{3}r$ and $2r$.

Therefore the perimeter of $\mathcal{T}$ has length $6 \times \sqrt{3}r$, so that

$$\frac{\text{circumference of } \mathcal{C}}{\text{perimeter length of } \mathcal{T}} = \frac{2\pi r}{6\sqrt{3}r}$$

$$= \frac{\pi}{3\sqrt{3}}.$$

Also, the shaded triangle has area $\frac{1}{2} \times \sqrt{3}r \times r$. Hence $\mathcal{T}$ has area $6 \times \frac{1}{2} \times \sqrt{3}r \times r = 3\sqrt{3}r^2$,

so that

$$\frac{\text{area of } \mathcal{C}}{\text{area of } \mathcal{T}} = \frac{\pi r^2}{3\sqrt{3}r^2}$$

$$= \frac{\pi}{3\sqrt{3}}.$$

It follows that

$$\frac{\text{area of } \mathcal{C}}{\text{area of } \mathcal{T}} = \frac{\text{circumference of } \mathcal{C}}{\text{perimeter length of } \mathcal{T}},$$

as required.

3. Pablo plans to take several unit cubes and arrange them to form a larger cube. He will then paint some of the faces of the larger cube. When the paint has dried, he will split the larger cube into unit cubes again.

Suppose that Pablo wants exactly 150 of the unit cubes to have no paint on them at all. How many faces of the larger cube should he paint?

Solution

Suppose that the larger cube is made up of $n \times n \times n$ smaller cubes.

Now the unpainted smaller cubes form a cuboid, and we can work out the number of unpainted smaller cubes in the form abc. Here a is either n (if neither the left nor the right face is painted), or $n - 1$ (if exactly one of the two faces is painted), or $n - 2$ (if both are). Similarly, b is $n, n - 1$ or $n - 2$ depending on which of the front and back faces are painted, and c is $n, n - 1$ or $n - 2$ depending on which of the top and bottom faces are painted.

So we are trying to express 150 as a product of three numbers that differ by at most 2. Now the prime factorisation of 150 is $2 \times 3 \times 5 \times 5$. Combining the 2 and 3 gives $150 = 5 \times 5 \times 6$, which is of the desired form. Any other option has the form $150 = 1 \times r \times s$, or $150 = 2 \times r \times s$ or $150 = 3 \times r \times s$, and none of these is possible since one of r and s will differ from the first factor by more than 2 (indeed, one of r and s will be greater than 7, because $3 \times 7 \times 7 < 150$). Thus $5 \times 5 \times 6$ is the only way of writing 150 in the required form.

Finally, $abc = 5 \times 5 \times 6$ corresponds to either

$$abc = (n - 1) \times (n - 1) \times n \text{ with } n = 6,$$

or

$$abc = (n - 2) \times (n - 2) \times (n - 1) \text{ with } n = 7.$$

These in turn correspond to either two or five faces being painted: if he has made a $6 \times 6 \times 6$ cube he should paint two (adjacent) faces; if he has made a $7 \times 7 \times 7$ cube he should paint five of the six faces.

4. The vertices of a square have coordinates $(p, 0)$, (a, b), (c, d) and $(0, q)$, where a, b, c, d, p and q are all positive.

Prove that $p + q = \frac{1}{3}(a + b + c + d)$.

Solution

If we rotate the right-angled triangle with coordinates $(0, 0)$, $(p, 0)$ and $(0, q)$, about the centre of the square, through $90°$, $180°$ and $270°$, we form a new larger square, consisting of the original square and four congruent right-angled triangles, as shown. From its construction, we know that the sides of the larger square have length $p + q$.

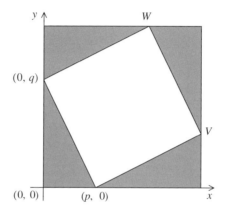

Let V and W be the other two vertices of the original square, as shown. Then V has coordinates $(p + q, p)$ and W has coordinates $(q, p + q)$.

Adding the sum of the coordinates of V to the sum of the coordinates of W, we obtain $(p + q) + p + q + (p + q) = 3(p + q)$.

But V and W are (a, b) and (c, d), in some order. Adding together these four coordinates in the same way, we obtain $a + b + c + d$.

Therefore

$$3(p + q) = a + b + c + d,$$

so that

$$p + q = \frac{1}{3}(a + b + c + d),$$

as required.

Note: We do not know which of V and W is (a, b), and which is (c, d). Given the way we have set out the proof, it does not matter.

5. When Anne entered the room, the mean age increased by 4 years. When Beth then entered the room, the mean age increased by a further 3 years. Anne and Beth were the same age.

How many people were in the room before Anne entered?

Solution

Let n be the number of people in the room before Anne entered, and let m years be the mean age of these n people. Therefore the sum of the ages of these n people is mn years. Finally, let the common age of Anne and Beth be y years.

When Anne entered the room, the total age increased by y to $mn + y$, and the number of people increased by 1 to $n + 1$. But the mean age increased by 4 years. Hence

$$m + 4 = \frac{mn + y}{n + 1},$$

which may be rearranged to give

$$mn + m + 4n + 4 = mn + y,$$

that is,

$$m + 4n + 4 = y. \tag{1}$$

When Beth entered the room, the mean age increased by a further 3 years. Hence

$$m + 7 = \frac{mn + 2y}{n + 2},$$

which may be rearranged to give

$$mn + 2m + 7n + 14 = mn + 2y,$$

that is,

$$2m + 7n + 14 = 2y. \tag{2}$$

Doubling equation (1) and then subtracting equation (2), we obtain $n - 6 = 0$, so that $n = 6$.

Hence there were 6 people in the room before Anne entered.

6. Two snails slither at the same speed around the perimeter of triangle XYZ, in which $\angle Y$ is a right angle. They start together at X, one travelling clockwise, the other anticlockwise, until they meet at the point P on YZ.

Prove that

$$\frac{2}{XY} + \frac{1}{YP} = \frac{1}{PZ}.$$

Solution

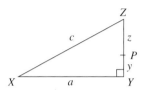

The two snails meet at the point P on YZ. It is convenient to introduce single letter names for the lengths, so let $XY = a$, $XZ = c$, $YP = y$ and $PZ = z$, as shown.

Since the two snails slither at the same speed

$$a + y = c + z,$$

so that

$$c = a + y - z. \tag{1}$$

From Pythagoras' theorem in triangle XYZ, we have

$$a^2 + (y + z)^2 = c^2.$$

Substituting from equation (1), we get

$$a^2 + (y + z)^2 = (a + y - z)^2.$$

When both sides of this equation are expanded, we notice that the terms a^2, y^2 and z^2 (all the square terms) appear on each side. Hence these terms may all be eliminated. Equating the remaining terms on each side, we obtain

$$2yz = 2ay - 2az - 2yz,$$

that is,

$$4yz + 2az = 2ay.$$

Now dividing throughout by $2ayz$, we get

$$\frac{2}{a} + \frac{1}{y} = \frac{1}{z}$$

which is

$$\frac{2}{XY} + \frac{1}{YP} = \frac{1}{PZ},$$

as required.

Solutions to the 2013 Olympiad Maclaurin Paper

1. Positive integers a, b, c and d are such that

$$a + \cfrac{1}{b + \cfrac{1}{c + \cfrac{1}{d}}} = \frac{20}{13}.$$

   What are the values of a, b, c and d?

   Solution
   Since

   $$\frac{20}{13} = 1 + \frac{7}{13}$$

   it follows that $a = 1$ and

   $$\cfrac{1}{b + \cfrac{1}{c + \cfrac{1}{d}}} = \frac{7}{13}.$$

   Therefore

   $$b + \cfrac{1}{c + \cfrac{1}{d}} = \frac{13}{7}$$

   $$= 1 + \frac{6}{7}$$

   and so $b = 1$.
   Continuing this process, we find that $c = 1$ and $d = 6$.
   Note: The expression

   $$1 + \cfrac{1}{1 + \cfrac{1}{1 + \cfrac{1}{6}}}$$

   is an example of a continued fraction.

2. The positive integer n is such that $n^2 + 20$ is exactly divisible by $n + 2$.

   What are the possible values of n?

   Solution
   We are given that $n^2 + 20$ is exactly divisible by $n + 2$. Since

   $$n^2 + 20 = (n - 2)(n + 2) + 24$$

   it follows that 24 is exactly divisible by $n + 2$.
   Now the divisors of 24 are ± 1, ± 2, ± 3, ± 4, ± 6, ± 8, ± 12 and ± 24. However, n is positive, so $n + 2$ is at least 3.
   Therefore the possible values of $n + 2$ are 3, 4, 6, 8, 12 and 24, and the corresponding values of n are 1, 2, 4, 6, 10 and 22.

3. A circle has centre O and diameter AB. The points C and D lie on the arc $ACDB$ so that AD bisects $\angle BAC$. The line AC is extended to E so that $DE = DA$.

Prove that $\angle CDE$ is a right angle.

Solution

Let $\angle BAD$ and $\angle DAC$ be $x°$, and let $\angle DBA$ be $y°$, as shown in the figure.

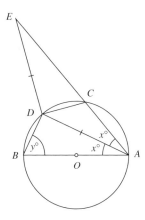

By 'angle in a semicircle', we have $\angle ADB = 90°$, so that $x + y = 90$ from the angle sum of triangle ADB.

Since $DE = DA$, from 'base angles of an isosceles triangle' we have $\angle CED = \angle DAC$, so that $\angle CED = x°$.

Also, from 'external angle of a cyclic quadrilateral' we have $\angle DCE = \angle DBA$, so that $\angle DCE = y°$.

Finally, from the angle sum of triangle DCE it follows that

$$\angle CDE = 180° - x° - y° = 180° - 90° = 90°,$$

as required.

4. Two coins are biased in such a way that, when they are both tossed once:

    (i)   the probability of getting two heads is the same as the probability of getting two tails;

    (ii) the probability of getting one head and one tail is $\frac{5}{8}$.

For each coin, what is the probability of getting a head?

Solution

Let p be the probability of a head on one coin and let q be the probability of a head on the other coin.

Then from condition (i) we have

$$pq = (1 - p)(1 - q),$$

from which, after simplifying, we obtain

$$p + q = 1. \tag{1}$$

Also, from condition (ii) we have

$$p(1 - q) + q(1 - p) = \frac{5}{8},$$

which may be simplified to

$$p + q - 2pq = \frac{5}{8}.$$

Substituting from equation (1), we find

$$1 - 2pq = \frac{5}{8},$$

from which we obtain

$$pq = \frac{3}{16}. \tag{2}$$

From equations (1) and (2) we deduce that p and q are the roots of the qudratic equation

$$16x^2 - 16x + 3 = 0$$

that is

$$(4x - 3)(4x - 1) = 0,$$

so that $x = \frac{3}{4}$ or $x = \frac{1}{4}$. Hence, the two required probabilities are $\frac{1}{4}$ and $\frac{3}{4}$.

84

5. Three squares are drawn on the outside of a right-angled triangle, whose shorter sides have lengths a and $2a$. The whole figure is then surrounded by a rectangle, as shown.

What is the ratio of the area of the shaded region to the area of the rectangle?

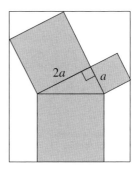

Solution
The areas of the two upper squares are a^2 and $4a^2$, so by Pythagoras' theorem the area of the lower square is $5a^2$, and therefore the sides of the lower square have length $\sqrt{5}a$. Hence the total shaded area is

$$a^2 + 4a^2 + 5a^2 + \tfrac{1}{2}a \times 2a = 11a^2.$$

Now the four shaded triangles in the following figure are all similar, because their corresponding angles are equal. (In fact, two of these triangles are congruent.)

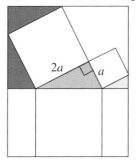

But the original right-angled triangle has sides of length a, $2a$ and $\sqrt{5}a$, so each of these similar triangles has side lengths in the ratio $1 : 2 : \sqrt{5}$.
From this, the breadth of the rectangle is

$$\frac{1}{\sqrt{5}} \times 2a + \sqrt{5}a + \frac{2}{\sqrt{5}} \times a = \frac{9\sqrt{5}}{5}a$$

and the height is

$$\sqrt{5}a + \frac{2}{\sqrt{5}} \times 2a + \frac{1}{\sqrt{5}} \times 2a = \frac{11\sqrt{5}}{5}a.$$

Hence the area of the rectangle is

$$\frac{9\sqrt{5}}{5}a \times \frac{11\sqrt{5}}{5}a = \frac{99}{5}a^2.$$

Therefore the ratio of the area of the shaded region to the area of the rectangle is

$$11a^2 : \frac{99}{5}a^2 = 5 : 9.$$

6. All the faces of three identical cubes are to be painted so that 9 faces are green and 9 are yellow. After the paint has dried, the cubes are going to be placed in a velvet bag and given as a gift. So only the colouring can be used to tell two cubes apart.

How many different gifts are possible?

Solution

It is worth first paying attention to the number of different ways in which a cube can be painted using one colour, say green, to paint various numbers of faces, with all the remaining faces of the other colour.

If 0, 1, 5 or 6 faces are painted green, then there is only one way. If two faces are painted green, then these might be opposite or adjacent faces, so there are two possible ways. If three faces are painted green, then the faces might form a 'collar' (with two opposite faces and one other) or a 'cap' (with no opposite faces), so there are two possible ways.

Now we consider the distribution of faces between the three cubes, in each case counting the number of possible gifts. Note that the order of cubes is not important. The numbers in the first three columns are the number of faces painted green; clearly the remaining faces are painted yellow.

Cube A	Cube B	Cube C	Gifts
6	3	0	$1 \times 2 \times 1 = 2$
6	2	1	$1 \times 2 \times 1 = 2$
5	4	0	$1 \times 2 \times 1 = 2$
5	3	1	$1 \times 2 \times 1 = 2$
5	2	2	3
4	4	1	3
4	3	2	$2 \times 2 \times 2 = 8$
3	3	3	4

In the 5, 2, 2 case, there is just one way to colour cube A, and cubes B and C can either be two opposites, two adjacents or one of each, so there are three different gifts. In the 4, 4, 1 case the argument is the same. In the 3, 3, 3 case, the number of collars can be either 0, 1, 2 or 3, with the remainder being caps, so there are four different gifts.

This yields a total of 26 different gifts.

Comments on the IMOK Olympiad Papers and Scripts

General comments (Gerry Leversha)

Both candidates and their teachers will find it helpful to know something of the general principles involved in marking Olympiad-type papers. The preliminary paragraphs therefore serve as an exposition of the 'philosophy' which has guided both the setting and marking of all such papers at all age levels, both nationally and internationally.

What we are looking for, essentially, is solutions to problems. This approach is therefore rather different from what happens in public examinations, such as GCSE, AS and A level, where credit is given for the ability to carry out individual techniques regardless of how these techniques fit into a protracted argument. Such marking is cumulative; a candidate may gain 60% of the available marks without necessarily having a clue about how to solve the final problem. Indeed, the questions are generally structured in such a way as to facilitate this approach, divided into many parts and not requiring an overall strategy for tackling a multi-stage argument.

In contrast to this, Olympiad-style problems are marked by looking at each question synoptically and deciding whether the candidate has some sort of overall strategy or not. An answer which is essentially a solution, but might contain either errors of calculation, flaws in logic, omission of cases or technical faults, will be marked on a '10 minus' basis. One question we often ask is: if we were to have the benefit of a two-minute interview with this candidate, could they correct the error or fill the gap? On the other hand, an answer which shows no sign of being a genuine solution is marked on a '0 plus' basis; up to 3 marks might be awarded for particular cases or insights. It is therefore important that candidates taking these papers realise the importance of the rubric about trying to finish whole questions rather than attempting lots of disconnected parts.

Cayley (comments from James Cranch)

IMOK Cayley is the UKMT individual and difficult competition targeted at students up to Year 9 in England and Wales, Year S2 in Scotland and Year 10 in Northern Ireland. Between 500 and 600 students participate annually: the format is one paper containing six hard problems, roughly arranged in presumed order of difficulty.

When selecting problems for the paper, we deliberately choose problems which are unusual: reflex applications of routine techniques should not suffice to solve them. The mark schemes are constructed accordingly: a student will only get significant credit for work which exerts control over the problem, and indeed will only get any marks at all for ideas which are useful. What follows are my personal observations, after the marking session. My team of fifteen markers was pleased by the variation and strength of ideas that it found; certainly it is good to see so many students wrestling with challenging problems.

1. There were many ways of solving this problem, and also many ways of going wrong along the way. One can go about this problem by a lengthy check of many possible candidate integers; if carried out studiously, this can of course work correctly. On the other hand, a sufficiently laborious check is almost bound to fail, so we could not rate failed attempts of this sort particularly highly.

   There were various clever insights which reduce the amount of trawling, and which should therefore be worth marks in their own right: for example, pointing out that the answer should be divisible by 28. Ideas which seek to reconcile that fact with the fact that the answer is square are even better!

   We were unable to give much credit to scripts which rapidly obtained the correct answer, but where the justification was lacunary or incoherent. After all, there were a good few attempts which rapidly obtained the wrong answer in a comparably convincing way.

2. This question was found to be the easiest on the paper. Many candidates managed to provide a reasoned argument, starting with standard facts about angles, ending with the desired conclusion. Most solutions began with the observation that the external angles of a convex polygon sum to 360°. There were some impressive methods using only more basic facts, for example, those which extended *EA* and *ED* to meet *BC*, and then from there could reason only about triangles and straight lines.

3. The crux of this problem is consideration of the first two terms, *a* and *b*, of the sequences as described: the first two terms determine the whole sequence, and if they are positive the whole sequence is.

   Thus a natural step, worth significant partial credit, is to reach the equation $8a + 13b = 260$ for the eighth term. A number of students obtained this and couldn't go any further; others guessed either or both of the correct solutions but couldn't justify that those were all. As ever, exhaustive searching is undesirable. In this case a suitable alternative is to use divisibility arguments: it can be seen directly from that equation that *a* is a multiple of 13, and this immediately restricts the problem to being of a manageable character.

88

4. We saw two approaches to this problem: a common, low-tech method where divisibility arguments are used to calculate one digit of the required answer at a time, and a less common, high-tech method, where it is deduced from algebraic rearrangement that the number is an integer of the form $(10^k - 1) \div 7$.

The two approaches are in fact closely connected: the former is in fact simulating the division algorithm on a number of the form $10^k - 1$ for unknown k.

It was heartbreaking to see a number of students find a condition of the form $7 \mid (10^k - 1)$ and then fail to solve it (or even declare, based perhaps on poor experiences with $k < 6$, that there were no solutions). Of course, it is rare indeed that one meets a fourteen-year-old who knows Fermat's little theorem, but this is an example of a situation where a small amount of experience in number theory might improve the student's chance of intuiting what is necessary.

5. A large number of students simply found a solution, either by guesswork or by more organised analysis, and then stopped. In order to obtain a good mark, it is vital to continue the analysis to classify all solutions.

One vital step in the analysis is obtaining a bound on solutions: for example, one may reason that the innermost $(n - 2)^3$ small cubes can never be painted, and this is greater than 150 for $n \geqslant 8$ (where n is the side length of the larger cube).

It is logically less important, but certainly still worthwhile, to reason that for $n \leqslant 5$ there are not enough small cubes to provide 150. Indeed, this only rules out five cases, whereas the upper bound rules out infinitely many to make the problem finite.

Having obtained such bounds, one must of course carefully check each of the remaining cases! If things are done as I indicate, $n = 6$ and $n = 7$ are all that remains, and in fact both turn out to be possible.

6. Only few students were confident in attempting this problem. Of those who tried it, many took as given the most interesting portion of the problem: that the outer semicircles have the same radius as the inner circle. This requires some technique to prove, and it is easy to guess that many of these students assumed it out of wishful thinking, having tried and failed to prove it.

Hamilton (comments from Stephen Power)

The Hamilton paper as a whole proved to be a good test of the candidates as the problems varied in difficulty from the relatively straightforward to the rather tricky. It was also pleasing to see that almost all candidates managed to get to grips with at least one problem and very low marks were relatively rare. At the other end of the spectrum, candidates scoring over 40 marks out of a possible 60 did very well indeed and to reach the giddy heights of scoring over 50 was exceptionally good.

The variety and quality of the scripts was impressive–well done to all who took part.

The most important repeated error was for candidates to start from the result they were supposed to be proving. This is a very bad idea and resulted in rather a lot of wasted time. In particular, this error occurred regularly in responses to Questions 2, 4 and 6. Even if candidates did not make this error early in Question 2, there was still the problem later on of showing that the desired equation was true. This should be done carefully, evaluating each side separately, and then finally showing that the two quantities are equal to each other.

The other general difficulty was that sometimes when a candidate found one solution that worked they just stopped at that point, presumably thinking they had finished. They failed to check for other solutions or, if they thought they had found all possible solutions, they did not *prove* that there were no more. Candidates need to realise that Olympiad problems are not just about finding a solution, they are about finding all possible solutions and justifying that all solutions have been found.

A final general point, some otherwise perfect solutions were marred by the fact that no words were used to explain what the candidate had done. It is a shame that marks were lost for the sake of an occasional helpful word or two.

1. This was a relatively straightforward problem which could be completed in a few lines of accurate algebra. One method is to expand the brackets in both the equation $(x + 1)(y + 1) = 20$ and the expression $(x + 2)(y + 2)$ and then to replace xy in each by 10. The equation then reduces to $x + y = 9$ which helps when evaluating the expression.

   An alternative method involves substituting $y = \frac{10}{x}$ into the given equation, expanding the brackets and then solving the resulting quadratic to find y. Then the corresponding values of x are found. These values are substituted into $(x + 2)(y + 2)$, which, after plenty of simplification, reduces in each case to the answer of 32. Unfortunately, the quadratic does not factorise and so candidates adopting this approach had to work with the surd forms. This method is best avoided unless no other option is apparent since the level of care needed to carry through the solution to its conclusion is high.

2. This problem produced a variety of methods, including a very pleasing one which splits the triangle into three identical isosceles triangles, each with one vertex at the centre of the original triangle. Using this dissection means that the perpendicular height of each triangle is the radius of the circle and so all four required quantities can be expressed easily in terms of the side length of the large triangle and the radius of the circle.

In general, most candidates either worked from the radius of the circle until they found the perpendicular height of the triangle in terms of the radius, or they started with the side length of the triangle and found the radius in terms of this length.

As mentioned already, care was needed to establish the required result in a logically correct way.

A few candidates used 1 unit as the radius of the circle and, if it was clear that this was not a case of plucking an easy value out of the air, then this was accepted as valid.

3. This problem was found to be harder and less familiar than others. Candidates needed to find upper and lower bounds for the problem. The lower bound, spotted by most candidates, comes from noting that the side length of the original cube, n say, has to be more than 5 otherwise there will not be enough cubes to have 150 unpainted. The (slightly more subtle) upper bound is found by considering the $(n - 2)^3$ cubes that will always remain unpainted no matter how many faces Pablo paints. So n has to be less than 8. This means that 6 and 7 are the only possible values of n and both need to be checked carefully to see if they lead to solutions.

Far too many candidates found one solution for one case and then stopped. Failure to realise that there could be more solutions led to low marks for candidates who presumably thought that they had solved the problem.

4. Many candidates assumed that the diagonals of the square are parallel to the axes. Of course, this is not true in general.

Drawing a diagram carefully helped candidates to see that surrounding the square with a larger square with sides parallel to the axes gives rise to four congruent triangles. Justification of the congruence of these triangles was needed to achieve full marks. Consideration of the coordinates and their relationships to each other and to the side length of the larger square quickly leads to four equations, expressing a, b, c

and d in terms of p and q. The required final result is obtained by adding these equations and rearranging.

A few alternative approaches were seen, for example, using triangles *inside* the original square.

5. Generally, two approaches to this problem were seen. The first approach constructs fractions representing the mean after Anne's arrival and after Beth's arrival, and relates each fraction to the given increase in the mean. This gives two equations in three unknowns, which can be solved simultaneously since one of the unknowns is automatically eliminated.

A second, more intuitive, approach was used by some candidates, who split the ages of Anne and Beth into parts consisting of the previous average age and then enough blocks of 4 years (for Anne) or 3 years (for Beth) to increase everyone's ages, including their own, by the amount needed to reach the new mean. When Anne and Beth's ages are equated, this method produces one equation in two unknowns. Since one of the variables is automatically eliminated this equation leads to the answer of 6 people originally in the room.

Some candidates claimed they could take the original average age to be a particular number of years (for example, 2 years, or sometimes even 0 years). This claim was not totally unreasonable as the problem is framed in such a way that all the quantities involved are relative. A different problem might have included, for example, doubling an age, in which case the relative nature disappears and letting the original average age be a particular value would not work. If the candidate had made it clear that they understood that this problem was of a type that allowed considering the average age to be a particular value then they were given full credit.

6. This problem was answered well by very few candidates. There were three key points. Firstly that the snails travel equal distances, secondly that the triangle is right-angled so Pythagoras' theorem may be applied, and finally that P splits YZ into two line segments. A single equation in the three lengths required is obtained by combining these ideas algebraically. The process of rearranging this equation into the required form was found difficult and was achieved by relatively few candidates.

Maclaurin (comments from Gerry Leversha)

1. This is really just arithmetic. It was sufficient for candidates to demonstrate that they could carry out the algorithm to turn a rational number into a simple continued fraction. No proof of uniqueness of a, b, c, d was required, since we wanted this to be an opportunity for weaker candidates to solve a whole problem. One common mistake, made by those who adopted a more 'algebraic' approach, was to assume that if two fractions were equal, so were their numerators and denominators. In fact, an argument using coprimality could, in some cases, make this approach work.

2. This number theory problem required the candidates to find bounds for the values of n and so render the search procedure finite. This can be done by forming a polynomial identity which allows algebraic 'long division' to take place and so leads to the fact that $(n + 2) \mid 24$. It was only necessary to consider positive factors greater than 2. We did not penalise candidates who believed that zero was a positive integer. However, if the solution $n = -1$ was included, arising from $n + 2 = 1$, we did penalise this, since if you are going to allow this value of n, the logical consequence is to look at all negative factors of 24.

3. This geometry problem needs an appeal to isosceles triangles, angle in a semicircle and a fact about cyclic quadrilaterals. We required the use of these results to be mentioned explicitly. Solutions which appealed to symmetry were sometimes suspect and, as usual, we were careful to penalise attempts which assumed what was meant to be proved.

4. The criterion for reaching the threshold between '10 minus' and '0 plus' was the formation of two simplified simultaneous equations about probabilities, such as $p + q = 1$ and $pq = \frac{3}{16}$. It was clear that many candidates were then unable to form a quadratic equation and solve it, which is disappointing since this is on the GCSE curriculum. Many candidates were very clumsy in choosing variables to use in forming equations. A common assumption made was that the two coins must be 'complementary' in that the probabilities of head and tail were reversed. This can easily be deduced from the equation $(1 - p)(1 - q) = pq$, of course, but we were not happy with a bland statement and no justification.

5. The key stage in solving this problem is to find a way of calculating the side lengths of the bounding rectangle. This requires consideration of triangles which are similar to the original $(1, 2, \sqrt{5})$ triangle. Some indication of why the triangles were similar was required.

6. This problem required the candidates to address two questions:
   I. How many ways can 9 be divided into three parts, in order?
   II. In how many ways can a cube be painted using one colour, say green, to paint various numbers of faces, with all the remaining faces of the other colour?

Candidates then needed to combine these two factors in the final enumeration. We were also looking for coherent communication of method. We were very pleased with the number of successful solutions and the clarity of the exposition. The 'difficult' partitions were (5, 2, 2), (4, 4, 1) and (3, 3, 3), and it was here that most mistakes were made.

Marking

The marking was carried out on the weekend of 22nd – 24th March in Leeds. There were three marking groups led by James Cranch, Stephen Power and Gerry Leversha. The other markers are listed later in this book.

IMOK certificates

All participating students who qualified automatically were awarded a certificate. These came in three varieties: Participation, Merit and Distinction.

Intermediate Mathematical Olympiad and Kangaroo 2013

of

received a

CERTIFICATE of DISTINCTION

Chairman, United Kingdom Mathematics Trust

THE UKMT INTERMEDIATE MATHEMATICAL OLYMPIAD AND KANGAROO

The IMOK is the follow-on round for the Intermediate Mathematical Challenge and is organised by the UK Mathematics Trust. For each year group, the top scoring 500 or so IMC pupils are invited to participate in the Olympiad, and the next 1700 are invited to participate in the European Kangaroo. Schools may also enter additional pupils to the Olympiad upon payment of a fee; the Kangaroo is by invitation only.

The Olympiad is a two-hour examination which includes six demanding questions requiring full written solutions. The problems are designed to include interesting and attractive mathematics and may involve knowledge or understanding beyond the range of normal school work.

The one-hour multiple choice European Kangaroo requires the use of logic as well as mathematical understanding to solve amusing and thought-provoking questions. The 'Kangourou sans Frontières' is taken by students in over forty countries in Europe and beyond.

The UKMT is a registered educational charity. See our website www.ukmt.org.uk for more information.
Donations would be gratefully received and can be made at
www.donate.ukmt.org.uk if you would like to support our work in this way.

IMOK Olympiad awards

As in recent years, medals were awarded in the Intermediate Mathematical Olympiad. Names of medal winners are listed below. Book prizes were awarded to the top 50 or so pupils in each year group. For those in the Cayley the prize was *How Many Socks Make a Pair?* by Rob Eastaway; in the Hamilton, *The History of Mathematics, a very short introduction* by Jacqueline Stedall; and in the Maclaurin, *Letters to a Young Mathematician* by Ian Stewart.

How many 4-digit integers have digits which are four consecutive numbers in some order?

For example:

IMOK medal winners

Cayley

Hugo Aaronson	St Paul's School, London
Babatomi Adebiyi	Twyford CofE High School, Acton
Samuel Ahmed	King's College School, London
Agnijo Banerjee	Grove Academy, Dundee
Luke Barratt	Backwell School, North Somerset
Joe Benton	St Paul's School, London
Patrick Bevan	Perse School, Cambridge
Colin Brown	Winchester College
Rosie Cates	Perse School, Cambridge
Alex Chen	Westminster Under School
Yifei Chen	Cardiff High School
James Chong	Charterhouse
Jongihn Chung	Perse School, Cambridge
Robert Clark	St Paul's School, London
Nathanie Cleland	Gillingham School, Dorset
Timothy Cooper	Myton School
Adam Cox	Marling School, Stroud
Jacob Coxon	Magdalen College School
William Davies	Reading School
Richard Efezeybek	Bournemouth School
Krishan Emmanuel	Harrow School
Wendi Fan	North London Collegiate School

Ian Fan	Dr Challoner's Grammar School, Amersham
Douni Fosterhall	Henrietta Barnett School, London
Ludo Fraser-Taliente	Eton College, Windsor
Kit Fraser-Taliente	Eton College, Windsor
Alex Fruh	St Aloysius College
Henry Griffiths	Brooke Weston Academy
Elizabeth Hayman	Bartholomew School
Curtis Ho	Harrow School
Alex Horner	City of London School
Charlie Hu	City of London School
Matthew Hutton	Royal Grammar School (Newcastle)
Bhang Hyoungjo	North London Collegiate School Jeju
Tiger Ji	Westminster School
Toby Jowitt	King Edward's School, Birmingham
Jenny Jung	Beijing Dulwich International School
Gyu Hyun Jung	North London Collegiate School Jeju
Om Kanchanasakdic	Bangkok Patana School
Hyerin Kang	North London Collegiate School Jeju
Ryan Kang	Westminster Under School
Taeho Kang	British School Muscat
Jia Kim	Wycombe Abbey School, High Wycombe
Jaehyeon Kim	Perse School, Cambridge
Ragyeom Kim	British International School of Shanghai (Puxi)
Sunjin Kim	North London Collegiate School Jeju
Siwoo Kim	King Edward's School, Birmingham
Yuma Kitahara	Westminster School
Steve Ko	British International School Vietnam
Joanna Lake	Henrietta Barnett School, London
Hanna Lee	North London Collegiate School Jeju
Alex Lee	Taipei European School
Jimmy Liu	Reading School
Jacob Mair	Burnham Grammar School, Slough
Diamor Marke	Wallington County Grammar Sch., Surrey
Rory McLaurin	Hampstead School, London
Adam Mombru	Eton College, Windsor
Protik Moulik	Westminster School
William Muraszko	Charter School, London

Neel Nanda	Latymer School, London
Michael Ng	Aylesbury Grammar School
Daisuke Nishikiori	Overseas Family School
Oyku su Okkan	American Collegiate Institute
Joshua Oliver	St Albans School
Nicholas Palmer	St Paul's School, London
Daniel Pavesio	Westminster School
Matthew Penn	Redland Green School, Bristol
Thomas Pycroft	Whitchurch High School
Otto Pyper	Eton College, Windsor
Benedict Randall Shaw	Betty Layward Primary School, London
Mukul Rathi	Nottingham High School
Thomas Read	Perse School, Cambridge
William Saunter	St Paul's School, London
Uijun Seo	North London Collegiate School Jeju
Akhi l Seth	Harrow School
Nishadh Shakir	Dr Challoner's Grammar School, Amersham
Pratap Singh	Perse School, Cambridge
Sinem Sinmaz	American Collegiate Institute
Roan Talbut	Perse School, Cambridge
Euan Tebbutt	Twycross House School
Yujie Teng	Harrow International School, Beijing
Daniel Townsend	Colchester Royal Grammar School
Jim Tse	Coombe Boys' School, Surrey
Yuriy Tumarkin	Durham Johnston School
Laurence Vansomeren	Kings College School, Cambridge
David Veres	King Edward VI School, Southampton
Clemens Vonstengel	City of London School
Helen Wang	Tiffin Girls' School, Kingston-upon-Thames
Alex Wang	Eton College, Windsor
Naomi Wei	City of London Girls' School
Lennie Wells	St Paul's School, London
Joel Williams	St George's School
Bill Xuan	King Edward's School, Birmingham
Harvey Yau	Ysgol Dyffryn Taf
Minghua Yin	Reading School
Jack You	Eton College, Windsor

Jun Young Hoo	North London Collegiate School Jeju
Sechan Yun	Perse School, Cambridge
Duo Zhao	Simon Langton Girls' School
Liam Zhou	Westminster School

Hamilton

Kaushal Alate	UWCSEA Dover Campus
Howard Au	Winchester College
George Bateman	Marlborough School
Alistair Bayliss	Perins Community School
Jamie Bell	King Edward VI Five Ways S., Birmingham
William Brassington	London Oratory School
Wenbo Cao	Highgate School, London
Matthew Chaffe	Littleover Community School, Derby
James Chan	Lancing College
Zhuchan Chen	Overseas Family School
James Chen	Ruthin School
Jason Cheung	Renaissance College
Minhyuk Choi	Winchester College
Euijin Choi	Wilson's School, Surrey
Calvin Chow	Concord College
Jeffrey Chu	Tonbridge School
Nathen Chung	King Edward's School, Birmingham
Esha Dasgupta	Sutton Coldfield Grammar School for Girls
John Dawson	Friends' School Lisburn
Friso De graaf	St Paul's School, London
Nicholas Dyson	Bootham School
Angel Fang	Longridge Towers School
Harry Goodburn	Wilson's School, Surrey
Caroline Harwin	Kendrick School, Reading
Jeremy Ho	King Edward's School, Birmingham
Donald Hobson	Webster's High School
Matthias Hoffmanvagenheim	Manchester Grammar School
Lawrence Hollom	Churcher's College
Haolin Hou	Oakham School
Michael Hu	Bristol Grammar School
Lucas Huysmans	Beaumont School
Suk joon Hwang	UWCSEA Dover Campus

Jeongseok Hyun	British Int. School of Shanghai (Puxi)
Kiwan Hyun	North London Collegiate School Jeju
Sumire Isomura	Mount School, London
Nicholas Jelicic	King's College School, London
Matthew Johnson	Whitgift School, Surrey
Jeon Jongheon	Winchester College
Tomoka Kan	St Paul's Girls' School, Hammersmith
Shane Kang	British International School Vietnam
Anthony Kattuman	Perse School, Cambridge
Muhammed Khan	King Edward VI Camp Hill Boys' S., Birmingham
Hyunjin Kim	British Int. School of Shanghai (Puxi)
Young Kim	Claremont Fan Court School
Thomas Knowles	Eton College, Windsor
Seonwo o Ko	Bromsgrove International School Thailand
Xiangjia Kong	Ermysted's Grammar School
Yoonmo Koo	Sir James Henderson School
John Kwon	Winchester College
Kirsten Land	Hornsey School for Girls, London
Howard Lao	Ashford School
Filipp Lavrentiev	Magdalen College School
Suelynn Lee	Cranbrook School, Kent
Jinju Lee	Badminton School, Bristol
June Lee	Norwich School
Yoo jin Lee	UWCSEA Dover Campus
Ethan Lewis	Archbishop Holgate's School
Jackie Li	St Paul's Girls' School, Hammersmith
Andy Lin	Battle Abbey School, East Sussex
Nian Liu	Gryffe High School
Sophie Maclean	Watford Grammar School for Girls
Colin Mao	Beijing Dulwich International School
Callum Mclean	Harrow School
Stephen Mitchell	St Paul's School, London
Conor Murphy	Eltham College, London
Popo Nittayawan	St Stephen's International School
Sabrina Niu	Harrow International School, Beijing
Jack Palmer	St Paul's School, London
Claire Pan	Plymouth College
Krit Patarapak	Charterhouse

Philip Peters	Haberdashers' Aske's School for Boys
Rebecca Poon	George Watson's College
Edward Rong	Westminster School
Lee Sanghyeon	Kolej Tuanku Jaafar
Daniel Saunders	Bradfield School, Sheffield
Sam Seo	North London Collegiate School Jeju
Harry Sha	Beijing Dulwich International School
Ben Sharples	Tadcaster Grammar School
Bemin Sheen	Tiffin School, Kingston-upon-Thames
Xinyu Shen	Winterbourne International Academy, Bristol
Finlay Stafford	Newfield School, Sheffield
Elliott Suen	West Island School (ESF)
Yeonju Suh	North London Collegiate School Jeju
Alan Sun	City of London School
Coco Sun	St Mary's School, Dorset
Adrian Tang	West Island School (ESF)
Lucy Wang	St Mark's RC School, Harlow
Yifan Wang	Roedean School, Brighton
Jessica Wang	South Island School
Bill Wangjiachen	King Edward's School, Birmingham
Sam Watt	Monkton Combe School, Bath
Alfred Wong	Reading School
Zheneng Xie	King Ecgbert School, Sheffield
Christopher Ye	Beijing Dulwich International School
Minsoo Yeo	North London Collegiate School Jeju
Helena Yu	Ratcliffe College
Cindy Yu	Wycombe Abbey School, High Wycombe
Joseph Zhu	Oxford Spires Academy

Maclaurin

Olivia Aaronson	St Paul's Girls' School, Hammersmith
Ashwin Agarwal	Eton College, Windsor
Harshvadhan Bakshi	UWCSEA Dover Campus
Jamie Bamber	Perse School, Cambridge
Nodar Barbakadze	St Paul's School, London
Mark Bobrovnikov	Whitgift School, Surrey
Joseph Boorman	Eton College, Windsor
James Bowler	Queen Elizabeth Grammar S., Wakefield
Clement Chan	King Edward's School, Birmingham

John Chen	Sedbergh School, Cumbria
Guy Cheng	Winchester College
Cyrus Cheng	Wells Cathedral School
Joanna Cheng	South Island School
Daniel Chiverton	Bishop Challoner RC School
Yejin Choi	North London Collegiate School Jeju
Kevin Choi	Sha Tin College
Horace Chu	German Swiss International School
Wan fung Chui	West Island School (ESF)
Alexander Cliffe	Casterton Business and Enterprise College
Stephen Cole	Cockermouth School, Cumbria
Samuel Coy	Forest School, London
Robert Davidson	Trinity School, Croydon
Joe Davies	Lawrence Sheriff School
Luofei Dong	King's School Ely, Cambridgeshire
George Dunlop	Winchester College
Chris Eum	Harrow International School, Beijing
Barnaby Fogg	Queen Elizabeth High S., Gainsborough
George Fortune	Altrincham Grammar S. for Boys, Cheshire
James Fraser	Winchester College
Joshua Garfinkel	Latymer School, London
Luke Gostelow	Hampton School, Middlesex
Alex Gunasekera	Magdalen College School
Georgina Hansen	St Paul's Girls' School, Hammersmith
Phil Hardalupas	St Paul's School, London
Liu He	Concord College
Shinichi Hirata	ACS International School
Kevin Ho	Tonbridge School
Chanhee Hong	Frankfurt International School
Liam Hughes	Robert Smyth School
David Hui	The King's School Worcester
Andrew Hui	Queen Elizabeth's School, Barnet
Oliver Hulme	Beverley Grammar School
Byungjun Hwang	Beijing Dulwich International School
Jared Jeyaretnam	Westminster School
Stephen Jones	Magdalen College School
Gareth Jones	Clifton College, Bristol
Bumsue Jun	North London Collegiate School Jeju
Hrutvik Kanabar	Eton College, Windsor

Gyeong-Hyun Kim	Eton College, Windsor
Daniel Kim	Westminster School
Min Kim	Monkton Combe School, Bath
Samuel Kittle	Simon Langton Boys' Grammar School
Balaji Krishna	Stanwell School
Kelvin Leung	Loughborough Grammar School
Jihon Lim	Renaissance College
Milton Lin	Taipei European School
Chen Lu	Eton College, Windsor
Cong Lu	Robert Gordon's College
Yuan Ma	Concord College
Georgina Majury	Down High School
Bhavik Mehta	Queen Elizabeth's School, Barnet
Harry Metrebian	Winchester College
Rachel Mok	Headington School
Junya Morioka	Haberdashers' Aske's School for Boys
Yuen Ng	Rainham Mark Grammar School
Andrew Orr	Hampton School, Middlesex
Kiryun Park	Dulwich College
James Pigden	Dame Alice Owen's School
Noah Porcelli	Cherwell School
Mukunth Raveendran	Haberdashers' Aske's School for Boys
Alex Rice	Judd School
Marcus Roberts	The Grammar School at Leeds
Bony Roy	Aylesbury High School
Ethan Sciamma	St Paul's School, London
Ayush Shah	Overseas Family School
Chikashi Shirakawa Rison	King's School Ely, Cambridgeshire
Edward Sides	Notre Dame High School, Sheffield
Polina Sklarevica	Sidcot School, Somerset
Toby Swann	Cowbridge Comprehensive School
Dhruv Tapasvi	The British School, New Delhi
Marguerite Tong	St Paul's Girls' School, Hammersmith
John Trusted	Eton College, Windsor
Paul Vallis	Plymouth College
Kavin Vijayakumar	Bancroft's School, Essex
Benjie Wang	Cantell College
Kim Ward	King Edward VI School, Southampton
Fraser Waters	Redland Green School, Bristol

Matthew Wilson	St Edmund's College
Timothy Xu	Brighton College
Jensen Yang	Taipei European School
Jeremy Yang	Beijing Dulwich International School
Joanna Yass	North London Collegiate School
David You	Beijing Dulwich International School
Bohan Yu	Cherwell School
Yi Zhang	Culford School
Danshu Zhang	Blackheath High School, London
Roy Zhang	Reading School
Zigan Zhen	Bellerbys College, Brighton
Caroline Zhou	Kent College (Canterbury)

National Mathematics Summer Schools
July 7th–12th and July 14th–19th, 2013

In 2013, as in recent years, there were two summer schools. Participants for the first week were selected predominantly on the basis of performance in the Intermediate Challenge, and were from schools which had not recently been represented at a summer school; those for the second week were predominantly selected on the basis of scores in the Hamilton or Maclaurin Intermediate Mathematical Olympiad papers.

Week One

As in 2012, the first week was under the auspices of Vicky Neale and her report follows:

Where were you when Andy Murray won Wimbledon? A group of enthusiastic mathematicians were converging on Woodhouse Grove School, located between Leeds and Bradford, for five days of intensive mathematics. Some of the staff were coming to their first summer school, others were old hands, but the venue was new for all of us. We were joined by six seniors, who had all been to a UKMT camp before, and also by forty-one juniors having their first taste of a maths summer school. They arrived a little nervously, not quite knowing what to expect and not knowing anyone, but they soon settled in and by the end of the week there was much tearful hugging at the prospect of departure.

After the excitement of the tennis, and of trying to find the right bedrooms, we got stuck in to the maths. The students were in six teams, named after the mathematicians Lovelace, Maclaurin, Noether, Pappus, Quetelet and (Mary Ellen) Rudin. One of the first tasks on Sunday evening was to learn a little more about the lives and work of these mathematicians.

We spent each morning working on team activities, concentrating on number theory and geometry. The students, with the help of the seniors, tackled a sequence of challenging problems that led to them discovering all sorts of interesting mathematics. The geometry team session on Thursday morning was led by the seniors, who had been given 24 hours' notice that they were going to do this. We asked them to prepare activities on the theme of cyclic quadrilaterals, and they did an excellent job. In fact, the seniors did an excellent job all week.

In the afternoons, we had sessions on an eclectic mix of mathematics, from fractals to the pigeonhole principle, cyclotomic polynomials to spherical geometry, slicing spaces to learning to count. In parallel, the seniors had their own programme of sessions on more advanced topics, including further number theory and functional equations.

The evenings saw a range of activities. On Monday evening, we used the school theatre to show a mathematical film, which led to a great discussion afterwards. Tuesday evening was devoted to mathematical relays, which was good fitness training for the bowling on Wednesday. And Thursday saw the traditional mathemusical extravaganza, which demonstrated what a diverse range of talents the students have alongside mathematics. Following the seniors' performance, some of us were lost for words.

We were fortunate to have beautiful sunshine and warm weather all week (possibly even too warm, sometimes). The students were able to sit outside on the grass, with the more energetic opting to play football and frisbee, while the staff sat on the terrace enjoying the sunshine and discussing mathematics (honest). The geometry equipment was as popular as ever, and the students made good use of our mathematical mini-library.

All too soon, it was Friday lunchtime and time to go home. Parents appeared to collect their offspring, while other students went off to the station in taxis. The prize for most novel form of departure goes to the student who was collected by his family's prize-winning pedigree sheep.

We were fortunate to have a fantastic group of students, seniors and staff. It was a pleasure to work with them all week. We're looking forward to next year!

Week Two

And as in 2012, the second week was under the auspices of James Gazet and his report follows:

This was the second week of the 2013 National Mathematics Summer School, held at a new location: Woodhouse Grove School on the outskirts of Leeds and Bradford. Forty-two Juniors attended, supported by a sextet of unobtrusively super-effective Seniors. James Gazet directed with kindly aplomb. Junior Masterclasses on Infinity were taken by Andras Zsák and Paul Russell gave the Senior Masterclasses on Ramsey Theory.

Some tutors had first to recover from their nostalgia for The Queen's Foundation, helped by the superb setting of Woodhouse Grove and the excellent food. In some aspects, the hot and sunny weather was kind to the Summer School but some of the accommodation became too hot to work in and to live in comfortably. All the students deserve praise for the way they coped with the hot conditions. These did not appear to affect their appetite for mathematics: it was one of those Summer Schools where Juniors and Seniors were often to be seen poring over problems outside 'normal' working time.

As students arrived, they received personalised starter packs and later their T-shirts (this year's scarlet was well received). After domestic arrangements had been sorted out and Sunday dinner consumed, teams attempted a variety of 'ice-breaker' problems. Some new activities included a request for students to become living sculptures making the number '1745'. Any black marks on clothing were probably acquired in groups whose members chose to lie down on the playground during this activity. Happily, it was clear from the start of the competitions on Monday that all members of the Summer School had quickly identified with their teams.

Andras Zsák's five detailed *Masterclasses on Infinity* ran through the week: the students were adroitly introduced to the idea of countability via the study of injective amd surjective functions, and the students clearly appreciated the careful way in which the ideas were drawn out.

From mid-morning to lunch, Monday to Thursday, teams took part in the individual, team and relay competitions. Some sections contained some new questions this year. The competitive spirit mounted steadily during the week and overall the Fibonaccis were the winners. To the Team Choice section the 2013 Seniors made a notable contribution through their astute sharing out of questions and support of their Juniors. The competitions were followed by the now standard discussion of points raised by the marking, during the relays and the Team Choice solutions.

Afternoon topics for Juniors were: Colouring Problems, Combinatorics, Conic Sections, Modular Arithmetic, an introduction to Number Theory, the Pigeonhole Principle and some topics in Ratio and Circle Geometry. This group of tutors was composed of Summer School veterans, passing on the fruits of their experience. This year they were current or recently retired schoolteachers with their perspectives on the teaching and learning of demanding but inspiring topics.

On Monday evening Michael Bradley explained a solution of Conway's 'Soldiers' problem, introduced the previous day. Many of the Junior pupils had made some progress with the problem before Michael demonstrated a theoretical approach. This was followed on Tuesday evening by talks and workshops prepared and presented by the Seniors. They introduced the Juniors to Euler's Theorem $V - E + F = 2$ via model building and looked at some applications such as the 6-colour theorem and creating solids from pentagons and hexagons. This session provided the Juniors with more of the mathematical model-building that was popular throughout the week.

Non-mathematical activities occupied the two remaining evenings. On Wednesday there was a bowling trip to Shipley. This expedition was followed by the traditional evening concert on Thursday. The 2013 event was less instrumental than usual, mainly featuring piano and voice and including a crop of jokes. The penultimate item, before the rendition of 'The Complex Number Song', was a sung 'Senior Surprise', reflecting on the week's varied mathematical activities.

On Friday morning, the Infinity Masterclass was followed by two final relays. The week's problem-solving finished with an updated version of Gerry Leversha's mathematics-related general knowledge quiz.

Thanks are due to the Seniors for their input into a smoothly running week. Their own Masterclasses were followed by afternoon sessions given by other members of the staff team.

Pupils attending from Sunday 7th July - Friday 12th July

Robyn Bell	Durham High School for Girls
Tayla Bick	Sutton High School, Surrey
William Brassington	London Oratory School
Sze-Ching Cheung	Queens Park Community School, London
David Clarke	Solihull School
George Collison	Wisbech Grammar School
Sean Cuddihy	Royal Hospital School, Suffolk
Alice Cullen	Pocklington School, near York
John Dawson	Friends' School, Lisburn
Louis de Mendonça	Exeter School
Laura Embrey	King's School, Macclesfield
Kerem Ergene	Brighton College
Scott Fulton	Largs Academy, North Ayrshire
Jemma Gillan	Strathearn School, Belfast
Alice Guillaume	James Allen's Girls' School, London
Matt Gurtler	Lancing College, West Sussex
Kevin Ho	Tonbridge School, Kent
Jack Hodkinson	Queen Elizabeth Grammar School, Wakefield
Shamel Hok	Roundhay School, Leeds
Michael Hu	Bristol Grammar School
Andrew Huang	Chesham Grammar School, Buckinghamshire
Rachel Hunt	Wimbledon High School, Wimbledon
Mei Jie	International College Sherborne S., Dorset
Penelope Jones	Withington Girls' School, Manchester
Hannah Keenan	St Patrick's High School, Keady, Armagh
Howard Lao	Ashford School, Kent
Xiusi Li	Francis Holland School, London
Jaeyeon (Vincent) Lim	Epsom College, Surrey
Junyi Liu	Southbank International School, London
Cameron Low	King Henry VIII School, Coventry
Cong Lu	Robert Gordon's College, Aberdeen
Dmitry Lubyako	Summer Fields School, Oxford

108

Henry Mckay	King's College School, London
Callum Melly	Colfe's School, London
James Mulholland	Chigwell School, Essex
Conor Murphy	Eltham College, London
Kerry Murphy	Casterton School, Lancashire
Hannah Patrick	Rydal Penrhos School, Colwyn Bay, Conwy
Imogen Pearce	Haileybury and Imperial Service Col., Hertford
Felix Prutton	Bungay High School, Suffolk
Alistair Pryke	Royal Grammar School, Worcester
Kyle Ragbir	John Lyon School, Harrow
Michael Savery	St Bede's RC School, Bristol
Patrick Semark	St Albans School
Helen Shao	Putney High School
Angus Shaw	George Heriot's School, Edinburgh
Esther Shindler	Menorah High School, London
Alicia Thomas	Bishop Hedley High School, Merthyr Tydfil
Charlie Thompson	Elizabeth College, Guernsey
Greg Torlinski	St Thomas Aquinas School, Birmingham
William Underwood	Monmouth School
Fraser Waters	Redland Green School, Bristol
Simon Whitaker	Bedford Modern School
Natalie Wood	Newport Free Grammar School, Essex
Jeanette Wu	Ockbrook School, near Derby
Jingxuan Yang	Culford School, Suffolk
Gordon Yip	Bedford Prep School

Pupils attending from Sunday 14th July - Friday 19th July

Olivia Aaronson	St Paul's Girls' School, Hammersmith
Ashwin Agarwal	Eton College, Windsor
Howard Au	Winchester College
Jamie Bamber	Perse School, Cambridge
Jamie Bell	King Edward VI Five Ways S., Birmingham
Mark Bobrovnikov	Whitgift School, Surrey
Lydia Buckingham	Wellington School, Somerset
Wenbo Cao	Highgate School, London
Matthew Chaffe	Littleover Community School, Derby
Daniel Chiverton	Bishop Challoner RC School, Basingstoke

Euijin Choi	Wilson's School, Surrey
Nathen Chung	King Edward's School, Birmingham
Samuel Coy	Forest School, London
Olivia Dadge	Nottingham High School for Girls
Esha Dasgupta	Sutton Coldfield Grammar School for Girls
Joe Davies	Lawrence Sheriff School, Rugby
George Dunlop	Winchester College
Catherine Evans	St Mary's School, Cambridge
Harry Goodburn	Wilson's School, Surrey
Luke Gostelow	Hampton School, Middlesex
Caroline Harwin	Kendrick School, Reading
Donald Hobson	Webster's High School, Angus
Matthias Hoffmanvagenheim	Manchester Grammar School
Lucas Huysmans	Beaumont School, St Albans
Sumire Isomura	Mount School, London
Jongheon (Jim) Jeon	Winchester College
Tomoka Kan	St Paul's Girls' School, Hammersmith
Gyeong-Hyun Kim	Eton College, Windsor
Min Kim	Monkton Combe School, Bath
Samuel Kittle	Simon Langton Boys' Grammar S., Canterbury
Balaji Krishna	Stanwell School, Vale of Glamorgan
Kirsten Land	Hornsey School for Girls, London
Jinju Lee	Badminton School, Bristol
Suelynn Lee	Cranbrook School, Kent
Jackie Li	St Paul's Girls' School, Hammersmith
Nian Liu	Gryffe High School, Renfrewshire
Chen Lu	Eton College, Windsor
Sophie Maclean	Watford Grammar School for Girls
Georgina Majury	Down High School, Co. Down
Callum Mclean	Harrow School
Stephen Mitchell	St Paul's School, London
Yiyi Painter	Nottingham High School for Girls
Jack Palmer	St Paul's School, London
Krit Patarapak	Charterhouse, Godalming, Surrey
Philip Peters	Haberdashers' Aske's School for Boys, Herts
Rebecca Poon	George Watson's College, Edinburgh
Noah Porcelli	The Cherwell School, Oxford

110

Mukunth Raveendran	Haberdashers' Aske's School for Boys, Herts
Imogen Richards	School of St Helen and St Katharine, Abingdon
Marcus Roberts	The Grammar School at Leeds
Edward Rong	Westminster School
Bony Akangsha Roy	Aylesbury High School
Sony Abhipsha Roy	Aylesbury High School
Ethan Sciamma	St Paul's School, London
Xinyu Shen	Winterbourne International Academy, Bristol
Supamathy Sivaneswaran	Nonsuch High School for Girls, Surrey
Finlay Stafford	Newfield School, Sheffield
Alan Sun	City of London School
Marguerite Tong	St Paul's Girls' School, Hammersmith
Danishia Vijayakumar	North London Collegiate School
Kavin Vijayakumar	Bancroft's School, Essex
Eva Wang	Caterham School, Surrey
Sam Watt	Monkton Combe School, Bath
Alfred Wong	Reading School
Cindy Yu	Wycombe Abbey School, High Wycombe
Joseph Zhu	Oxford Spires Academy

Seniors in Week 1	Jiali Gao	Monica Gupta	James Hodgson
	Freddie Illingworth	Rachel Newhouse	Yuen Ng
	Sreya Saha		

Seniors in Week 2	Oliver Feng	Jennie Han	Eleanor Holderness
	Gareth Jones	Remy Naylor	Ramsay Pyper
	Linden Ralph	Kasia Warburton	

Staff in Week 1	Vicky Neale	Andrew Jobbings	Stephen O'Hagan
	Jack Shotton	Alan Slomson	Vinay Kathotia
	Lizzie Kimber	Jo Harbour	Alex Neville

Staff in Week 2	Anne Andrews	Robin Bhattacharyya	Michael Bradley
	James Gazet	Ina Hughes	Gerry Leversha
	Paul Russell	Andras Zsák	

Senior Mathematical Challenge and British Mathematical Olympiads

The Senior Challenge took place on Tuesday 6th November 2012. Once again it was sponsored by the Institute of Actuaries. There were 98,580 entries and around 1400 candidates took part in the next stage, British Mathematical Olympiad Round 1, held on Friday 30th November 2012. The Senior Kangaroo was held on the same day, around 1750 candidates were eligible.

UK SENIOR MATHEMATICAL CHALLENGE

Tuesday 6 November 2012

Organised by the **United Kingdom Mathematics Trust**

and supported by

The Actuarial Profession
making financial sense of the future

RULES AND GUIDELINES (to be read before starting)

1. Do not open the question paper until the invigilator tells you to do so.
2. **Use B or HB pencil only.** Mark *at most one* of the options A, B, C, D, E on the Answer Sheet for each question. Do not mark more than one option.
3. Time allowed: **90 minutes.**
   No answers or personal details may be entered on the Answer Sheet after the 90 minutes are over.
4. The use of rough paper is allowed.
   Calculators, measuring instruments and squared paper are forbidden.
5. Candidates must be full-time students at secondary school or FE college, and must be in Year 13 or below (England & Wales); S6 or below (Scotland); Year 14 or below (Northern Ireland).
6. There are twenty-five questions. Each question is followed by five options marked A, B, C, D, E. Only one of these is correct. Enter the letter A-E corresponding to the correct answer in the corresponding box on the Answer Sheet.
7. **Scoring rules**: all candidates start out with 25 marks;
   0 marks are awarded for each question left unanswered;
   4 marks are awarded for each correct answer;
   1 mark is deducted for each incorrect answer.
8. **Guessing**: Remember that there is a penalty for wrong answers. Note also that later questions are deliberately intended to be harder than earlier questions. You are thus advised to concentrate first on solving as many as possible of the first 15-20 questions. Only then should you try later questions.

The United Kingdom Mathematics Trust is a Registered Charity.

http://www.ukmt.org.uk

1. Which of the following cannot be written as the sum of two prime numbers?

    A 5   B 7   C 9   D 10   E 11

2. The diagram shows an equilateral triangle, a square and a regular
    pentagon which all share a common vertex. What is the value of θ?

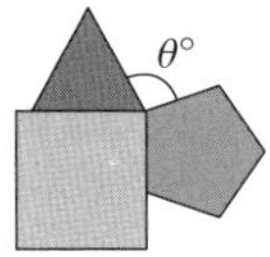

    A 98   B 102   C 106   D 110   E 112

3. The price of my favourite soft drink has gone up by leaps and bounds over the past
    ten years. In four of those years it has leapt up by 5p each year, whilst in the other
    six years it has bounded up by 2p each year. The drink cost 70p in 2002. How
    much does it cost now?

    A £0.77   B £0.90   C £0.92   D £1.02   E £1.05

4. According to one astronomer, there are one hundred thousand million galaxies in
    the universe, each containing one hundred thousand million stars. How many stars
    is that altogether?

    A 10^{13} B 10^{22} C 10^{100} D 10^{120} E 10^{121}

5. All six digits of three 2-digit numbers are different. What is the largest possible
    sum of three such numbers?

    A 237   B 246   C 255   D 264   E 273

6. What is the sum of the digits of the largest 4-digit palindromic number which is divisible
    by 15? [Palindromic numbers read the same backwards and forwards, e.g. 7227.]

    A 18   B 20   C 24   D 30   E 36

7. Given that $x + y + z = 1$, $x + y - z = 2$ and $x - y - z = 3$, what is the value of xyz?

    A -2 B $-\frac{1}{2}$ C 0   D $\frac{1}{2}$ E 2

8. The diagrams below show four types of tile, each of which is made up of one or
    more equilateral triangles. For how many of these types of tile can we place three
    identical copies of the tile together, without gaps or overlaps, to make an equilateral
    triangle?

    A 0   B 1   C 2   D 3   E 4

9. Pierre said, "Just one of us is telling the truth". Qadr said, "What Pierre says is not true".
    Ratna said, "What Qadr says is not true". Sven said, "What Ratna says is not true".
    Tanya said, "What Sven says is not true".
    How many of them were telling the truth?

    A 0   B 1   C 2   D 3   E 4

10. Let N be the smallest positive integer whose digits add up to 2012. What is the first
    digit of $N + 1$?

    A 2   B 3   C 4   D 5   E 6

11. Coco is making clown hats from a circular piece of cardboard. The circumference of the base of each hat equals its slant height, which in turn is equal to the radius of the piece of cardboard. What is the maximum number of hats that Coco can make from the piece of cardboard?

A 3   B 4   C 5   D 6   E 7

12. The number 3 can be expressed as the sum of one or more positive integers in four different ways:

$$3; \quad 1 + 2; \quad 2 + 1; \quad 1 + 1 + 1.$$

In how many ways can the number 5 be so expressed?

A 8   B 10   C 12   D 14   E 16

13. A cube is placed with one face on square 1 in the maze shown, so that it completely covers the square with no overlap. The upper face of the cube is covered in wet paint. The cube is then 'rolled' around the maze, rotating about an edge each time, until it reaches square 25. It leaves paint on all of the squares on which the painted face lands, but on no others. The cube is removed on reaching the square 25. What is the sum of the numbers on the squares which are now marked with paint?

5	6	7	8	9
4	19	20	21	10
3	18	25	22	11
2	17	24	23	12
1	16	15	14	13

A 78   B 80   C 82   D 169   E 625

14. Six students who share a house all speak exactly two languages. Helga speaks only English and German; Ina speaks only German and Spanish; Jean-Pierre speaks only French and Spanish; Karim speaks only German and French; Lionel speaks only French and English whilst Mary speaks only Spanish and English. If two of the students are chosen at random, what is the probability that they speak a common language?

A $\frac{1}{2}$ B $\frac{2}{3}$ C $\frac{3}{4}$ D $\frac{4}{5}$ E $\frac{5}{6}$

15. Professor Rosseforp runs to work every day. On Thursday he ran 10% faster than his usual average speed. As a result, his journey time was reduced by x minutes. How many minutes did the journey take on Wednesday?

A $11x$ B $10x$ C $9x$ D $8x$ E $5x$

16. The diagram shows the ellipse whose equation is $x^2 + y^2 - xy + x - 4y = 12$. The curve cuts the y-axis at points A and C and cuts the x-axis at points B and D. What is the area of the inscribed quadrilateral $ABCD$?

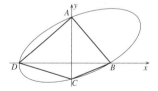

A 28   B 36   C 42   D 48   E 56

17. The diagram shows a pattern found on a floor tile in the cathedral in Spoleto, Umbria. A circle of radius 1 surrounds four quarter circles, also of radius 1, which enclose a square. The pattern has four axes of symmetry. What is the side length of the square?

A $\dfrac{1}{\sqrt{2}}$ B $2 - \sqrt{2}$ C $\dfrac{1}{\sqrt{3}}$ D $\dfrac{1}{2}$ E $\sqrt{2} - 1$

18. The diagram shows two squares, with sides of length $\frac{1}{2}$, inclined at an angle 2α to one another. What is the value of x?

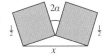

A $\cos\alpha$ B $\dfrac{1}{\cos\alpha}$ C $\sin\alpha$ D $\dfrac{1}{\sin\alpha}$ E $\tan\alpha$

19. The numbers 2, 3, 4, 5, 6, 7, 8 are to be placed, one per square, in the diagram shown so that the sum of the four numbers in the horizontal row equals 21 and the sum of the four numbers in the vertical column also equals 21. In how many different ways can this be done?

A 0   B 2   C 36   D 48   E 72

20. In trapezium $PQRS$, $SR = PQ = 25$cm and SP is parallel to RQ. All four sides of $PQRS$ are tangent to a circle with centre C. The area of the trapezium is 600cm^2. What is the radius of the circle?

A 7.5cm   B 8cm   C 9cm   D 10cm   E 12cm

21. Which of the following numbers does *not* have a square root in the form $x + y\sqrt{2}$, where x and y are positive integers?

A $17 + 12\sqrt{2}$ B $22 + 12\sqrt{2}$ C $38 + 12\sqrt{2}$ D $54 + 12\sqrt{2}$ E $73 + 12\sqrt{2}$

22. A semicircle of radius r is drawn with centre V and diameter UW. The line UW is then extended to the point X, such that UW and WX are of equal length. An arc of the circle with centre X and radius $4r$ is then drawn so that the line XY is a tangent to the semicircle at Z, as shown. What, in terms of r, is the area of triangle YVW?

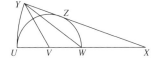

A $\dfrac{4r^2}{9}$ B $\dfrac{2r^2}{3}$ C r^2 D $\dfrac{4r^2}{3}$ E $2r^2$

23. Tom and Geri have a competition. Initially, each player has one attempt at hitting a target. If one player hits the target and the other does not then the successful player wins. If both players hit the target, or if both players miss the target, then each has another attempt, with the same rules applying. If the probability of Tom hitting the target is always $\frac{4}{5}$ and the probability of Geri hitting the target is always $\frac{2}{3}$, what is the probability that Tom wins the competition?

A $\dfrac{4}{15}$ B $\dfrac{8}{15}$ C $\dfrac{2}{3}$ D $\dfrac{4}{5}$ E $\dfrac{13}{15}$

24. The top diagram on the right shows a shape that tiles the plane, as shown in the lower diagram. The tile has nine sides, six of which have length 1. It may be divided into three congruent quadrilaterals as shown. What is the area of the tile?

A $\dfrac{1 + 2\sqrt{3}}{2}$ B $\dfrac{4\sqrt{3}}{3}$ C $\sqrt{6}$ D $\dfrac{3 + 4\sqrt{3}}{4}$ E $\dfrac{3\sqrt{3}}{2}$

25. How many distinct pairs (x, y) of real numbers satisfy the equation $(x + y)^2 = (x + 4)(y - 4)$?

A 0   B 1   C 2   D 3   E 4

Further remarks

The solutions are provided in a leaflet which is also set up to facilitate marking in centres who wished to continue to mark in house.

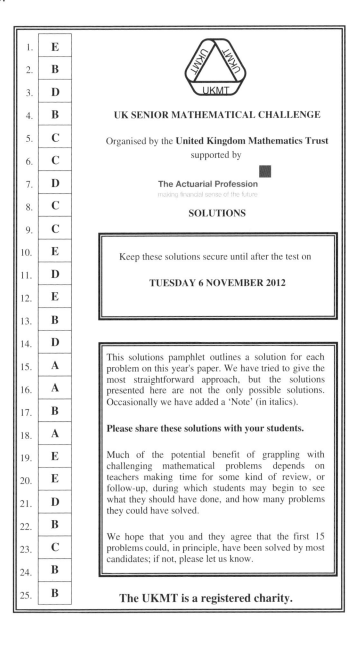

1.	E
2.	B
3.	D
4.	B
5.	C
6.	C
7.	D
8.	C
9.	C
10.	E
11.	D
12.	E
13.	B
14.	D
15.	A
16.	A
17.	B
18.	A
19.	E
20.	E
21.	D
22.	B
23.	C
24.	B
25.	B

UK SENIOR MATHEMATICAL CHALLENGE

Organised by the **United Kingdom Mathematics Trust**
supported by

The Actuarial Profession
making financial sense of the future

SOLUTIONS

Keep these solutions secure until after the test on

TUESDAY 6 NOVEMBER 2012

This solutions pamphlet outlines a solution for each problem on this year's paper. We have tried to give the most straightforward approach, but the solutions presented here are not the only possible solutions. Occasionally we have added a 'Note' (in italics).

Please share these solutions with your students.

Much of the potential benefit of grappling with challenging mathematical problems depends on teachers making time for some kind of review, or follow-up, during which students may begin to see what they should have done, and how many problems they could have solved.

We hope that you and they agree that the first 15 problems could, in principle, have been solved by most candidates; if not, please let us know.

The UKMT is a registered charity.

1. **E** If an odd number is written as the sum of two prime numbers then one of those primes is 2, since 2 is the only even prime. However, 9 is not prime so 11 cannot be written as the sum of two primes. Note that $5 = 2 + 3$; $7 = 2 + 5$; $9 = 2 + 7$; $10 = 3 + 7$, so 11 is the only alternative which is not the sum of two primes.

2. **B** The interior angles of an equilateral triangle, square, regular pentagon are $60°$, $90°$, $108°$ respectively. The sum of the angles at a point is $360°$. So $\theta = 360 - (60 + 90 + 108) = 102$.

3. **D** The cost now is $(70 + 4 \times 5 + 6 \times 2)\text{p} = £1.02$.

4. **B** One hundred thousand million is $10^2 \times 10^3 \times 10^6 = 10^{11}$. So the number of stars is $10^{11} \times 10^{11} = 10^{22}$.

5. **C** Let the required addition be 'ab' + 'cd' + 'ef', where a, b, c, d, e, f are single, distinct digits. To make this sum as large as possible, we need a, c, e (the tens digits) as large as possible; so they must be 7, 8, 9 in some order. Then we need b, d, f as large as possible, so 4, 5, 6 in some order. Hence the largest sum is $10(7 + 8 + 9) + (4 + 5 + 6) = 10 \times 24 + 15 = 255$.

6. **C** In order to be a multiple of 15, a number must be a multiple both of 3 and of 5. So its units digit must be 0 or 5. However, the units digit must also equal the thousands digit and this cannot be 0, so the required number is of the form '$5aa5$'. The largest such four-digit numbers are 5995, 5885, 5775. Their digit sums are 28, 26, 24 respectively. In order to be a multiple of 3, the digit sum of a number must also be a multiple of 3, so 5775 is the required number. The sum of its digits is 24.

7. **D** Add the first and third equations: $2x = 4$, so $x = 2$. Add the first two equations: $2x + 2y = 3$, so $y = -\frac{1}{2}$. Substitute for x and y in the first equation: $2 + \left(-\frac{1}{2}\right) + z = 1$ so $z = -\frac{1}{2}$. Therefore $xyz = 2 \times \left(-\frac{1}{2}\right) \times \left(-\frac{1}{2}\right) = \frac{1}{2}$.

8. **C** If an equilateral triangle is split into a number of smaller identical equilateral triangles then there must be one small triangle in the top row, three small triangles in the row below, five small triangles in the row below that and so on. So the total number of small triangles is 4 or 9 or 16 etc. These are all squares and it is left to the reader to prove that the sum of the first n odd numbers is n^2. So, for three copies of a given tile to form an equilateral triangle, the number of triangles which comprise the tile must be one third of a square number.
Only the tiles made up of three equilateral triangles and twelve equilateral triangles satisfy this condition. However, it is still necessary to show that three copies of these tiles can indeed make equilateral triangles. The diagrams above show how they can do this.

9. **C** If Pierre is telling the truth then Qadr is not telling the truth. However, this means that Ratna is telling the truth, so this leads to a contradiction as Pierre stated that just one person is telling the truth. So Pierre is not telling the truth, which means that Qadr is telling the truth, but Ratna is not telling the truth. This in turn means that Sven is telling the truth, but Tanya is not. So only Qadr and Sven are telling the truth.

10. **E** It can be deduced that N must consist of at least 224 digits since the largest 223-digit positive integer consists of 223 nines and has a digit sum of 2007. It is possible to find 224-digit positive integers which have a digit sum of 2012.
The largest of these is 99 999 ...999 995 and the smallest is 59 999 ...999 999.
So $N = 59\,999\ldots 999\,999$ and $N + 1 = 60\,000\ldots 000\,000$ (223 zeros).

11. **D** Let the radius of the circular piece of cardboard be r. The diagram shows a sector of the circle which would make one hat, with the minor arc shown becoming the circumference of the base of the hat. The circumference of the circle is $2\pi r$. Now $6r < 2\pi r < 7r$. This shows that we can cut out 6 hats in this fashion and also shows that the area of cardboard unused in cutting out *any* 6 hats is less than the area of a single hat. Hence there is no possibility that more than 6 hats could be cut out.

12. E Two different ways of expressing 5 are $1 + 4$ and $4 + 1$. In the following list these are denoted as $\{1, 4:$ two ways$\}$. The list of all possible ways is $\{5:$ one way$\}$, $\{2, 3:$ two ways$\}$, $\{1, 4:$ two ways$\}$, $\{1, 2, 2:$ three ways$\}$, $\{1, 1, 3:$ three ways$\}$, $\{1, 1, 1, 2:$ four ways$\}$, $\{1, 1, 1, 1, 1:$ one way$\}$. So in total there are 16 ways.
{Different expressions of a positive integer in the above form are known as 'partitions'. It may be shown that the number of distinct compositions of a positive integer n is 2^{n-1}.}

13. B The table below shows the position of the face marked with paint when the base of the cube is on the 25 squares. Code: T - top; B - base; F - front; H - hidden (rear); L - left; R - right.

1	2	**3**	4	5	6	**7**	8	9	10	**11**	12	13	14	**15**	16	17	18	19	**20**	21	22	23	**24**	25
T	H	B	F	T	R	B	L	T	F	B	H	T	L	B	R	R	R	R	B	L	L	L	B	F

So the required sum is $3 + 7 + 11 + 15 + 20 + 24 = 80$.

14. D Note that each student has a language in common with exactly four of the other five students. For instance, Jean-Pierre has a language in common with each of Ina, Karim, Lionel and Mary. Only Helga does not have a language in common with Jean-Pierre. So whichever two students are chosen, the probability that they have a language in common is 4/5.

15. A Let Professor Rosseforp's usual journey take t minutes at an average speed of v metres/minute. Then the distance to work is vt metres. On Thursday his speed increased by 10%, i.e. it was $11v/10$ metres/minute. The time taken was $(t - x)$ minutes. Therefore $11v/10 \times (t - x) = vt$. So $11(t - x) = 10t$, i.e. $t = 11x$.

16. A At points A and C, $x = 0$. So $y^2 - 4y = 12$, i.e. $(y - 6)(y + 2) = 0$, i.e. $y = 6$ or $y = -2$. So C is $(0, -2)$ and A is $(0, 6)$. At points B and D, $y = 0$. So $x^2 + x = 12$, i.e. $(x - 3)(x + 4) = 0$, i.e. $x = 3$ or $x = -4$. So D is $(-4, 0)$ and B is $(3, 0)$. Therefore the areas of triangles DAB and DBC are $\frac{1}{2} \times 7 \times 6 = 21$ and $\frac{1}{2} \times 7 \times 2 = 7$. So $ABCD$ has area 28. {*It is left to the reader to prove that area $ABCD = \frac{1}{2}BD \times AC$.*}

17. B In the diagram, B is the centre of the quarter-circle arc AC; D is the point where the central square touches arc AC; F is the point where the central square touches arc CE; O is the centre of the circle. As both the circle and arc AC have radius 1, $OABC$ is a square of side 1. By Pythagoras' Theorem: $OB^2 = 1^2 + 1^2$. So $OB = \sqrt{2}$. Therefore $OD = OB - DB = \sqrt{2} - 1$. By a similar argument, $OF = \sqrt{2} - 1$. Now $DF^2 = OD^2 + OF^2 = 2 \times OD^2$ since $OD = OF$. So the side of the square is $\sqrt{2} \times OD = \sqrt{2}(\sqrt{2} - 1) = 2 - \sqrt{2}$.

18. A In the diagram, D is the midpoint of AC. Triangle ABC is isosceles since $AB = BC = \frac{1}{2}$. Therefore, BD bisects $\angle ABC$ and BD is perpendicular to AC. The angles at a point total $360°$, so $\angle ABC = 360° - 2 \times 90° - 2\alpha = 180° - 2\alpha$. Therefore $\angle ABD = \angle CBD = 90° - \alpha$. So $\angle BAD = \angle BCD = \alpha$. Therefore $x = AC = 2 \times AD = 2 \times AB \cos \alpha = 2 \times \frac{1}{2} \cos \alpha = \cos \alpha$.

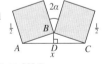

19. E Note that the number represented by x appears in both the horizontal row and the vertical column. Note also that $2 + 3 + 4 + 5 + 6 + 7 + 8 = 35$. Since the numbers in the row and those in the column have sum 21, we deduce that $x = 2 \times 21 - 35 = 7$.
We now need two disjoint sets of three numbers chosen from 2, 3, 4, 5, 6, 8 so that the numbers in both sets total 14. The only possibilities are $\{2, 4, 8\}$ and $\{3, 5, 6\}$. We have six choices of which number to put in the top space in the vertical line, then two for the next space down and one for the bottom space. That leaves three choices for the first space in the horizontal line, two for the next space and one for the final space. So the total number of ways is $6 \times 2 \times 1 \times 3 \times 2 \times 1 = 72$.

20. E The two tangents drawn from a point outside a circle to that circle are equal in length. This theorem has been used to mark four pairs of equal line segments on the diagram. In the circle the diameter, XY, has been marked. It is also a perpendicular height of the trapezium. We are given that $SR = PQ = 25\,\text{cm}$ so we can deduce that $(a + d) + (b + c) = 25 + 25 = 50$. The area of trapezium $PQRS = \frac{1}{2}(SP + QR) \times XY = 600\,\text{cm}^2$. Therefore $\frac{1}{2}(a + b + c + d) \times 2r = 600$. So $\frac{1}{2} \times 50 \times 2r = 600$, i.e. $r = 12$.

21. D $(x + y\sqrt{2})^2 = x^2 + 2xy\sqrt{2} + 2y^2$. Note that all of the alternatives given are of the form $a + 12\sqrt{2}$ so we need $xy = 6$. The only ordered pairs (x, y) of positive integers which satisfy this are $(1, 6), (2, 3), (3, 2), (6, 1)$. For these, the values of $x^2 + 2y^2$ are 73, 22, 17, 38 respectively. So the required number is $54 + 12\sqrt{2}$.

22. B Let the perpendicular from Y meet UV at T and let $\angle ZXV = \alpha$. Note that $\angle VZX = 90°$ as a tangent to a circle is perpendicular to the radius at the point of contact. Therefore $\sin \alpha = \frac{r}{3r} = \frac{1}{3}$. Consider triangle YTX: $\sin \alpha = \frac{YT}{YX}$. So $YT = YX \sin \alpha = \frac{4r}{3}$. So the area of triangle $YVW = \frac{1}{2} \times VW \times YT = \frac{1}{2} \times r \times \frac{4r}{3} = \frac{2r^2}{3}$.

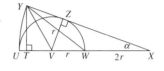

23. C Tom wins after one attempt each if he hits the target and Geri misses. The probability of this happening is $\frac{4}{5} \times \frac{1}{3} = \frac{4}{15}$. Similarly the probability that Geri wins after one attempt is $\frac{2}{5} \times \frac{1}{5} = \frac{2}{15}$. So the probability that both competitors will have at least one more attempt is $1 - \frac{4}{15} - \frac{2}{15} = \frac{3}{5}$.

Therefore the probability that Tom wins after two attempts each is $\frac{3}{5} \times \frac{4}{15}$. The probability that neither Tom nor Geri wins after two attempts each is $\frac{3}{5} \times \frac{3}{5}$. So the probability that Tom wins after three attempts each is $\left(\frac{3}{5}\right)^2 \times \frac{4}{15}$ and, more generally, the probability that he wins after n attempts each is $\left(\frac{3}{5}\right)^{n-1} \times \frac{4}{15}$.

Therefore the probability that Tom wins is $\frac{4}{15} + \left(\frac{3}{5}\right) \times \frac{4}{15} + \left(\frac{3}{5}\right)^2 \times \frac{4}{15} + \left(\frac{3}{5}\right)^3 \times \frac{4}{15} + \ldots$.

This is the sum to infinity of a geometric series with first term $\frac{4}{15}$ and common ratio $\frac{3}{5}$. Its value is $\frac{4}{15} \div \left(1 - \frac{3}{5}\right) = \frac{2}{3}$.

24. B The diagram shows one of the three quadrilaterals making up the tile, labelled and with a line BE inserted. Note that it is a trapezium. As three quadrilaterals fit together, it may be deduced that $\angle ABC = 360° \div 3 = 120°$, so $\angle BAD = 60°$. It may also be deduced that the length of AB is $1 + x$, where x is the length of BC. Now $\cos \angle BAD = \cos 60° = \frac{1}{2} = \frac{1-x}{1+x}$. So $1 + x = 2 - 2x$, i.e. $x = \frac{1}{3}$. The area of $ABCD$ is $\frac{1}{2}(AD + BC) \times CD = \frac{1}{2}\left(1 + \frac{1}{3}\right) \times \frac{4}{3}\sin 60°$ $= \frac{2}{3} \times \frac{4}{3} \times \frac{\sqrt{3}}{2} = \frac{4\sqrt{3}}{9}$. So the area of the tile is $3 \times \frac{4\sqrt{3}}{9} = \frac{4\sqrt{3}}{3}$.

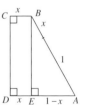

25. B Starting with $(x + y)^2 = (x + 4)(y - 4)$ and expanding both sides gives $x^2 + 2xy + y^2 = xy - 4x + 4y - 16$, i.e. $x^2 + (y + 4)x + y^2 - 4y + 16 = 0$. To eliminate the xy term we let $z = x + \frac{1}{2}y$ and then replace x by $z - \frac{1}{2}y$. The equation above becomes $z^2 + 4\left(z - \frac{1}{2}y\right) + \frac{3}{4}y^2 - 4y + 16 = 0$. However,

$$z^2 + 4\left(z - \tfrac{1}{2}y\right) + \tfrac{3}{4}y^2 - 4y + 16 = (z + 2)^2 + \tfrac{3}{4}y^2 - 6y + 12$$

$$= (z + 2)^2 + \tfrac{3}{4}\left(y^2 - 8y + 16\right) = (z + 2)^2 + \tfrac{3}{4}(y + 4)^2.$$

So the only real solution is when $z = -2$ and $y = 4$; i.e. $x = -4$ and $y = 4$.

The answers

The table below shows the proportion of pupils' choices. The correct answer is shown in bold. [The percentages are rounded to the nearest whole number.]

Qn	A	B	C	D	E	Blank
1	3	3	6	8	**77**	2
2	7	**69**	5	5	5	8
3	1	1	3	**93**	1	2
4	3	**74**	10	2	9	3
5	4	4	**78**	5	2	7
6	13	5	**55**	7	4	15
7	6	9	7	**50**	6	22
8	37	21	**14**	5	6	15
9	5	17	**58**	11	2	6
10	17	8	5	7	**23**	40
11	16	18	5	**21**	2	38
12	8	9	15	12	**52**	4
13	22	**54**	5	5	2	12
14	21	14	7	**36**	9	13
15	**24**	41	12	1	3	18
16	**35**	3	3	5	3	51
17	11	**9**	4	8	5	64
18	**18**	7	5	7	4	59
19	11	15	18	5	**6**	45
20	3	3	3	6	**15**	71
21	7	2	3	**8**	4	77
22	3	**8**	2	6	2	79
23	18	12	**6**	5	5	53
24	3	**5**	2	4	3	83
25	8	**9**	7	3	3	69

SMC 2012: Some comments on the pupils' choice of answers as sent to schools in the letter with the results

It is pleasing to see that overall the students were more successful than last year, with the average mark going up from 49.5 to 53.4. As usual, there is a lot of interest in looking at the distribution of the answers to the different questions. We hope you will be interested in comparing the answers given by your students with the national distribution.

In general, the first few questions were well done, but only in the case of question 3, answered correctly by 93% of the students, should we be really satisfied with the outcome. Overall, in question 1 nearly one-quarter of the students thought that either 5 or 7 or 9 or 10 cannot be written as the sum of two primes. In question 2, over a fifth of the students gave the wrong answer to a straightforward question about angles in regular polygons, with one in twelve not even answering it. In question 4, a similar proportion of students could not cope with a question about indices. The topics involved in these questions - regular polygons, primes, factors and indices - may not occur very frequently in post-16 mathematics, but nevertheless they are topics which students at this level should be familiar with, and should expect to meet in a typical SMC paper.

The outcome on the early questions 7 and 8 was also a disappointment. There is a lot of scope for arithmetical errors in question 7, so a high proportion of wrong answers was perhaps to be expected, but it is a surprise that more than one-fifth of the candidates did not attempt the question. Whilst it is very possible that the students had never seen three simultaneous linear equations involving three unknowns before, a little thought would show that the equations are easy to solve. We aim to avoid routine questions. So students should enter the SMC knowing that the correct method for tackling a question will not always be immediately obvious, and that some thought will be required.

Question 8 does not require any technique, but just the willingness to draw a few diagrams. So the lack of success with this question was a surprise.

We received a few queries about the correct answer to question 13, and we are grateful to Fairy Maths Tutor who has posted on YouTube an excellent animation which explains the solution very clearly

http://www.youtube.com/watch?v=QLt0p89kdv8

Please bring this to the attention of your students.

The response to question 16 was encouraging. Over 70% of the students who attempted this question gave the correct answer. The later questions are more testing, and so students who gained a certificate can rightly be proud of their achievement.

The SMC marks

The profile of marks obtained is shown below.

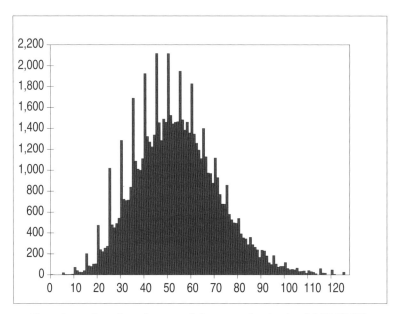

Bar chart showing the actual frequencies in the 2012 SMC

The average score increased slightly from 49.5 in 2011 to 53.4 in 2012.
We had received comments from schools and colleges that many SMC
entrants who gain certificates in the IMC were not awarded SMC
certificates. This was discouraging and occurred because SMC entrants
are largely drawn from the more successful IMC students. In recognition
of this, the UKMT has decided to award certificates to the top 60% of
SMC students from now on. On this basis the cut-off marks were set at

GOLD – 77 or over   SILVER – 62 to 76   BRONZE – 49 to 61

Candidates who scored 93 or more were invited to take part in BMO 1 and
those who scored 82 or more were invited to take part in the new Senior
Kangaroo.

122

A sample of one of the certificates is shown below.

UK SENIOR MATHEMATICAL CHALLENGE
2012

of

received a

SILVER CERTIFICATE

The Actuarial Profession
making financial sense of the future

Chairman, United Kingdom Mathematics Trust

THE UNITED KINGDOM SENIOR MATHEMATICAL CHALLENGE

The Senior Mathematical Challenge (SMC) is run by the UK Mathematics Trust. The SMC encourages mathematical reasoning, precision of thought, and fluency in using basic mathematical techniques to solve interesting problems. It is aimed at those in full-time education and with sufficient mathematical competence to undertake a post-16 course.

The problems on the SMC are designed to make students think. Most are accessible, yet still challenge those with more experience; they are also meant to be memorable and enjoyable.

Mathematics controls more aspects of the modern world than most people realise—from iPods, cash machines, telecommunications and airline booking systems to production processes in engineering, efficient distribution and stock-holding, investment strategies and 'whispering' jet engines. The scientific and industrial revolutions flowed from the realisation that mathematics was both the language of nature, and also a way of analysing—and hence controlling—our environment. In the last fifty years old and new applications of mathematical ideas have transformed the way we live.

All these developments depend on mathematical thinking—a mode of thought whose essential style is far more permanent than the wave of technological change which it has made possible. The problems on the SMC reflect this style, which pervades all mathematics, by encouraging students to think clearly about challenging problems.

The SMC was established as the National Mathematics Contest in 1961. In recent years there have been over 90,000 entries from around 2000 schools and colleges. Certificates are awarded to the highest scoring 60% of candidates (Gold : Silver : Bronze 1 : 2 : 3).

The UKMT is a registered charity. For more information please see our website www.ukmt.org.uk. Donations to support our work would be gratefully received and can be made by visiting our Virgin moneygiving page at www.donate.ukmt.org.uk.

The next stages

Subject to certain conditions, candidates who obtained a score of 93 or over in the 2012 Senior Mathematical Challenge were invited to take the British Mathematical Olympiad Round One and those who scored from 82 to 92 were invited to take part in a new event, The Senior Kangaroo. This was an extension of the 2011 trial year. It made use of Kangaroo questions as well as a few others and is not a multiple choice paper but can be marked by character recognition as all the answers are three-digit numbers.

SENIOR 'KANGAROO' MATHEMATICAL CHALLENGE

Friday 30th November 2012

Organised by the United Kingdom Mathematics Trust

The Senior Kangaroo paper allows students in the UK to test themselves on questions set for the best school-aged mathematicians from across Europe and beyond.

RULES AND GUIDELINES (to be read before starting):

1. Do not open the paper until the Invigilator tells you to do so.

2. Time allowed: **1 hour.**

3. The use of rough paper is allowed; **calculators** and measuring instruments are **forbidden.**

4. **Use B or HB pencil only** to complete your personal details and record your answers on the machine-readable Answer Sheet provided. **All answers are written using three digits, from 000 to 999.** For example, if you think the answer to a question is 42, write 042 at the top of the answer grid and then code your answer by putting solid black pencil lines through the 0, the 4 and the 2 beneath.

   Please note that the machine that reads your Answer Sheet will only see the solid black lines through the numbers beneath, not the written digits above. You must ensure that you code your answers or you will not receive any marks. There are further instructions and examples on the Answer Sheet.

5. The paper contains 20 questions. Five marks will be awarded for each correct answer. There is no penalty for giving an incorrect answer.

6. The questions on this paper challenge you **to think**, not to guess. Though you will not lose marks for getting answers wrong, you will undoubtedly get more marks, and more satisfaction, by doing a few questions carefully than by guessing lots of answers.

Enquiries about the Senior Kangaroo should be sent to:
Maths Challenges Office, School of Maths Satellite,
University of Leeds, Leeds, LS2 9JT
Tel. 0113 343 2339
www.ukmt.org.uk

1. How many zeroes are there at the end of the number which is the product of the first 2012 prime numbers?

2. The size of the increase from each term to the next in the list a, $225\frac{1}{2}$, c, d, 284 is always the same. What is the value of a?

3. On the grid shown in the diagram, the shaded squares form a region, A.

   What is the maximum number of additional grid squares which can be shaded to form a region B such that B contains A and that the lengths of the perimeters of A and B are the same?

4. Five cards are laid on a table, as shown. Every card has a letter on one side and a number on the other side.

   Peter says: "For every card on the table, if there is a vowel on one side of the card, then there is an even number on the other side."

   What is the smallest number of cards Sylvia must turn over in order to be certain that Peter is telling the truth?

5. Susan has two pendants made of the same material. They are equally thick and weigh the same. The first pendant is in the shape of an annulus created from two concentric circles, with diameters 8 cm and 12 cm, as shown. The shape of the second pendant is a disc. The diameter of the second pendant is written in the form $a\sqrt{b}$, where a is an integer and b is a prime integer.

   What is the value of $a + b$?

   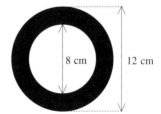

6. Given that $4^x = 9$ and $9^y = 256$, what is the value of xy?

7. When 1001 is divided by a single-digit number, the remainder is 5.
   What is the remainder when 2012 is divided by the same single-digit number?

8. The three prime numbers a, b and c are such that $a > b > c$, $a + b + c = 52$ and $a - b - c = 22$.
   What is the value of abc?

9. The diagram shows a circle touching a sector of another circle in three places. The ratio of the radius of the sector to the radius of the small circle is 3:1. The ratio of the area of the sector to the area of the small circle, written in its simplest form, is $p \ : \ q$.

What is the value of $p + q$?

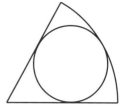

10. Sixteen teams play in a volleyball league. Each team plays one game against every other team. For each game, the winning team is awarded 1 point, and the losing team 0 points. There are no draws. After all the games have been played and the teams have been ranked according to their total scores, the total scores form a sequence where the difference between consecutive terms is constant.

How many points did the team in first place receive?

11. Last year there were 30 more boys than girls in the school choir. This year the number of choir members has increased by 10%, the number of girls has increased by 20% and the number of boys by 5%.

How many members does the choir have this year?

12. The cells of a 4 × 4 grid are coloured black and white as shown in Figure 1. One move allows us to exchange the colourings of any two cells positioned in the same row or in the same column.

What is the minimum number of moves needed to obtain Figure 2?

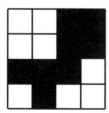

Figure 1   Figure 2

13. A circular stained-glass window is shown in the diagram. The four smaller circles are the same size and are positioned at equal intervals around the centre of the large circle. The letters R, G and B have been placed in regions of red, green and blue glass respectively. The total area of the green glass is 400.

What is the area of the blue glass?

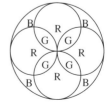

126

14. The diagram shows a cuboid. In triangle XYZ, the lengths of XY, XZ and YZ are 9, 8 and $\sqrt{55}$ respectively.
What is the length of the diagonal XA shown?

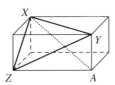

15. The equation $x^2 - bx + 80 = 0$, where $b > 0$, has two integer-valued solutions. What is the sum of the possible values of b?

16. Given that $a + b = 5$ and $ab = 3$, what is the value of $a^4 + b^4$?

17. David removed one number from ten consecutive natural numbers. The sum of the remaining numbers was 2012.

Which number did he remove?

18. The diagram shows a square divided into six smaller squares labelled A, B, C, D, E and F. Two squares are considered to be adjacent if they have more than one point in common. The numbers 1, 2, 3, 4, 5 and 6 are to be placed in the smaller squares, one in each, so that no two adjacent squares contain numbers differing by 3.

How many different arrangements are possible?

A	B	C
		D
	F	E

19. A rectangle which has integer-length sides and area 36 is cut from a square with sides of length 20 so that one of the sides of the rectangle forms part of one of the sides of the square.

What is the largest possible perimeter of the remaining shape?

20. How many subsets of the set $\{1,\ 2,\ 3,\ 4,\ 5,\ 6,\ 7,\ 8,\ 9,\ 10\}$ exist in which the sum of the largest element and the smallest element is 11?

Further remarks

A solutions leaflet was provided.

SENIOR 'KANGAROO' MATHEMATICAL CHALLENGE

Friday 30th November 2012

Organised by the United Kingdom Mathematics Trust

SOLUTIONS

1. **1** In general, each zero at the end of an integer arises because, in the prime factorisation of the integer, there is a factor of 2 and a factor of 5 that can be paired to give a factor of 10. For example, $38\,000 = 2^4 \times 5^3 \times 19$ so 2 and 5 may be paired three times giving a factor of 1000. The product of the first 2012 prime numbers only contains a single factor of 2 and a single factor of 5 so there is only one zero at the end.

2. **206** Let the increase from one term to the next be i. From $225\frac{1}{2}$ to 284 the increase is $3i$ so $284 - 225\frac{1}{2} = 3i$. Therefore $3i = 58\frac{1}{2}$ and hence $i = 19\frac{1}{2}$. To find the value of a, we need to decrease $225\frac{1}{2}$ by i which gives $a = 206$.

3. **16** The diagram shows a region R, say, that certainly contains the region A, and has the same perimeter as A. We claim that R is the region with the largest possible area with these properties and so is B, the region required. To see this, observe that adding any number of extra grid squares to R will only increase the perimeter and so will not give a region of the type required. Therefore, the maximum number of additional grid squares that can be added is 16.

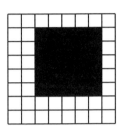

4. **2** For Sylvia to be certain that Peter is telling the truth, she must check that the card showing the letter E has an even number on the other side and that the card showing the number 7 does not have a vowel on the other side. The other three cards do not need to be checked since K is not a vowel and cards with even numbers on one side may have any letter on the other side.

5. **9** For the weights of the two equally thick pendants to be the same, the area of the annulus must be equal to the area of the disc. The area of the annulus is $\pi \times 6^2 - \pi \times 4^2$ which is 20π. Since the area of a disc of radius r is πr^2, we have $\pi r^2 = 20\pi$ and so $r = \sqrt{20} = 2\sqrt{5}$. Thus the diameter of the second pendant is $2 \times 2\sqrt{5}$ which is $4\sqrt{5}$. So $a + b = 4 + 5 = 9$.

6. **4** We have $4^{xy} = \left(4^x\right)^y = 9^y = 256$. However $256 = 4^4$ so $xy = 4$.

7. **2** Let the single-digit number be k. Since the remainder is 5, k is larger than 5. Also k is a single-digit number so k is less than 10. Thus k is 6, 7, 8 or 9. However, the remainder when 1001 is divided by k is 5 so 996 is a multiple of k. Since 996 is not divisible by 7, 8 and 9 we conclude that $k = 6$. Finally, 2012 leaves a remainder of 2 when divided by 6.

8. **962** Adding the two given equations, we get $2a = 74$, which means $a = 37$. Substituting this value into the first equation we obtain $b + c = 15$. Therefore one of b and c is even and the other is odd. Since b and c are both prime, one of them is 2. This means the other is 13. Thus the product required is $2 \times 13 \times 37$, which is 962.

9. **5** Label the diagram as shown. Let the radius of the small circle be r, therefore $r = CD = CE$. We are told that the ratio of the radius of the sector to the radius of the small circle is 3 : 1 so $BD = 3 \times CD = 3r$. Therefore $BC = 2r$. Since triangle BCE is right-angled with two known sides, we have angle CBE is 30° and the area of the sector is a sixth of the area of a circle of radius $3r$. The ratio of the area of the sector to the area of the small circle is $\frac{1}{6}\pi (3r)^2 : \pi r^2$ which simplifies to $\frac{9}{6}\pi r^2 : \pi r^2$, this is, 3 : 2 in its simplest form. So $p + q = 5$.

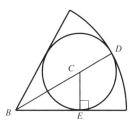

10. **15** Each team played 15 matches so the maximum possible score for any one team is 15 points. Since the total score for a team must be an integer, the gap between consecutive team scores is also an integer. With 16 teams and no negative total scores, the gap is 1 point. This means the total scores are 15 points, 14 points, 13 points , ..., 1 point, 0 points. Thus the team in first place scored 15 points, winning all their matches.

11. **99** Let the number of girls in the choir last year be x. This means there were $x + 30$ boys in the choir last year. This year there are 20% more girls, that is, $1.2x$ girls, and 5% more boys, that is, $1.05(x + 30)$ boys. The overall number in the choir this year is 10% more, that is, $1.1(x + x + 30)$. Putting these together, we get $1.1(2x + 30) = 1.2x + 1.05(x + 30)$. Multiplying out the brackets, we obtain $2.2x + 33 = 1.2x + 1.05x + 31.5$ and hence $15 = 0.05x$, so $x = 30$. The number in the choir this year is $2.2(2x + 30)$ which is therefore $2.2(2 \times 30 + 30)$. So there are 99 choir members this year.

12. **4** In the diagram, the squares labelled A, B, C, D, E and F all need to switch colour (from black to white or white to black, as appropriate). This could take as few as 3 exchanges, if the squares were distributed helpfully. Unfortunately, this is not the case. For example, each of A and F can only be paired with B. This means that it is impossible to use just three exchanges. So if we can perform the required switches in four exchanges, this must be the minimum number needed. This can be done in a number of ways, for example, exchange A and B, exchange C and D, exchange E and X, exchange X and F.

A		B
	C	D
	E	X
		F

13. **400** Let the radius of each of the small circles be r. So the area of the whole window is $\pi (2r)^2$, which is $4\pi r^2$. Therefore $4\pi r^2 = 4(R + G + B)$ and $\pi r^2 = R + G + B$. Now consider the area of one of the small circles. This is πr^2 but is also R + 2G. Equating these expressions for πr^2 gives R + G + B = R + 2G, which simplifies to B = G. Thus the area of the blue glass is equal to the area of the green glass.

Alternative: Note that the area of the large circle is equal to the area of four smaller circles since $\pi (2r)^2 = 4 \times \pi r^2$. But

the area of the window = the area of the 4 smaller circles − 4G + 4B.

Hence B = G.

14. **10** Let $BX = p$, $BY = q$ and $BZ = r$. Using Pythagoras' theorem in $\triangle BXY$, $\triangle BXZ$ and $\triangle BYZ$ respectively, we obtain the equations: $p^2 + q^2 = 81$, $p^2 + r^2 = 64$ and $q^2 + r^2 = 55$. Adding all three equations, we get $2(p^2 + q^2 + r^2) = 81 + 64 + 55$ that is $p^2 + q^2 + r^2 = 100$. By applying Pythagoras' theorem to $\triangle BXZ$ and $\triangle AXZ$, we find that the length of the diagonal XA is $\sqrt{p^2 + q^2 + r^2}$, which is $\sqrt{100} = 10$.

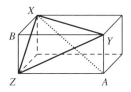

15. **186** The possible quadratic equations are $(x-80)(x-1)=0$, $(x-40)(x-2)=0$, $(x-20)(x-4)=0$, $(x-16)(x-5)=0$, $(x-10)(x-8)=0$. These equations give the values of b as 81, 42, 24, 21 and 18 respectively. The sum of the possible values of b is 186.

16. **343** Expanding $(a+b)^4$ gives $a^4+4a^3b+6a^2b^2+4ab^3+b^4$. We can rearrange this to give $a^4+b^4=(a+b)^4-\left(4a^3b+6a^2b^2+4ab^3\right)$ which can be written in the form $a^4+b^4=(a+b)^4-\left(4ab(a^2+b^2)+6a^2b^2\right)$. Now using $a^2+b^2=(a+b)^2-2ab$ we can write $a^4+b^4=(a+b)^4-\left(4ab\big((a+b)^2-2ab\big)+6(ab)^2\right)$, that is $a^4+b^4=(a+b)^4-4ab(a+b)^2+2(ab)^2$. Substituting $a+b=5$ and $ab=3$, we obtain $a^4+b^4=5^4-\left(4\times 3(5^2-2\times 3)+6\times 3^2\right)$ which reduces to 343.

Note: For a quicker solution, observe that $a^2+b^2=(a+b)^2-2ab=5^2-2\times 3=19$ so that $a^4+b^4=\left(a^2+b^2\right)^2-2a^2b^2=19^2-2(ab)^2=361-18=343$.

17. **223** Let the smallest of the ten original numbers be x. The sum of all ten numbers is $x+(x+1)+(x+2)+\ldots+(x+9)$, which equals $10x+45$.

Let the number removed be $x+a$ where $0\leqslant a\leqslant 9$. Removing this number from the ten original numbers leaves 2012 so $10x+45-(x+a)=2012$, that is, $9x=1967+a$. Dividing by 9, we get $x=218\frac{5}{9}+\frac{a}{9}$. Since x is an integer, $a=4$. Hence $x=219$ and the number removed, $x+a$, is 223.

18. **96** The numbers 1, 2, 3, 4, 5 and 6 can be paired uniquely (1 with 4, 2 with 5, and 3 with 6) so that the difference between the numbers in each pair is 3. Any of the six numbers can be placed in position F but once that has been done, the partner of this number must be placed in position C as, otherwise, the square containing F would be adjacent to a square containing a number that differs by 3. Any of the remaining four numbers may be placed at position A, but then the number placed at B must be one of the two numbers from the pair that has so far been left unused. Finally, the two unused numbers may be positioned at D and E, in either order. Thus the number of possible arrangements is $6\times 4\times 2\times 2$, which is 96.

19. **116** Let the lengths of the sides of the rectangle be a and b, where $a<b$. For the rectangle to be cut from the square, $b<20$. But $ab=36$ and a and b are integers, so the greatest possible value of b is 18. Note that cutting the rectangle so that it shares a corner with the original square and so two sides of the rectangle form part of two sides of the original square would still leave the remaining shape with a perimeter of 80. Cutting the rectangle from the square with one side of length a taken to be part of one of the sides of the square will give a perimeter of $80+2b$. Similarly, if the side of length b is taken to be part of one of the sides of the square, the perimeter of the new shape will be $80+2a$. For the largest perimeter, it is clearly better to do the former since a is less than b. Now $80+2b$ is largest when b is largest, so putting $b=18$ we obtain the largest perimeter, which is 116.

20. **341** If the smallest element was 1 then the largest element would be 10 (to give a sum of 11). Of the remaining possible elements, 2 could be included or not, 3 could be included or not and so on. This means that there are 2^8 possible subsets with smallest element 1 and largest element 10. Similarly there are 2^6 possible subsets with smallest element 2 and largest element 9, there are 2^4 possible subsets with smallest element 3 and largest element 8, there are 2^2 possible subsets with smallest element 4 and largest element 7, and there is one possible subset with smallest element 5 and largest element 6. In total this means there are $2^8+2^6+2^4+2^2+1=341$ possible subsets.

Certificates
These were awarded at two levels, Merit and Participation.

Senior Kangaroo 2012

of

received a
CERTIFICATE of PARTICIPATION

Chairman, United Kingdom Mathematics Trust

THE UKMT SENIOR KANGAROO

The Senior Kangaroo is one of the follow-on rounds for the Senior Mathematical Challenge (SMC) and is organised by the UK Mathematics Trust (UKMT). Around 2,500 high-scoring students in the SMC are invited to participate in the Senior Kangaroo and to test themselves on questions set for the best school-aged mathematicians from across Europe and beyond.

The Senior Kangaroo is a one-hour examination comprising 20 questions; all answers are written using 3 digits, from 000 to 999. The problems involve amusing and thought-provoking situations which require the use of logic as well as mathematical understanding.

The UKMT is a registered charity. For more information please see our website www.ukmt.org.uk. Donations to support our work would be gratefully received and can be made by visiting www.donate.ukmt.org.uk.

132

British Mathematical Olympiads

Within the UKMT, the British Mathematical Olympiad Subtrust has control of the papers and everything pertaining to them. The BMOS produces an annual account of its events which, for 2012-2013, was edited by James Aaronson and Tim Hennock (both of Trinity College, Cambridge). Much of this report is included in the following pages.

United Kingdom Mathematics Trust

British Mathematical Olympiad

Round 1 : Friday, 30 November 2012

Time allowed *Three and a half hours.*

Instructions • *Full written solutions – not just answers – are required, with complete proofs of any assertions you may make. Marks awarded will depend on the clarity of your mathematical presentation. Work in rough first, and then write up your best attempt. Do not hand in rough work.*

• *One **complete** solution will gain more credit than several unfinished attempts. It is more important to complete a small number of questions than to try all the problems.*

• *Each question carries 10 marks. However, earlier questions tend to be easier. In general you are advised to concentrate on these problems first.*

• *The use of rulers, set squares and compasses is allowed, but calculators and protractors are forbidden.*

• *Start each question on a fresh sheet of paper. Write on one side of the paper only. On each sheet of working write the number of the question in the top **left**-hand corner and your name, initials and school in the top **right**-hand corner.*

• *Complete the cover sheet provided and attach it to the front of your script, followed by your solutions in question number order.*

• *Staple all the pages neatly together in the top **left**- hand corner.*

• *To accommodate candidates sitting in other time zones, please do not discuss the paper on the internet until 8am GMT on Saturday 1 December.*

Do not turn over until told to do so.

133

 United Kingdom Mathematics Trust

2012/13 British Mathematical Olympiad
Round 1: Friday, 30 November 2012

1. Isaac places some counters on the squares of an 8 by 8 chessboard so that there is at most one counter in each of the 64 squares. Determine, with justification, the maximum number that he can place without having five or more counters in the same row, or in the same column, or on either of the two long diagonals.

2. Two circles S and T touch at X. They have a common tangent which meets S at A and T at B. The points A and B are different. Let AP be a diameter of S. Prove that B, X and P lie on a straight line.

3. Find all real numbers x, y and z which satisfy the simultaneous equations $x^2 - 4y + 7 = 0$, $y^2 - 6z + 14 = 0$ and $z^2 - 2x - 7 = 0$.

4. Find all positive integers n such that $12n - 119$ and $75n - 539$ are both perfect squares.

5. A triangle has sides of length at most 2, 3 and 4 respectively. Determine, with proof, the maximum possible area of the triangle.

6. Let ABC be a triangle. Let S be the circle through B tangent to CA at A and let T be the circle through C tangent to AB at A. The circles S and T intersect at A and D. Let E be the point where the line AD meets the circle ABC. Prove that D is the midpoint of AE.

The British Mathematical Olympiad 2012-2013

The Round 1 paper was marked by volunteers in December. Below is a list of the prize winners.

Round 1 Prize Winners

The following contestants were awarded prizes:

Gold Medals

Andrew Carlotti	Sir Roger Manwood's School, Kent
Madhi Elango	Queen Elizabeth's School, Barnet
Ian Fan	Dr Challoner's Grammar School, Amersham
Oliver Feng	Eton College, Windsor
Gabriel Gendler	Queen Elizabeth's School, Barnet
Alex Harris	Perse School, Cambridge
Maria Holdcroft	Willink School, Reading
Daniel Hu	City of London School
Freddie Illingworth	Magdalen College School, Oxford
Matthew Jasper	St Crispin's School, Wokingham
Sahl Khan	St Paul's School, London
Edward Kirkby	Alton College, Hampshire
Yuting Li	Westminster School, London
Matei Mandache	Loughborough Grammar School
Ramsay Pyper	Eton College, Windsor
Linden Ralph	Hills Road VI Form College, Cambridge
Harvey Yau	Ysgol Dyffryn Taf, Carmarthenshire

Silver Medals

Modi Anurag	Uppingham School, Rutland
Philip Boylesmith	The Grammar School at Leeds
Alex Burgess	Hemel Hempstead School
Sili Chen	City of London Freemen's School
Ioannis Coward	Campion School, Athens
Monika Dec	Leweston School, Dorset
Alex Fairclough	Reading School
Hongmin Gao	Merchiston Castle School, Edinburgh
Frank Han	Dulwich College, London
Chenshan Hu	Brighton College
Willie Hung	Taipei European School
Andrei Ionescu	British School of Brussels
Marc Jeffreys	Woodbridge School, Suffolk
Mikita Kudlovich	St Clare's, Oxford

Viet Hang Le	South Nottinghamshire College
Suyi Li	Langley Grammar School, Berkshire
Warren Li	Fulford School, York
Liheng Ma	Wuxi Number 1 High School, China
Remy Naylor	Worthing VI Form College
Anh Nguyen	Ruthin School,
Chris Sear	Parmiter's School, Watford
Sam Shepherd	Hayes School, Kent
Jeremy Soper	Taunton School (Upper School)
Joseph Tomkinson	Holmes Chapel Comp. School, Cheshire
Vladimir Vankov	Royal Grammar School, Newcastle
Samuel Walsh	St Bede's College, Manchester
Lawrence Wang	Harrow School
Tony Wang	Culford School, Suffolk
Ziming Wang	Ruthin School, Denbighshire
Adam Weller	Reading School
Ruijia Wu	Headington School, Oxford
Yuchen Yang	Dulwich College, London
Qin Zou	Notre Dame Sixth Form College, Leeds

Bronze Medals

Samuel Banks	King Henry VIII School, Coventry
Keith Barker	Wilson's School, Surrey
Joe Benton	St Paul's School, London
Mikhai Bobkov	Oundle School, Northants
Joseph Boorman	Eton College, Windsor
Peter Buchan	Reigate Grammar School, Surrey
Jake Choules	Eton College, Windsor
Sangwoo Doh	Beijing Dulwich International School
Tsz Hin Fung	Colchester Royal Grammar School
Humphrey Galbraith	Winchester College
Daniel Heydecker	St Albans School
James Hodgson	St Bernard's Convent School, Slough
Ellie Holderness	Latymer Upper School, Hammersmith
Xijie Hou	Ruthin School, Denbighshire
Liam Hughes	Robert Smyth School, Market Harborough
Jeon Jongheon	Winchester College
Patrick Kidger	Torquay Boys' Grammar School
Arthur Kung	Shrewsbury School

Elizabeth Lee	Loughborough High School
Yiting Li	Cheltenham Ladies College
Milton Lin	Taipei European School
Akuan Liu	Cherwell School, Oxford
Norman McGregor	Bell Baxter High School, Fife
Fangda Mei	St Peter & St Paul School, Lincoln
Harry Metrebian	Winchester College
Masaya Murata	St Michael's Catholic Grammar S., London
Nhat Ngo	St Andrew's Tutorial Centre, Cambridge
Quan Minh Nguyen	Tettenhall College, Wolverhampton
Marcus Nielsen	Aylesbury Grammar School
Alistair O'Neill	St Olave's Grammar School, Kent
Robert Pearcehiggins	Cherwell School, Oxford
Yingting Qian	St Mary's School, Cambridge
Adam Richardson	Sir Joseph Williamson's Maths S., Rochester
Hoseong Seo	Abbey College, Cambridge
William Simmons	Harvey Grammar School, Folkestone
Dylon Sivam	Haberdashers' Aske's S. for Boys, Herts
Cheng Sun	Hills Road VI Form College, Cambridge
Xiaoyang Sun	Wuxi Number 1 High School, China
Siddhart Swaroop	King's College School, London
Alvin Sy	Tonbridge School, Kent
Maria Tatulea Codrean	Dollar Academy, Clackmannanshire
Matthew Temple	King's School, Chester
Iain Timmins	Wyggeston & QE I College, Leicester
Marius Tirlea	Westminster School
Ben Walker	Marlborough School, Oxon
Jensen Yang	Taipei European School
Winter Yang	St George's College, Addlestone, Surrey
Changul Yeum	Ruamrudee International School, Thailand
Daniel Zhang	King Edward VI School, Southampton
Jinfeng Zhang	Caterham School, Surrey

United Kingdom Mathematics Trust

British Mathematical Olympiad
Round 2: Thursday, 31 January 2013

Time allowed *Three and a half hours.*
Each question is worth 10 marks.

Instructions • *Full written solutions – not just answers – are required, with complete proofs of any assertions you may make. Marks awarded will depend on the clarity of your mathematical presentation. Work in rough first, and then draft your final version carefully before writing up your best attempt.*
*Rough work **should** be handed in, but should be clearly marked.*

• *One or two **complete** solutions will gain far more credit than partial attempts at all four problems.*

• *The use of rulers and compasses is allowed, but calculators and protractors are forbidden.*

• *Staple all the pages neatly together in the top **left**-hand corner, with questions 1, 2, 3, 4 in order, and the cover sheet at the front.*

• To accommodate candidates sitting in other time zones, please do not discuss any aspect of the paper on the internet until 8am GMT on Friday 1 February.

In early March, twenty students eligible to represent the UK at the International Mathematical Olympiad will be invited to attend the training session to be held at Trinity College, Cambridge (4-8 April). At the training session, students sit a pair of IMO-style papers and eight students will be selected for further training. Those selected will be expected to participate in further correspondence work and to attend further training sessions. The UK Team of six for this summer's International Mathematical Olympiad (to be held in Santa Marta, Colombia, 18-28 July 2013) will then be chosen.

Do not turn over until told to do so.

138

 United Kingdom Mathematics Trust

2012/ 2013 British Mathematical Olympiad
Round 2: Thursday, 31 January 2013

1. Are there infinitely many pairs of positive integers (m, n) such that both m divides $n^2 + 1$ and n divides $m^2 + 1$?

2. The point P lies inside triangle ABC so that $\angle ABP = \angle PCA$. The point Q is such that $PBQC$ is a parallelogram. Prove that $\angle QAB = \angle CAP$.

3. Consider the set of positive integers which, when written in binary, have exactly 2013 digits and more 0s than 1s. Let n be the number of such integers and let s be their sum. Prove that, when written in binary, $n + s$ has more 0s than 1s.

4. Suppose that $ABCD$ is a square and that P is a point which is on the circle inscribed in the square. Determine whether or not it is possible that PA, PB, PC, PD and AB are all integers.

The British Mathematical Olympiad 2012-2013
Round 2

The second round of the British Mathematical Olympiad was held on Thursday 31st January 2013. Some of the top scorers from this round were invited to a residential course at Trinity College, Cambridge.

Leading Scorers

40	Daniel Hu	City of London School
40	Matei Mandache	Loughborough Grammar School
39	Sahl Khan	St Paul's School, London
38	Andrew Carlotti	Sir Roger Manwood's School, Kent
33	Warren Li	Fulford School, York
30	Edward Kirkby	Alton College, Hampshire
29	Gabriel Gendler	Queen Elizabeth's School, Barnet
	Frank Han	Dulwich College
28	Tianbei Li	Concord College, Shrewsbury
27	Marius Tirlea	Westminster School
26	Hongmin Gao	Merchiston Castle School, Edinburgh
24	Harry Metrebian	Winchester College
22	Ramsay Pyper	Eton College, Windsor
21	Pascal Bose	St Olave's Grammar School, Kent
20	Oliver Feng	Eton College, Windsor
	Liam Hughes	Robert Smyth School, Market Harborough
	Freddie Illingworth	Magdalen College School, Oxford
	Gareth Jones	Clifton College, Bristol
	Hoseong Seo	Abbey College, Cambridge
	Joseph Tomkinson	Holmes Chapel Comp. School, Cheshire
19	Matthew Jasper	St Crispin's School, Wokingham
18	Linden Ralph	Hills Road VI Form College, Cambridge
17	Madhi Elango	Queen Elizabeth's School, Barnet
	Remy Naylor	Worthing VI Form College
16	Maria Holdcroft	Willink School, Reading
	Harvey Yau	Ysgol Dyffryn Taf, Carmarthenshire
14	Alex Fellows	Hills Road VI Form College, Cambridge
	Neel Nanda	Latymer School, London
13	Joe Benton	St Paul's School, London
	George Fortune	Altrincham Grammar S. for Boys, Cheshire

140
IMO 2013

The 2013 International Mathematical Olympiad took place in Santa Marta, Colombia from 18 - 28 July 2013. The Team Leader was Dr Geoff Smith (University of Bath) and the Deputy Leader was Dominic Yeo (Worcester College, Oxford). A full account of the 2013 IMO and the UK preparation for it appears later in the book. The members of the team were Andrew Carlotti, Gabriel Gendler, Daniel Hu, Sahl Khan, Warren Li and Matei Mandache. The reserves were Frank Han, Maria Holdcroft and Freddie Illingworth. In addition to the Leader and Deputy Leader, the team were accompanied by Beverley Detoeuf (UKMT) to deal with pastoral aspects.

Introduction to the BMO problems and full solutions

The 'official' solutions are the result of many hours' work by a large number of people, and have been subjected to many drafts and revisions. The contestants' solutions included here will also have been redrafted several times by the contestants themselves, and also shortened and cleaned up somewhat by the editors. As such, they do not resemble the first jottings, failed ideas and discarded pages of rough work with which any solution is started.

Before looking at the solutions, pupils (and teachers) are encouraged to make a concerted effort to attack the problems themselves. Only by doing so is it possible to develop a feel for the question, to understand where the difficulties lie and why one method of attack is successful while others may fail. Problem solving is a skill that can only be learnt by practice; going straight to the solutions is unlikely to be of any benefit.

It is also important to bear in mind that solutions to Olympiad problems are not marked for elegance. A solution that is completely valid will receive a full score, no matter how long and tortuous it may be. However, elegance has been an important factor influencing our selection of contestants' answers.

BMO Round 1 – Questions and Solutions

1. Isaac places some counters on the squares of an 8 by 8 chessboard so that there is at most one counter in each of the 64 squares. Determine,with justification, the maximum number that he can place without having five or more counters in the same row, or in the same column, or on either of the two long diagonals.

(*Proposed by Dr Jeremy King*)

The key to this problem is to realise that, if we focus only on the constraint that there can be only at most four counters in each row, the maximum number of counters we can put on the board is 32. (Of course, we could also do the same by considering only the columns.) This can be attained in a variety of ways.

Solution by Abigail Hayes, Stretford Grammar School

We know that there must be fewer than 5 counters in each row, column and long diagonal, so the maximum in each is 4 counters.

If we had more than 32 counters, then there would be at least 5 in one row, which cannot happen. Hence, there can be at most 32 counters.

Here is an example which attains this bound:

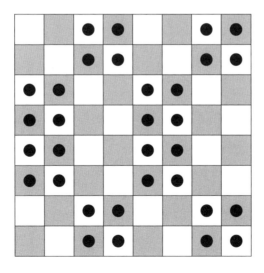

2. Two circles S and T touch at X. They have a common tangent which meets S at A and T at B. The points A and B are different. Let AP be a diameter of S. Prove that B, X and P lie on a straight line.

(*Proposed by Richard Freeland*)

There are a few different ways to approach this problem, mostly using the alternate segment theorem and other standard circle facts. Whilst a good diagram is always helpful, it is important not to *assume* accidentally that PXB is a straight line as part of the proof, just because it looks that way in the diagram!

Solution 1 by Harry Metrebian, Winchester College

Let the centres of circles S and T be O_1 and O_2 respectively; let the other end of the diameter of T through B be Q and let the common tangent to both circles at X pass through a point L on the same side of X as the line AB and a point M on the other side of X.

We know that O_1XO_2 is a straight line as the lines O_1X and O_2X are both perpendicular to the tangent at X.

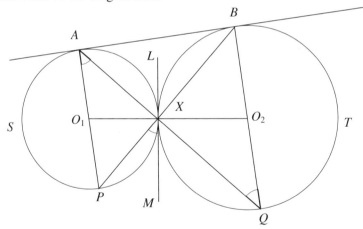

Since tangents and radii meet at right angles,

$$\angle PAB = \angle ABQ = 90°.$$

Therefore the lines AP and BQ are parallel. So, by alternate angles,

$$\angle PO_1X = \angle BO_2X.$$

Since the angle subtended by a chord at the centre of a circle is twice that subtended by the same chord at the circumference,

$$\angle PAX = \tfrac{1}{2}\angle PO_1X = \tfrac{1}{2}\angle BO_2X = \angle BQX.$$

By the alternate segment theorem,

$$\angle PXM = \angle PAX = \angle BQX = \angle BXL.$$

Since LXM is a straight line, BXP is also a straight line by the converse of the vertically opposite angles theorem.

Solution 2 by Aatreyee Mimi Das, Heckmondwike Grammar School

Let the other end of the diameter of T through B be Q. Let the tangent to circles S and T at X meet AB at V, and let M be a point on XV the other side of X from V.

Note that $\angle PXA = 90°$ because AP is a diameter. Similarly $\angle BXQ = 90°$. Let $\angle APX = y°$. Then by the alternate segment theorem, $\angle BAX = y°$. Also let $\angle XQB = z°$; then $\angle XBA = z°$ also by the alternate segment theorem.

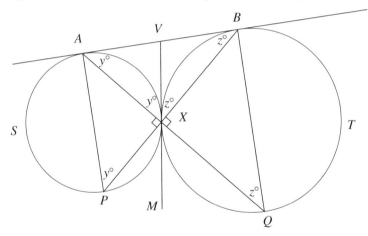

Using the alternate segment theorem again, it must be the case that $\angle AXV = y°$ and $\angle VXB = z°$. Then $\angle AXB = y° + z°$. But then the sum of the angles in triangle BAX is

$$\angle XBA + \angle BAX + \angle AXB$$
$$= z° + y° + (y° + z°)$$
$$= 2(y° + z°).$$

Since this must be 180°, it follows that $\angle AXB = y° + z° = 90°$. Therefore

$$\angle PXB = \angle PXA + \angle AXB = 90° + 90° = 180°,$$

and so PXB is a straight line.

3. Find all real numbers x, y and z which satisfy the simultaneous equations $x^2 - 4y + 7 = 0$, $y^2 - 6z + 14 = 0$ and $z^2 - 2x - 7 = 0$.

(*Proposed by Dr David Monk*)

It might not seem obvious where to start with this curious looking set of simultaneous equations, but there turns out to be a useful trick that leads to the solution. Most successful solutions used the method below.

Solution by the markers

Sum all three equations, to yield

$$x^2 - 4y + 7 + y^2 - 6z + 14 + z^2 - 2x - 7 = 0.$$

This can be rearranged to form

$$(x - 1)^2 + (y - 2)^2 + (z - 3)^2 = 0.$$

Since all squares are nonnegative, this can only happen if all three terms are equal to 0. Therefore, *if there is any solution*, it must be that $x = 1$, $y = 2$ and $z = 3$.

We must check against the *original* equations to see if this is indeed a solution, and it turns out that $x = 1$, $y = 2$, $z = 3$ does satisfy them. Therefore this is the unique solution.

4. Find all positive integers n such that $12n - 119$ and $75n - 539$ are both perfect squares.

(Proposed by Richard Freeland)

The key in this question is to somehow reduce the problem to a finite set of cases each of which we can then check. A typical way of doing this is to find some factorisation of an integer, as the solution below does.

Solution by Alex Harris, Perse School

Firstly, let $a^2 = 12n - 119$ and $b^2 = 75n - 539$.

We have $n = \dfrac{a^2 + 119}{12}$, from the definition of a. So we can use the definition of b to derive

$$\frac{75(a^2 + 119)}{12} - 539 = b^2,$$

i.e. $25(a^2 + 119) - 4 \times 539 = 4b^2,$

and hence

$$25a^2 - 4b^2 = -819.$$

This can be rearranged and factorised to give

$$(2b - 5a)(2b + 5a) = 819.$$

So we know that the integers $2b - 5a$ and $2b + 5a$ multiply together to give 819. Since we can assume that a and b are nonnegative, which means that $2b + 5a$ is at least as big as $2b - 5a$, we have a limited set of possibilities for $(2b - 5a, 2b + 5a)$: (1, 819), (3, 273), (7, 117), (9, 91), (13, 63) and (21, 39).

Only the second, third and fifth give integer values for a, so (a, b) can be (27, 69), (11, 31) or (5, 19).

We can substitute into the formula for n above to determine its possible values. The first does not give an integer, so we are left with $n = 20$ or $n = 12$. We can easily check that both these values of n work.

5. A triangle has sides of length at most 2, 3 and 4 respectively. Determine, with proof, the maximum possible area of the triangle.

(Proposed by Dr Jeremy King)

Whilst there are some very neat, short solutions to this problem, it is important to justify carefully why the given triangle is maximal.

Solution 1 by Gavin O'Connell, Bristol Grammar School

Let θ be the largest angle of the triangle. Thus, θ is the angle between the two shorter sides, of lengths a and b.

The area of the triangle is given by $A = \frac{1}{2}ab \sin \theta$, where $a \leqslant b$ are the shorter sides. But we have

$$a \leqslant 2,$$

$$b \leqslant 3,$$

and

$$\sin \theta \leqslant 1.$$

Hence $A \leqslant 3$, with equality when the triangle is right-angled with legs 2 and 3. This gives a hypotenuse of length $\sqrt{13} < 4$, which is valid.

Thus, the maximum area is 3.

Solution 2 by Warren Li, Fulford School

If the sides of the triangle are of lengths a, b and c, and the circumradius is R, then it is well known that the area of the triangle is $A = \dfrac{abc}{4R}$.

Without loss of generality, let $a \leqslant b \leqslant c$. We have $c \leqslant 2R$, $a \leqslant 2$ and $b \leqslant 3$, so $A \leqslant \dfrac{ab}{2} \leqslant 3$.

The proof is then completed in a manner similar to Solution 1.

6. Let *ABC* be a triangle. Let *S* be the circle through *B* tangent to *CA* at *A* and let *T* be the circle through *C* tangent to *AB* at *A*. The circles *S* and *T* intersect at *A* and *D*. Let *E* be the point where the line *AD* meets the circle *ABC*. Prove that *D* is the midpoint of *AE*.

(*Proposed by Dr Gerry Leversha*)

There is a wide variety of ways to approach this problem. Some students used a similar triangles argument along the lines of the first solution below; some other methods involved considering the centres of circles *S* and *T*, as in the second solution. Another method is to observe that the circumcentre of *ABC* lies on the circle through *B*, *D*, *C*, and extend the line *ADE* to meet this circle again.

Solution 1 by Oliver Feng, Eton College
Let $\angle ABD = \alpha$ and $\angle DCA = \beta$.

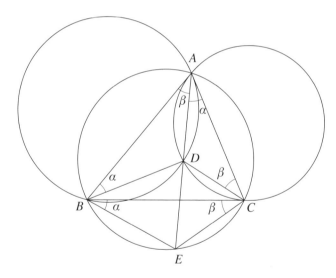

Then $\angle CAD = \angle ABD = \alpha$ and $\angle DAB = \angle DCA = \beta$, by the alternate segment theorem. So $\triangle ABD$ is similar to $\triangle CAD$. Therefore, $\dfrac{AB}{BD} = \dfrac{AC}{AD}$ and so $AD = \dfrac{AC \times BD}{AB}$ ... (1).

Also, $\angle CBE = \angle CAE = \alpha$ and $\angle ECB = \angle EAB = \beta$ by the theorem of angles in the same segment. Similarly $\angle BED = \angle BEA = \angle BCA$. Further, $\angle DBE = \angle CBE + \angle DBC = \angle ABD + \angle DBC = \angle ABC$. So $\triangle DBE$ and $\triangle ABC$ are similar.

Hence, $\dfrac{DB}{DE} = \dfrac{AB}{AC}$, and so $DE = \dfrac{AC \times BD}{AB}$... (2). By (1) and (2) $AD = DE$ so that D is the midpoint of AE.

Solution 2 by Ian Fan, Dr Challoner's Grammar School

Denote the centres of circles S and T respectively by O_S and O_T, and let $\angle CAE = \phi$ and $\angle DAB = \theta$.

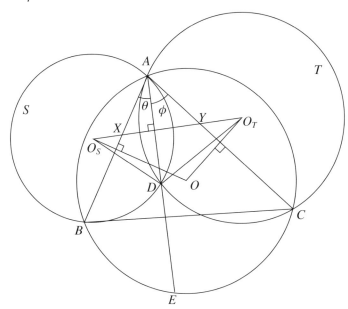

We can see that

$$\angle O_T O_S O = 90° - \angle BXO_S = \angle DAB = \theta$$

and

$$\angle OO_T O_S = 90° - \angle O_T YC = \angle CAE = \phi.$$

Then

$$\angle O_T O_S D = 90° - \angle O_S DA = 90° - \angle DAO_S = \phi$$

since the line AC is tangent to circle S. Similarly, $\angle DO_T O_S = \theta$. Combining this with what we deduced above,

$$\angle O_T O_S O = \angle DO_T O_S$$

and

$$\angle OO_T O_S = \angle O_T O_S D.$$

Therefore the two triangles $\triangle O_T O_S D$ and $\triangle O_S O_T O$ share the side $O_S O_T$ and the two angles at O_S and O_T (but the other way round). So one is a reflection of the other. Consider this reflection. It maps O_S to O_T and vice versa, so it must be a reflection in a line perpendicular to $O_S O_T$. Since D maps to O (and vice versa), this line must also be perpendicular to the line DO. So DO is parallel to $O_S O_T$.

Since $O_S O_T$ is perpendicular to the line ADE, it must also be the case that DO is perpendicular to ADE. As $\triangle AOE$ is isosceles with $AO = EO$, this implies that D is the midpoint of AE.

BMO Round 2 – Questions and Solutions

1. Are there infinitely many pairs of positive integers (m, n) such that both m divides $n^2 + 1$ and n divides $m^2 + 1$?

(Proposed by Dr Geoff Smith)

As with many problems involving finding infinitely many solutions to a condition, it is best to try a few small cases first and try to spot a pattern in them, and then to prove that this pattern gives your infinite set of solutions. Trying the values of n up to five gives us the solutions $(1, 1)$, $(1, 2)$, $(2, 5)$, $(5, 13)$, which is very suggestive – all the numbers here are Fibonacci numbers, in fact, 1, 2, 5, 13 consists of alternate terms of the Fibonacci sequence. This leads us to the solution below.

Solution by Andrew Carlotti, Sir Roger Manwood's School

Let us denote by F_n the nth Fibonacci number. We claim that $(n, m) = (F_{2k-1}, F_{2k+1})$ is a solution for all positive integers k.

First of all we show that, for all positive integers k,

$$F_{2k+1}^2 + 1 = F_{2k-1} \cdot F_{2k+3}. \tag{1}$$

This will be proved by induction on k.

For $k = 1$, it is true since

$$F_3^2 + 1 = 2^2 + 1 = 5 = 1 \times 5 = F_1 \cdot F_5.$$

Now we do the induction step; we suppose therefore that $F_{2k-1}^2 + 1 = F_{2k-3} \cdot F_{2k+1}$. Note first that $F_{2k+3} = 3F_{2k+1} - F_{2k-1}$, by repeatedly applying the relation $F_{m+2} = F_{m+1} + F_m$. Then

$$
\begin{aligned}
F_{2k-1} \cdot F_{2k+3} &= F_{2k-1}\left(3F_{2k+1} - F_{2k-1}\right) \\
&= 3F_{2k+1} \cdot F_{2k-1} - F_{2k-1}^2 \\
&= 3F_{2k+1} \cdot F_{2k-1} - \left(F_{2k-3} \cdot F_{2k+1} - 1\right) \\
&= F_{2k+1}\left(3F_{2k-1} - F_{2k-3}\right) + 1 \\
&= F_{2k+1} \cdot F_{2k+1} + 1 \\
&= F_{2k+1}^2 + 1.
\end{aligned}
$$

This completes the proof of (1). But then it follows immediately that

$$F_{2k-1} \mid \left(F_{2k+1}^2 + 1\right)$$

and

$$F_{2k+1} \mid \left(F_{2k-1}^2 + 1\right)$$

for all positive integers k.

2. The point P lies inside triangle ABC so that $\angle ABP = \angle PCA$. The point Q is such that $PBQC$ is a parallelogram. Prove that $\angle QAB = \angle CAP$.

(*Proposed by Dr Andrew Jobbings*)

There were several distinct elegant solutions offered by candidates to this problem. With a configuration as simple as this, there was a strong temptation to add lots of extra lines and points and start a calculation-heavy 'angle chase', but this was generally unsuccessful. Adding a single extra point, on the other hand, was often very profitable, particularly when it was chosen to take advantage of the parallel lines and equal angles already present, as in the first solution below. Some candidates were also able to use a careful analysis of the sine function to deduce the conclusion from a trigonometric identity derived from the original configuration.

Solution 1 by Hongmin Gao, Merchiston Castle School

Translate the triangle $\triangle ABQ$ to form a new, congruent triangle $\triangle DPC$. This has side DC parallel to AQ, side DP parallel to AB and side PC parallel to BQ. Therefore $\angle QAB = \angle CDP$. Also extend the line BP to meet DC at M.

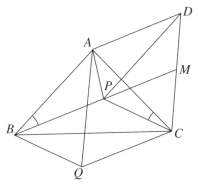

Lines AD, BP and CQ are parallel, as are AB and DP. Thus

$$\angle ABP = \angle DPM = \angle PDA.$$

Since $\angle ABP = \angle PCA$, it follows that $\angle PCA = \angle PDA$. Therefore the points A, P, C and D lie on the same circle, by the converse of the angles in the same segment theorem.

Therefore $\angle CAP = \angle CDP$, and so $\angle CAP = \angle QAB$.

Solution 2 by Philip Leung, Harrow School (slightly edited)

Extend the line BP to meet AC at E and CP to meet AB at D. Let $\angle PDA = x°$ and $\angle PBA = y°$.

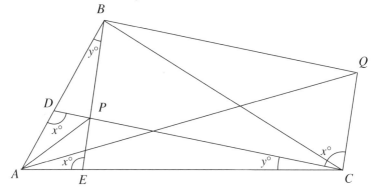

By the Sine Rule on $\triangle BDP$,

$$\frac{DP}{\sin y°} = \frac{PB}{\sin \angle BDP} = \frac{PB}{\sin x°}.$$

By the Sine Rule on $\triangle ACD$,

$$\frac{AD}{\sin y°} = \frac{CA}{\sin x°}.$$

Therefore

$$\frac{AD}{CA} = \frac{DP}{PB} = \frac{DP}{QC},$$

and so

$$\frac{QC}{CA} = \frac{DP}{AD}.$$

Since $\angle ABP = \angle PCA$ and the angle at A is shared between the two triangles, $\triangle BAE$ and $\triangle CAD$ are similar. So $\angle BEA = x°$. But as QC is parallel to BPE, $\angle QCA = x°$.

Combined with the knowledge that the ratio of sides $QC : CA$ and $DP : AD$ are equal, this tells us that $\triangle ADP$ is similar to $\triangle ACQ$ by SAS similarity.

So $\angle PAB = \angle CAQ$. Hence $\angle QAB = \angle CAP$.

3. Consider the set of positive integers which, when written in binary, have exactly 2013 digits and more 0s than 1s. Let n be the number of such integers and let s be their sum. Prove that, when written in binary, $n + s$ has more 0s than 1s.

(Proposed by Dr Jeremy King)

The crux of this problem is careful manipulation of binomial coefficients. All successful solutions followed a similar line to the one we present below.

Solution by Warren Li, Fulford School: By definition, n is the number of binary representations with 2013 digits, first digit 1, and at least 1007 digits 0. Summing over all possible values for the number of digits 0 and then employing the identity $\binom{a}{b} = \binom{a}{a-b}$,

$$n = \sum_{i=1007}^{2012} \binom{2012}{i}$$

$$= \frac{1}{2} \sum_{i=0}^{2012} \binom{2012}{i} - \frac{1}{2}\binom{2012}{1006}.$$

Since the sum $\sum_{i=0}^{m} \binom{m}{i} = 2^m$,

$$n = 2^{2011} - \binom{2011}{1005}.$$

Now, s can be written as $\sum_{i=0}^{2012} a_i 2^i$, where a_i denotes the number of binary representations which have a 1 at digit i. We note that $a_{2012} = n$, and that for all other i,

$$a_i = \sum_{i=1007}^{2011} \binom{2011}{i}$$

$$= \frac{1}{2} \sum_{i=0}^{2011} \binom{2011}{i} - \frac{1}{2}\left(\binom{2011}{1005} + \binom{2011}{1006}\right)$$

$$= 2^{2010} - \binom{2011}{1005}.$$

Hence, letting that constant value be a,

$$s = \sum_{i=0}^{2012} a_i 2^i$$

$$= 2^{2012}n + a\sum_{i=0}^{2011} 2^i$$

$$= 2^{2012}n + \left(2^{2010} - \binom{2011}{1005}\right)\left(2^{2012} - 1\right).$$

Thus

$$n + s = \left(2^{2012} + 1\right)\left(2^{2011} - \binom{2011}{1005}\right)$$

$$+ \left(2^{2012} - 1\right)\left(2^{2010} - \binom{2011}{1005}\right)$$

$$= 2^{4023} + 2^{4022} + 2^{2010} - 2^{2013}\binom{2011}{1005}.$$

Now that we have a formula for $n + s$, it is just left to show that we have enough digits 0. Since $n + s < 2^{4024}$, there are at most 4024 binary digits. Then

$$n + s = 2^{2013}\left(2^{2010} + 2^{2009} - \binom{2011}{1005}\right) + 2^{2010},$$

meaning that 2012 of the last 2013 digits are 0.

Finally, we note that the only way in which $n + s$ will not have more 0 digits that 1 digits is if it has 4024 digits, and all of the digits unaccounted for are 1, i.e.

$$n + s = 2^{2013}\left(1 + 2 + 2^2 + \dots + 2^{2010}\right) + 2^{2010}.$$

However this is clearly bigger than the given value for $n + s$.

4. Suppose that *ABCD* is a square and that *P* is a point which is on the circle inscribed in the square. Determine whether or not it is possible that *PA*, *PB*, *PC*, *PD* and *AB* are all integers.

(Proposed by Dr Jeremy King)

Solutions to this problem broadly fell into two categories. The first solution presented involves showing that *P* has rational coordinates and then derives a contradiction, while the second relates *PA*, *PC* and *AB* by an equation with no integer solutions, and we present two ways of deriving this equation.

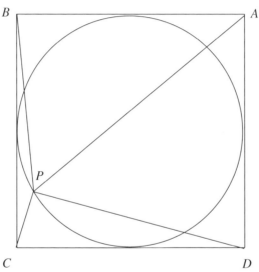

Solution 1 by Matei Mandache, Loughborough Grammar School

We shall assume all five lengths are integers and obtain a contradiction. Give the points *A*, *B*, *C*, *D* and *P* cartesian coordinates (a, a), $(-a, a)$, $(-a, -a)$, $(a, -a)$ and (b, c) respectively. Then *a* is rational, as $2a$ is an integer.

By Pythagoras, we learn that

$$AP^2 = 2a^2 + b^2 + c^2 - 2ab - 2ac$$

$$BP^2 = 2a^2 + b^2 + c^2 + 2ab - 2ac$$

$$CP^2 = 2a^2 + b^2 + c^2 + 2ab + 2ac$$

$$DP^2 = 2a^2 + b^2 + c^2 - 2ab + 2ac.$$

From these we derive

$$BP^2 - AP^2 = 4ab$$

and

$$CP^2 - BP^2 = 4ac.$$

Therefore b and c are rational.

We note that we can scale up our solution by an integer factor (in fact, the lowest common denominator of a, b and c) to generate a solution with a, b and c integers. Furthermore, if they are all even, we can scale down repeatedly by a factor of 2 until at least one of them is odd.

Now, from the constraint that P lies on the incircle, we note that $b^2 + c^2 = a^2$. Given that not all of a, b and c are even, the only other option, since squares modulo 4 are always 0 or 1, is that exactly one of b and c is even. Without loss of generality, assume that b is even, and a and c are odd.

Now, from the above formulae for BP^2 and CP^2, we note that they are both odd. This yields that they are both 1 modulo 8, and so $8 \mid CP^2 - BP^2$. However, the right-hand quantity is just $4ac$, which is not divisible by 8 as a and c are odd. This yields our contradiction.

Solution 2 by Daniel Hu, City of London School

Let O be the centre of the inscribed circle, so that it lies on AC. Let the circle have radius r, so $AB = 2r$ and $AC = 2\sqrt{2}r$.

Drop the perpendicular from P to AC, and let it meet AC at H, so $OH^2 + HP^2 = OP^2$. Without loss of generality, assume that H lies between O and C. Hence

$$PC^2 = HP^2 + HC^2$$

$$= HP^2 + \left(\sqrt{2}r - OH\right)^2$$

$$= HP^2 + OH^2 + 2r^2 - 2\sqrt{2}r \times OH.$$

Similarly, $AP^2 = HP^2 + OH^2 + 2r^2 + 2\sqrt{2}r \times OH$, and we obtain

$$PC^2 + AP^2 = 2HP^2 + 2OH^2 + 4r^2$$

$$= 2r^2 + 4r^2$$

$$= 6r^2.$$

Hence

$$2PA^2 + 2PC^2 = 3AB^2. \tag{1}$$

Write this as $2b^2 + 2c^2 = 3a^2$.

Suppose that this equation has a nonzero solution, and let (a, b, c) be the solution with a minimal. Since squares mod 3 are 0 and 1, 3 must divide b and c. So write $b = 3b'$ and $c = 3c'$, so $6b'^2 + 6c'^2 = a^2$. Now, we note that $3 \mid a$, so $a = 3a'$, to give $2b'^2 + 2c'^2 = 3a'^2$, so that (a', b', c') is a nonzero solution with $a' < a$, contradicting the minimality assumption. This is an example of a general technique known as infinite descent.

Solution 3 by Tianbei Li, Concord College (slightly edited)

To derive equation (1) in Solution 2, we may use cartesian coordinates. We can scale so that A, B, C and D are at (a, a), $(-a, a)$, $(-a, -a)$, $(a, -a)$ and P is at $(a \cos \theta, a \sin \theta)$. Then

$$PA^2 = a^2\left((1 - \cos \theta)^2 + (1 - \sin \theta)^2\right)$$
$$= a^2\left(3 - 2 \cos \theta - 2 \sin \theta\right)$$

and

$$PC^2 = a^2\left((1 + \cos \theta)^2 + (1 + \sin \theta)^2\right)$$
$$= a^2\left(3 + 2 \cos \theta + 2 \sin \theta\right).$$

Therefore

$$PA^2 + PC^2 = 6a^2,$$

and

$$2AP^2 + 2PC^2 = 3AB^2.$$

We can then finish as in Solution 2.

Olympiad Training and Overseas Competitions

Various training camps are held throughout the year to select and prepare students for participation in the UK team at forthcoming International Mathematical Olympiads and other international events.

Oxford Training Camp

The training programme for the academic year 2012-13 began in late August 2012 with a camp at The Queen's College, Oxford for students new to IMO preparation, and overseen by Dr Peter Neumann.

The academic programme was fairly structured and very intense. Essentially there were four 'lecture/tutorial courses' plus some one-off lectures/presentations, all supported by the company acting as tutors circulating and helping the students with the problem-solving activities that were a crucial part of the courses. There were two 100-minute sessions each morning Monday to Friday. These were a lecture course on Geometry by Geoff Smith (5) and five lectures on Problem Solving by Jack Shotton (1), Paul Russell (2) and James Cranch (2). On Monday, Tuesday, Thursday and Friday there were three afternoon sessions, each lasting 60 to 75 minutes. Four of these formed a course on Number Theory by Vicky Neale, another a sequence on Combinatorics by James Cranch (2), Ed Crane (1) and Paul Russell (1); then there were lectures by Ed Crane on Recurrence Relations, by Jack Shotton on Functional Equations, by Hannah Roberts on Inequalities and by Paul Russell on Induction. On the Tuesday evening Yves Capdeboscq, Fellow of Queen's, kindly came to give an inspirational lecture entitled 'From Averages to Weak Limits' to show the students something of his area of research.

On the final Saturday morning the majority of the students sat the four-and-a-half-hour Oxford Mathematical Olympiad under IMO conditions and rules of engagement.

On the non-academic side Rosie Cretney (Open University, ex-Queen's), Sally Anne Huk (Tues–Fri), Penny Thompson (Tues–Fri) and Peter Neumann took primary responsibility for the children's welfare, assisted by Bev Detoeuf on the first evening.

James, Rosie, Hannah, Sally Anne, Penny and others organised various activities for the evenings. We had a quiz evening, a talent show, a mathematical relay and a film evening. On the Wednesday afternoon a highly successful punting expedition during a one-hour gap in the rain was followed by time exploring Oxford and its shops, colleges and museums.

The students at the Oxford camp were: Samuel Bodansky (The Grammar School Leeds); Ian Fan (Dr Challoner's Grammar School); George Fortune (Altrincham Grammar School for Boys); Jiali Gao (Wolverhampton Girls' High School); Monica Gupta (Tiffin Girls' School); Yair Halberstadt (Hasmonean High School); Jennie Han (Redland High School); Alex Harris (Perse School); Maria Holdcroft (Willink School); Liam Hughes (Robert Smyth School); Stephen Jones (Magdalen College School); Gareth Jones (Clifton College); Warren Li (Fulford School); Rachel Newhouse (Skipton Girls' High School); Yuen Ng (Rainham Mark Grammar School); Ramsay Pyper (Eton College); Linden Ralph (Comberton Village College); Bryony Richards (South Wiltshire Grammar School); Sreya Saha (Altrincham Grammar School for Girls); Kasia Warburton (Reigate Grammar School); Harvey Yau (Ysgol Dyffryn Taf); Gloria Yin (St Paul's Girls' School)

Mathematical Olympiad for Girls

The UK Mathematical Olympiad for Girls (UK MOG) is held annually to identify students to engage in training for EGMO. Students who are not involved in training are still eligible for selection for the team.

The 2012 MOG paper was held on 20th September. The time allowed was 3 hours and the Instructions were essentially the same as those for the BMO papers shown earlier. The questions appear on the next page.

United Kingdom Mathematics Trust

UK Mathematical Olympiad for Girls
20 September 2012

1. The numbers a, b and c are real. Prove that at least one of the three numbers $(a + b + c)^2 - 9bc$, $(a + b + c)^2 - 9ca$ and $(a + b + c)^2 - 9ab$ is non-negative.

2. Let $S = \{a_1, a_2, \dots, a_n\}$ where the a_i are different positive integers. The sum of the elements of each non-empty proper subset of S is not divisible by n. Show that the sum of all elements of S is divisible by n. *Note that a proper subset of S consists of some, but not all, of the elements of S.*

3. Find all positive integers m and n such that $m^2 + 8 = 3^n$.

4. Does there exist a positive integer N which is a power of 2, and a different positive integer M obtained from N by permuting its digits (in the usual base 10 representation), such that M is also a power of 2? *Note that we do not allow the base 10 representation of a positive integer to begin with 0.*

5. Consider the triangle ABC. Squares $ALKB$ and $BNMC$ are attached to two of the sides, arranged in a "folded out" configuration (so the interiors of the triangle and the two squares do not overlap one another). The squares have centres O_1 and O_2 respectively. The point D is such that $ANCD$ is a parallelogram. The point Q is the midpoint of KN, and P is the midpoint of AC.
    (a) Prove that triangles ABD and BKN are congruent.
    (b) Prove that O_1QO_2P is a square.

Time allowed: 3 hours

Hungary Camp

Since 2001, there has been a visit to Budapest over the New Year to train with the Hungarian IMO squad, and this tradition continued in 2012-13, with 20 British and 20 Hungarian students attending.

Our thanks go to James Cranch for leading the camp so well, and his helpers Tim Hennock and Jo Harbour.

The attendees were: Joseph Benton (St Paul's School); Andrew Carlotti (Sir Roger Manwood's School); Madhi Elango (Queen Elizabeth's School); Yi Fan (Dr Challoner's Grammar School); Oliver Feng (Eton College); Hongmin Gao (Merchiston Castle School); Gabriel Gendler (Queen Elizabeth's School); Alexander Harris (Perse School); Maria Holdcroft (Willink School); Daniel Hu (City of London School); Freddie Illingworth (Magdalen College School); Matthew Jasper (St Crispin's School); Sahl Khan (St Paul's School); Edward Kirkby (Alton College); Suyi Li (Langley Grammar School); Warren Li (Fulford School); Matei Mandache (Loughborough Grammar School); Ramsay Pyper (Eton College); Linden Ralph (Comberton Village College); Harvey Yau (Ysgol Dyffryn Taf).

Romanian Master of Mathematics

The UK has competed in the Romanian Master of Mathematics (RMM) since 2008. Teams consist of six people; the UK does not name a reserve. As well as the individual competition, there are official team rankings, based on the scores of the top three contestants from each team only. As at the IMO, there are two papers, each of three questions, and each question marked out of 7 points (but the format varied at the first two competitions).

The UK was delighted to be invited to send a team to the Sixth edition of the Romanian Master of Mathematics contest, held in the Tudor Vianu National High School for Computer Science between the 27th February and 3rd March. The contest has become a regular part of the mathematical competition calendar, and is designed to be a hard competition for countries that perform strongly at the International Mathematical Olympiad.

This year, the team consisted of: Andrew Carlotti (Sir Roger Manwood's School); Gabriel Gendler (Queen Elizabeth's School); Daniel Hu (City of London School); Sahl Khan (St Paul's School); Warren Li (Fulford School); Matei Mandache (Loughborough Grammar School). The team leader was Jonathan Lee (University of Cambridge); Beverley Detoeuf of UKMT was the deputy leader, and Dan Schwarz (Romania) was an observer for the UK. A full report about the 2013 RMM can be found at http://www.bmoc.maths.org/home/rmm.shtml.

Trinity College Training Camp

The traditional Easter training and selection camp was once again held at Trinity College, Cambridge, and the UKMT are most grateful to Trinity College for its generous hosting of the event.

Twenty-one young UK mathematicians came to Cambridge for the Trinity College training session and IMO squad selection exams. The group included all candidates for the current year's IMO team along with some younger students with great potential for future international competitions. There were four or five sessions per day covering materials useful in IMO problems. Part way through and at the end of the five-day camp, students sat two IMO-style examinations, after which a final small UK IMO squad was selected to attend the final selection camp at Oundle School.

The attending students were: Andrew Carlotti (Sir Roger Manwood's School); Oliver Feng (Eton College); Hongmin Gao (Merchiston Castle School); Gabriel Gendler (Queen Elizabeth's School); Frank Han (Dulwich College); Maria Holdcroft (Willink School); Daniel Hu (City of London School); Liam Hughes (Robert Smyth School); Freddie Illingworth (Magdalen College School); Gareth Jones (Clifton College); Sahl Khan (St Paul's School); Edward Kirkby (Alton College); Elizabeth Lee (Loughborough High School); Warren Li (Fulford School); Matei Mandache (Loughborough Grammar School); Harry Metrebian (Winchester College); Ramsay Pyper (Eton College); Katya Richards (School of St Helen and St Katharine); Marius Tirlea (Westminster School); Kasia Warburton (Reigate Grammar School); Harvey Yau (Ysgol Dyffryn Taf).

We are very grateful to the following staff who gave excellent sessions and looked after the attendees: James Aaronson, Natalie Behague, Lex Betts, Robin Bhattacharyya, Ben Elliott, Mary Fortune, Richard Freeland, Adam Goucher, Zoltan Gyenes, Jo Harbour, Tim Hennock, Josh Lam, Imre Leader, Gerry Leversha, Joseph Myers, Vishal Patil, Hannah Roberts, Paul Russell, Jack Shotton, Geoff Smith and Dominic Yeo.

European Girls' Mathematical Olympiad

After a very successful first year in Cambridge, the baton for holding the 2013 event was passed to Luxembourg. EGMO was founded to increase the participation of girls in international mathematics competitions. The competition had grown since 2013; 22 countries participated and further countries had also hoped to join.

The selection for the EGMO team was made from performances at BMO1 and BMO2, the two rounds of the British Mathematical Olympiad. It has been encouraging to see an increase in the achievement and contribution of girls to the UK Olympiad effort this year; several girls attended training camps at Oxford and Hungary and selection for the EGMO team was a close-run affair. We hope that we will be able to build on the past year's efforts and continue to encourage girls to enjoy the beauty of mathematics. The team consisted of: Maria Holdcroft (Willink School); Elizabeth Lee (Loughborough High School); Katya Richards (School of St Helen and St Katharine) and Kasia Warburton (Reigate Grammar School). The reserve was Ellie Holderness (Latymer Upper School). The Team Leader was Hannah Roberts of Pembroke College, Oxford and the Deputy Leader was Jo Harbour of Mayfield Primary School, Cambridge. A full report about EGMO2013 can be found at

http://www.bmoc.maths.org/home/egmo.shtml

Balkan Mathematical Olympiad

The 2013 Balkan Mathematical Olympiad was held in Cyprus from 28 June until 3 July. The UK Team Leader was Dr Geoff Smith of the University of Bath and the Deputy Leader was Dr Gerry Leversha, formerly of St Paul's School. The United Kingdom participates as a guest nation in this competition, and we have a self-imposed rule that we will not send a student to it more than once. This creates a lot of churn, and gives many students the experience of international competition.

In normal circumstances, the Balkan MO is held in May, but this year that proved impossible. The Cyprus Mathematical Society stepped in to organize an emergency edition of the competition a couple of months later than usual. This had the effect that some regular guest countries, such as France and Saudi Arabia for example, were not in a position to participate.

The team was as follows: Oliver Feng (Eton College); William Gao (Merchiston Castle School); Frank Han (Dulwich College); Maria Holdcroft (Willink School); Freddie Illingworth (Magdalen College School) and Warren Li (Fulford School).
A full report of the Balkans MO can be found at

http://www.bmoc.maths.org/home/balkan.shtml

Oundle Selection Camp

The final team of six for the IMO was finalised at the end of May after a highly intensive training and selection camp held at Oundle School.
Our thanks go to the following students: Andrew Carlotti (Sir Roger Manwood's School); Gabriel Gendler (Queen Elizabeth's School); Frank Han (Dulwich College); Maria Holdcroft (Willink School); Daniel Hu (City of London School); Freddie Illingworth (Magdalen College School); Sahl Khan (St Paul's School); Warren Li (Fulford School); Matei Mandache (Loughborough Grammar School). And staff: Geoff Smith, Joseph Myers, Dominic Yeo and Beverley Detoeuf.

The International Mathematical Olympiad

In many ways, a lot of the events and activities described earlier in this book relate to stages that UK IMO team members will go through before they attend an IMO. At this stage, it is worth explaining a little about the structure of the Olympiad, both for its own sake as well as to fit the following report into a wider context.

An IMO is a huge event and takes several years to plan and to execute. In 2013, teams from more than 100 countries went to Colombia to participate. A team consists of six youngsters (although in some cases, a country may send fewer). The focus of an IMO is really the two days on which teams sit the contest papers. The papers are on consecutive days and each lasts $4\frac{1}{2}$ hours. Each paper consists of three problems, and each problem is worth 7 marks. Thus a perfect score for a student is 42/42. The students are ranked according to their personal scores, and the top half receive medals. These are distributed in the ratios gold:silver:bronze = 1:2:3. The host city of the IMO varies from year to year. Detailed contemporary and historical data can be found at

http://www.imo-official.org/

But, whilst these may be the focus, there are other essential stages, in particular the selection of the problems and, in due course, the co-ordination (marking) of scripts and awarding of medals.

As stated, an IMO team is built around the students but they are accompanied by two other very important people: the Team Leader and the Deputy Leader, (many teams also take Observers who assist at the various stages and some of these may turn out to be future Leaders). Some three or four days before the actual IMO examinations, the Team Leaders arrive in the host country to deal with the task of constructing the papers. Countries will have submitted questions for consideration over the preceding months and a short list of questions (and, eventually, solutions) are given to Team Leaders on arrival. The Team Leaders gather as a committee (in IMO parlance, the Jury) to select six of the short-listed questions. This can involve some very vigorous debate and pretty tough talking! But it has to be done. Once agreed, the questions are put into papers and translations produced into as many languages as necessary, sometimes over 50.

At some stage, the students, accompanied by the Deputy Leader, arrive in the host country. As is obvious, there can be no contact with the Team Leader who, by then, has a good idea of the IMO papers! The Leaders and the students are housed in different locations to prevent any contact, casual or otherwise.

On the day before the first examination, there is an Opening Ceremony. This is attended by all those involved (with due regard to security). Immediately after the second day's paper, the marking can begin. It may seem strange that students' scripts are 'marked' by their own Leader and Deputy. In fact, no actual marks or comments of any kind are put on the scripts themselves. Instead, having looked at scripts and decided what marks they think should be awarded, the Leader and Deputy have to justify their claim to others, called co-ordinators, who are supplied by the host country. Once all the marks have been agreed, sometimes after extremely protracted negotiation, the Jury decides where the medal boundaries should go. Naturally, this is a crucial part of the procedure and results in many tears as well as cheers.

Whilst the co-ordination of marks is going on, the students have time to relax and recover. There are often organised activities and excursions and there is much interaction and getting to know like-minded individuals from all corners of the world.

The grand finale is always the closing ceremony which includes the awarding of medals as well as speeches and numerous items of entertainment – some planned but others accidental.

54th International Mathematical Olympiad, Santa Marta, Colombia, 18-28 July 2013, Report by Geoff Smith (UK Team Leader)

The 54th International Mathematical Olympiad was held on the Caribbean coast of Colombia in July 2013. The students stayed in Santa Marta, and the leaders in Barranquilla, at the mouth of the Rio Magdalena. The UK Team Leader was Dr Geoff Smith of the University of Bath and the Deputy Leader was Dominic Yeo of Worcester College, Oxford. The person in charge of pastoral matters was our Observer C, Bev Detoeuf from the Leeds Office of UKMT.

The team was as follows:

Andrew Carlotti	Sir Roger Manwood's School, Kent
Gabriel Gendler	Queen Elizabeth's School, London
Daniel Hu	City of London School
Sahl Khan	St Paul's School, London
Warren Li	Fulford School, York
Matei Mandache	Loughborough Grammar School

The reserves were

Frank Han   Dulwich College, London
Maria Holdcroft   Willink School, Berkshire
Freddie Illingworth   Magdalen College School, Oxford

Andrew Carlotti was competing for the fourth time, and by securing a gold medal at IMO 2013, he now has the best IMO medal record of any British student. He has one bronze medal and three gold medals, won during 2010–13. This takes him above Simon Norton (3 gold medals, 2 special prizes) and the late John Rickard (3 gold medals, 3 special prizes).

The performance of the British team of 2013 is shown in the following table:

		P1	P2	P3	P4	P5	P6	Σ	Medal
UNK1	Andrew Carlotti	7	7	0	7	7	6	34	Gold
UNK2	Gabriel Gendler	7	5	0	7	6	0	25	Silver
UNK3	Daniel Hu	7	7	0	7	7	2	30	Silver
UNK4	Sahl Khan	7	0	0	7	7	0	21	Bronze
UNK5	Warren Li	7	7	0	7	7	0	28	Silver
UNK6	Matei Mandache	7	7	0	7	7	5	33	Gold

The cut-offs were 15 for bronze, 24 for silver and 31 for gold. There were 97 participating nations. The unofficial ranking of countries by total scores has the UK in 9th position overall, 2nd among European nations (behind Russia), and in 1st position among the nations of the European Union (by some margin). This represents the best team performance by a British side at an IMO since 1996 when we finished 5th.

Here are the top 30 places at IMO 2013. The full table can be found at

http://www.imo-official.org/year_country_r.aspx?year=2013

1. China (208), 2. South Korea (204), 3. USA (190), 4. Russia (187), 5. North Korea (184), 6. Singapore (182), 7. Vietnam (180), 8. Taiwan (176), 9. United Kingdom (171), 10. Iran (168), 11. Canada (163), 11. Japan (163), 13. Israel (161), 13. Thailand (161), 15. Australia (148), 16. Ukraine (146), 17. Mexico (139), 17. Turkey (139), 19. Indonesia (138), 20. Italy (137), 21. France (136), 22. Belarus (134), 22. Hungary (134), 22. Romania (134), 25. Netherlands (133), 26. Peru (132), 27. Germany (127), 28. Brazil (124), 29. India (122), 30. Croatia (119).

Of the remaining nations, Anglophone and Commonwealth scores include 31. Hong Kong (117), 31. Malaysia (117), 48. New Zealand (77), 56. Sri Lanka (65), 58. South Africa (64), 61. Bangladesh (60), 64. Cyprus (52), 76. Ireland (33), 79. Pakistan (25), 84. Nigeria (18), 86. Trinidad and Tobago (16), 95. Uganda (1).

Italy are to be congratulated for finishing top of the nations using the Euro. France finished above Germany, a singular event which had not happened since German re-unification. There seems to be a general trend that some of the countries of central and eastern Europe are getting lower IMO rankings, whereas the nations of the Far East have been doing very well recently. Indonesia obtained an excellent result, a sharp improvement on their previous performances, and Israel secured their best ranking position since 2000. As often happens, China sent a very strong team, and are to be congratulated for winning the event.

Problems of Day 1

1. Prove that for any pair of positive integers k and n, there exist k positive integers $m_1, m_2, \ldots, m_k$ (not necessarily different) such that

$$1 + \frac{2^k - 1}{n} = \left(1 + \frac{1}{m_1}\right)\left(1 + \frac{1}{m_2}\right)\ldots\left(1 + \frac{1}{m_k}\right).$$

2. A configuration of 4027 points in the plane is called *Colombian* if it consists of 2013 red points and 2014 blue points, and no three of the points of the configuration are collinear. By drawing some lines, the plane is divided into several regions. An arrangement of lines is *good* for a Colombian configuration if the following two conditions are satisfied:

   • no line passes through any point of the configuration;
   • no region contains points of both colours.

   Find the least value of k such that for any Colombian configuration of 4027 points, there is a good arrangement of k lines.

3. Let the excircle of triangle ABC opposite the vertex A be tangent to the side BC at the point A_1. Define the points B_1 on CA and C_1 on AB analogously, using the excircles opposite B and C, respectively. Suppose that the circumcentre of triangle $A_1B_1C_1$ lies on the circumcircle of triangle ABC. Prove that triangle ABC is right-angled.

   The excircle of triangle ABC opposite the vertex A is the circle that is tangent to the line segment BC, to the ray AB beyond B, and to the ray AC beyond C. The excircles opposite B and C are similarly defined.

Problems of Day 2

4. Let ABC be an acute-angled triangle with orthocentre H, and let W be a point on the side BC, lying strictly between B and C. The points M and N are the feet of the altitudes from B and C, respectively. Denote by ω_1 the circumcircle of BWN, and let X be the point on ω_1 such that WX is a diameter of ω_1. Analogously, denote by ω_2 the circumcircle of CWM, and let Y be the point on ω_2 such that WY is a diameter of ω_2. Prove that X, Y and H are collinear.

5. Let $\mathbb{Q}_{>0}$ be the set of positive rational numbers. Let $f : \mathbb{Q}_{>0} \to \mathbb{R}$ be a function satisfying the following three conditions:

   - for all $x, y \in \mathbb{Q}_{>0}$, we have $f(x)f(y) \geqslant f(xy)$;
   - for all $x, y \in \mathbb{Q}_{>0}$, we have $f(x + y) \geqslant f(x) + f(y)$;
   - there exists a rational number $a > 1$ such that $f(a) = a$.

   Prove that $f(x) = x$ for all $x \in \mathbb{Q}_{>0}$.

6. Let $n \geqslant 3$ be an integer, and consider a circle with $n + 1$ equally spaced points marked on it. Consider all labellings of these points with the numbers $0, 1, \ldots, n$ such that each label is used exactly once; two such labellings are considered to be the same if one can be obtained from the other by a rotation of the circle. A labelling is called *beautiful* if, for any four labels $a < b < c < d$ with $a + d = b + c$, the chord joining the points labelled a and d does not intersect the chord joining the points labelled b and c.

   Let M be the number of beautiful labellings, and let N be the number of ordered pairs (x, y) of positive integers such that $x + y \leqslant n$ and $\gcd(x, y) = 1$.

   Prove that

   $$M = N + 1.$$

Diary

The Director of IMO 2013 was Maria Losada (not be confused with Maria Falk de Losada, her mother and the chair of the jury). Maria Losada was immensely helpful to the Australian and UK teams, facilitating our early arrival, monitoring our hotel bookings, and inviting the UK team guide Maria Ximena Rueda to join us for our pre-IMO camp. Maria Losada does not play a large role in this diary, but she orchestrated the IMO, and without her work, and that of her team, the IMO could not have happened.

Sunday July 14th We have an early flight tomorrow, so some of us gather at a Holiday Inn near Heathrow Airport. This involves meeting the flight of Daniel and Matei, silver medallists from the International Physics Olympiad in Denmark. They are having to miss the physics closing ceremony to join us for the journey to Colombia. Our International Olympiad in Informatics (Computing) silver medallist, Andrew Carlotti, will be making his way from the IOI in Brisbane in the company of the Australian IMO team. They have to travel via New Zealand and Chile, and Andrew should arrive in Santa Marta a few hours before we do.

Monday July 15th We have ordered a giant taxi, but a merely large one arrives. We quickly arrange for a more impressive vehicle, and make our way to Terminal 5. We find Sahl there, so the party is as ready as it is going to get until we reach Colombia.

We are delighted to discover that our Iberia/Avianca flights will take our checked-in luggage all the way to Santa Marta. The first hop to Madrid goes easily enough. In Madrid we have to change terminals, and we do so in the hope that our luggage will move as swiftly.

The long journey to Bogota involves trays of baby-food, mysterious pastes which were presumably obtained as surplus goods from NASA. I am in the happy position of being moved to a row of seats with no other passengers. Ten hours later, or just four hours later if you are foolish enough to use local time, we find ourselves in Bogota. We are at a great altitude, so the conditions are not oppressive.

The students are hungry, and we quickly locate a traditional Colombian Japanese sushi and sashimi restaurant. The students spot a flight information board, and Gabriel convinces us that our flight to Santa Marta has been cancelled. I compound the error by taking him seriously. Eventually it turns out that we have been looking at the arrivals board.

The correct departure gate is unmarked, but by determined negotiation we eventually find ourselves waiting in the right place. At last there are a few maths T-shirts around, and it is clear that we are getting close to the IMO. Our Colombian guide Maria introduces herself, for she has kindly agreed to act as translator during the Australia-UK pre-IMO camp.

The flight to Santa Marta is in the dark, and when we arrive, we step off the aircraft into proper tropical air that you can chew. Our bags soon arrive, and we locate the mini-van which has been sent to meet us from the Santorini Hotel. It has been a long day, and while people are not yet irritable, the bonhomie is getting a bit forced. The chap in charge of loading the bags is of a certain age, and rather ponderous. Eventually we intervene and load the bags ourselves. We are then crammed into the van for the short journey to our hotel.

I can tell that we have arrived when I see the Australian leaders Angelo di Pasquale and Ivan Guo standing by the side of the road. There are various conflicting instructions as to what we should do with (a) our bags and (b) ourselves. Eventually we get out and Bev does battle with a UKMT credit card and the very confused check-in staff. After over half an hour (I kid you not) she succeeds in making the appropriate credit card payment, and leads the students off to the UK villa.

Then Dominic and I stroll up to the counter to collect our room keys, and are astonished when the staff explain that Bev has not paid for us, and we must pay before we are given our keys. We are exhausted, and not in the mood for a fight, so I pay using my UKMT credit card and we get our keys.

Dominic shoots down to the UK villa. He and Bev study our paperwork, and we discover that Bev had indeed paid for us. Dominic comes back to my room, takes my credit card, and gets the second payment reversed by the gentlemen in reception. Dominic is initially of the opinion that the receptionists are crooks, but having seen earlier events, I reassure him that they are just massively incompetent.

I am now drained after this prodigious journey, and am not best pleased when the clowns in the room next door decide to have loud conversations on their balcony until past 4am. As I drift off to sleep, someone sets off firecrackers to entertain the hotel at 5am. Things can only get better.

Tuesday July 16th The Australian and UK students each have their own villas, and we rearrange the social spaces to create exam rooms, borrowing furniture from the nearby pool area when necessary. While they sit the paper, I go to reception, and have my room changed to get away from the selfish idiots who were in room 511 last night.

We get bread, cold meats, cheese and tropical fruit drinks from a local supermarket, and have an improvised lunch when the exam is over.

The British students have bested the Australians on the first paper, but only by a narrow margin. I am impressed, because I know that the British side is very good. It seems that the Australians will not be a pushover this year, and that our continued possession of the Mathematics Ashes is in doubt. The contest is the final exam of the pre-IMO camp.

Wednesday July 17th After my first good night's sleep in Colombia, I am to be picked up by a mini-van taxi for the transfer to the city of Barranquilla while the students are sitting an exam. Checking out involves tangling once more with the characters in reception. To simplify matters, I take along an itemized list of my extras, so that settling up should be a straightforward process. They wave my list away, and start tapping at computer terminals. After the usual 30 minutes, they come up with a completely incorrect figure. I point out that they have failed to allow for the items associated with my second room. There is much slapping of palms on foreheads, and they decide simply to let me off those items, presumably because my taxi is due and it would take another 30 minutes to add two numbers together.

Mike Clapper of the Australian Maths Trust, together with his partner Jo, arrive from the airport just before my taxi turns up, and we exchange warm greetings. Their luggage has vanished somewhere between Brisbane and Santa Marta, but they seem happy enough just to have arrived.

My taxi parks outside, and I bid farewell. The van is cool and quick, and we drive to Barranquilla in under 2 hours. For much of the journey, the sea is on your right, and a large lake is on your left, and as your mind drifts, it is not clear which is which. It feels like you are travelling on a tropical *Afsluitdijk*, with pelicans and countless white herons for decoration. I am travelling with several other team leaders: Dieter Gronau from Germany, Raphael Steiner from Switzerland, Philipp Wirth from Liechtenstein and Bernd Kreussler from Ireland.

It is a curious feature of Colombian geography that it has cities and towns, but the villages are mostly missing. There is one small settlement in the middle of the journey, and there we could see the sharp disparities of wealth which bedevil Colombia and many other Ibero-American societies.

At length we arrive at the El Prado hotel in Barranquilla. This is not an ordinary modern hotel, but rather it dates from the 1930s, and is fit for Ernest Hemingway. The reception staff act as if they have never heard of the IMO, and give us room keys and the information that we will get free breakfast tomorrow. Since today's lunch is now overdue, this is disconcerting. I leave my luggage in my room, and conduct a random walk through the hotel. Eventually I spot IMO internet Tsar Matjaž Željko, and tail him until he leads me to the IMO office. I get the shortlist, and tokens that can be exchanged for meals.

Thursday July 18th I enter an email exchange with my brother Pete, who lives in Dubai. After a couple of decades of making things happen, he has recently written a book (Project Management: All You Need is Love) and is developing a literary bent. He sets himself the challenge of getting the British and Australian press interested in the Mathematics Ashes, and over the next few days he works on a blog with this purpose. We swap ideas during my night and his day, but the text is all his.

http://otherashes.wordpress.com/2013/07/19/and-so-it-begins/

The Mathematics Ashes has its origins in a hotel bar in IMO Vietnam, where, after several beers, the former Australian Mathematics Trust supremo Peter Taylor suggested this annual competition, and Peter Taylor is very much in on the gag. Joseph Myers keeps the Mathematics Ashes records in a more formal style.

http://www.bmoc.maths.org/home/ashes.shtml

Friday July 19th The jury has its first serious meeting. In my Observations of 2011 (http://www.imo-register.org.uk/2011-report-geoff.pdf) I made a 'modest proposal' to reform IMO voting protocols, and the case for change was made more pressing by the unbalanced papers of 2012. The new protocol involves forcing problems 1, 2, 4 and 5 to involve all four subject areas, and then choosing the best two hard problems on merit alone, unconstrained by subject type except that they should not be from the same area as one another.

The mechanism for producing the balance in the easy and medium problems is to choose eight problems. For each of the areas algebra, combinatorics, geometry and number theory the jury can choose the best easy and the best medium problem. The easy and medium positions can then be filled in $\binom{4}{2}$ = 6 ways. The jury pauses for reflection on the relative merits of the six choices, and then votes off possibilities one at a time. The idea is that each problem that appears on the paper must be the best available question in its category, and that the easy/medium problems, the ones which most students actually try to do, will be balanced.

There is an extended debate, and eventually the jury agrees to try the new protocol for one year as an experiment. Whether the new method is adopted again is a matter for future juries, and I suppose that will partly depend on how people judge the quality of the 2013 paper. Anyway, having lit the touchpaper, I sit back and wait for disaster.

The jury chair is Maria Falk de Losada, a formidable Colombian New Yorker who eats fools for breakfast. She wants us to discuss the merits of the problems. This is an excellent idea, but it is too soon. It turns out that many leaders (me included) want to be left alone to struggle with the shortlist problems in their rooms, and we persuade the chair to give us more time.

Saturday July 20th At length we have the solutions to the shortlist problems, and we can start to make rational judgements about the merits of the harder problems. We implement the new protocol, and a paper is produced. One well-known jury figure is convinced that the paper is too easy, and that we have really messed it up this year. I am not so sure. We have chosen a purely conceptual problem in position 2, and our experience with the 2011 windmill was that many students find such questions very difficult.

Viewing the internet late in the evening, I discover that the UK has retained the Mathematical Ashes by 1 point. The Australians set an easy Ashes paper to compress the marks.

Sunday July 21st Today is student arrival day in Santa Marta, but this is of little import at the jury site. The jury begins the day by working on the notation that will be used in the problems. Having established that, the English Language Committee kicks into life, with its open door entry qualification. Chris Tuffley of New Zealand constructs the computer file, and after our deliberations we make our proposal to the jury, and after further discussion we have the English language versions of the papers. A few hours later we approve the other IMO official languages, and finally the leaders go to work to produce the papers in all necessary languages.

Monday July 22nd The jury approves the final versions of the papers, and then we travel to the opening ceremony. This is held in a very large university hall. There are short and welcome speeches from various members of the Losada family, and a political address from the mayor of Barranquilla which set everyone thinking.

We then entered the important phase of the ceremony, when the teams paraded one by one round the arena, accompanied by various grotesque figures from the Colombian carnival. The conception was brilliant. This bizarre procession was accompanied by carnival music: horns, drums and accordions. No review that I might give would do it justice.

The UK team members, dapper in shirts, ties and panama hats, take their turn. Sahl is carried round by Gabriel, while Andrew, Daniel, Matei and Warren stroll round while waving.

At the end of the ceremony, the leaders depart for Cartagena, a beautiful old Spanish port along the coast. The architecture is beautiful, and we have a happy time wandering around the town. The city walls are intact, put there to protect Cartagena from English pirates. On the way back to our hotel, the driver gets lost in Barranquilla. This is no mean feat because the roads are set out and numbered on a grid system, American style. I wonder if he is related to the people working at reception in the Hotel Santorini?

Tuesday July 23rd Checking the internet in the morning, I discover that the baby who will become Prince George of Cambridge has been born. This is a disaster for my brother Pete's plan to get publicity for the Mathematics Ashes. The journalists who planned to give name checks to the team members in the British press have had their stories spiked. Their editors have given over space to the 'woman gives birth to baby' story. As Pete put it, we were 'bumped by the bump'.

174

It is the morning of the first exam, and the jury convenes to answer questions of clarification from the students. There are one or two technical problems, one of which is resolved by turning a television screen upside down.

The co-ordinators present their marking schemes. Initially there are no paper copies, and that makes it very hard to view the schemes in the round. This is sorted out fairly quickly.

In the evening we attend the mayor's reception, and listen to more of that carnival music. The most impressive aspect of the event was the extraordinarily powerful amplification system. You can imagine how much we enjoyed that.

On returning to the hotel, we find that the students' scripts are expected to arrive at about 11pm. I go to bed rather than wait.

Wednesday July 24th I pick up the UK scripts before breakfast. My initial reaction is that the jury has messed up very badly, and problems 1 and 2 must be far too easy, because the British students have demolished them. I prepare for the worst. No doubt the new voting protocol will be blamed, and I will lose all respect from my fellow jurors.

I ask other leaders how their students have done, and to my surprise it seems that many students have found problems 1 and 2 quite difficult. While I am sorry for the students personally, it is a relief that the paper has not been completely misjudged. The British students have done unusually well on paper 1. It is a shame that there is so little work on problem 3, not even many good diagrams.

We have a much more efficient Q & A session for the first 30 minutes of paper 2, and then listen to the well-presented marking schemes for the problems of day 2. We have lunch and then transfer to the students' site. There has been little time to work on the scripts of day 1. This is not a problem for me, because the British solutions fall easily into two categories: completely right or total rubbish. Many leaders will have more subtle issues to resolve, and I feel for them.

The students' site, the Irotama Resort, is a wonder to behold. It is a huge resort complex set right on the beach. Many people are housed in beach bungalows, but I am in a tall apartment block. In my suite we have our own bedrooms, but I share a common social area with Dieter Gronau of Germany and Gregor Dolinar of Slovenia. The apartment is well equipped, with a chilled water dispenser and a washing machine.

It is delightful to meet the UK team, and both Bev and Dominic. Everyone is well, and the students are claiming to have done better on day 2 than day 1. If this is true, we are going to have our best performance for years. I ask other leaders, and while problem 4 is widely regarded as accessible, problem 5 is viewed as quite challenging and problem 6 as very hard indeed.

In particular, Andrew Carlotti is an extremely happy bunny, and he looks almost certain to pick up his third gold medal. It also seems certain that all our team will get medals, and that many of them will be strong.

We leave Bev to keep an eye on the team, and Dominic and I go into mark maximization mode. It is really only problems 3 and 6 where we are likely to have complicated co-ordinations. Dominic takes the combinatorial problem 6 and this leaves me with the geometric problem 3. It is a long evening, but not as long as it might have been.

Thursday July 25th On the first day of co-ordination we address problems 1, 5 and 4. The marks harvest is 125/126, but we know that the second day of co-ordination will be a more testing experience.

The co-ordinators seem well prepared, and the co-ordination room is so well air-conditioned that there is an incentive to prolong discussion indefinitely. There are now ample opportunities to meet old friends among the deputies and observers, and of course to strike up new relationships.

Friday July 26th Our first co-ordination is on problem 3. One of our co-ordinators is Mark Saul, whom I have known for a long time. I lead. There are only two scripts of interest. Daniel Hu has not done the problem, but he has done the converse (that is, he has proved the reverse of what is required). The marking scheme helpfully and explicitly states that there are no marks available for doing this, but I begin by asking if case law has developed allowing partial credit. It has not, and we move on.

Next we examine Andrew Carlotti's script. This is all rough work, but he has circled a piece of work on page 9 which is interesting. It is written in his characteristic stream of consciousness style, but if carefully read, it is an outline of part of the necessary proof, a part which is worth 3 marks.

I have seen co-ordinators give full marks for material like this, and I have also seen them give zero. The extreme perspectives are (i) 'this is an essentially correct solution, but the student has written it up (probably under time pressure) very casually, but we are here to reward ideas, not neat and accurate presentation, so we allow this as a proof' and (ii) 'you have supplied a very interesting way to interpret these jottings, and we commend your ingenuity, but we are here to mark the student's script, not the quality of your interpretation'. Unfortunately the co-ordinators are firmly of the latter view, and though we obtain a second opinion from Jana Madjarova of Sweden, we cannot squeeze out a mark.

Dominic is to lead on the remaining two questions. Problem 2 is the geometric combinatorics problem proposed by Ivan Guo of Australia. We have four clear solutions, one clear non-solution, and an incomplete solution by Gabriel Gendler, written up against the clock. Dominic forecasts 5 points for Gabriel in advance, and that is exactly what we get, along with four 7s and a 0.

Finally we move to problem 6. After day 1, no student of any country had obtained a mark for this problem on the public display. We have three scripts with content. Andrew Carlotti gets 6, Matei Mandache gets 5 and Daniel Hu gets 2. This is roughly in line with Dominic's forecast, though he has to do some very hard work to convince the co-ordinators of our case. Dominic's mastery of his brief is excellent, and he tries very hard to persuade the co-ordinators that Daniel's script is worth more than 2, but they will not budge. Since the gold medal cut-off seems likely to be about Daniel's score, this could be very important.

In the evening we had the joint IMOAB and jury meeting. We begin by remembering those who have, in the language of Erdős, 'left'. This includes my friend and co-author Christopher Bradley, and I give a short summary of his contributions and career. The jury stands in respect.

There is an announcement about the film, being made in the UK at the moment, provisionally entitled *X PLUS Y*. This is a love story, the main players being two young people from different IMO teams. The IMO Foundation should be in a position to make use of the publicity to try to garner support for the IMO, and for this reason it is being reconfigured.

The runners and riders for the IMOAB elections are announced, nominations having been gathered at IMO 2013. There are many candidates for the positions on the IMOAB, but only two candidates for the IMOAB chair. I happen to know that each of these two candidates nominated the other, so we can expect the usual extremely amicable election at IMO 2014.

Finally we study the mark distribution at IMO 2013, and decide upon the medal cut-offs: 15 for bronze, 24 for silver and 31 for gold.

Saturday July 27th There is a tourism opportunity in the morning, but all the UK participants take a rest. At 3pm we have a brief meeting of countries interested in EGMO (the European Girls' Mathematical Olympiad). The event will be held next year during April 10-16 in Antalya, Turkey, but thus far we have no host country for EGMO 2015.

In the afternoon we visit the Santa Marta botanical gardens, adjacent to the house where Simon Bolivar died in 1830. We are gathering for the medal ceremony. At this moment I am approached by the leaders of Belarus, Igor Voronovich and Sergei Mazanik. They have just received a message from the Belarus Ministry of Education that they are prepared to support an edition of EGMO. We pencil in Belarus as hosts of EGMO 2015. I am very excited about this excellent news.

There is a brief ceremony involving some ornately dressed soldiers, and IMO chair Nazar Agakhanov lays a memorial wreath. After that we have an outdoor medal ceremony, and finally return to the Irotama hotel for the farewell dinner round the pool (which was brilliantly planned) and the presentation of the Microphone d'Or. The competition for the most garrulous juror is organized by Rafael Sánchez of Venezuela. Rafael has asked me to make the speech, so I prepare some offensive remarks. Unfortunately Angelo is busy trying to check-in the Australian team for the flights home. We find his deputy, Ivan Guo, and he kindly agrees to substitute for his leader.

The usual characters crowd on stage for the ceremony, and speeches are translated into all official languages. Ivan accepts the golden microphone with a few well-chosen insulting phrases about his leader, and honour is satisfied. Angelo beat me by one speech!

Sunday July 28th I wake up and check my email. There is a worrying message from Adam McBride that David Monk is in intensive care with heart problems. David has been a stalwart of UK IMO preparation since the 1960s, and he is known and loved internationally because of his beautiful problems. He is the most prolific author of IMO problems, having created no less than 13 over the years (he is sometimes given half a credit for another problem, but he repudiates this). He wrote the wonderful *New Problems in Euclidean Geometry* a few years ago (published by UKMT). At breakfast I share this disturbing news with other leaders and it gives us all pause for thought. (As I write this report, the good news is that David is recovering well, and has just been allowed home.)

Indra Haraksingh from Trinidad and Tobago kindly tries to give me a T-shirt. I am flattered by the 2XL size label, but explain that this is not realistic. I look for the UK guide Maria and am disappointed to discover that she has already left for Bogota. Good luck to her at MIT.

The UK team catches the 10:30 am bus and arrives in good time at Santa Marta's Simon Bolivar Airport. We meet a Uruguayan contestant who is desperate for a hamburger. Presumably this is a form of homesickness. The airport, and subsequently our plane, fills up with IMO teams.

At Bogota we have little time to change planes, but the team are hungry so they demolish a quick meal. I go on ahead, and hear repeated calls for 'Carlotti' over the tannoy. The whole team turns up oblivious to team member Andrew's new-found celebrity. My best guess is that he has dropped his passport in the loo, but no. It turns out that the Colombian customs authorities want to inspect his checked-in luggage. Bev and Andrew hurtle off to do the necessary. Fortunately they arrive back quickly, and we board as normal.

This time Bev has managed to persuade the airline not to ignore our food requirements, and people get the meals they want. This is an overnight flight, so we hope to sleep. I am initially disappointed to be trapped by an aisle seat passenger, but after inspecting her new neighbour, she magically disappears. It is a gift I have.

This means that I can spread sideways, leaving more space for my colleague Dominic. This is all very satisfactory. I insert earplugs which nearly, but not completely, cut out the loud conversation from the wretches behind who decide to flirt at volume while the rest of the plane is trying to sleep. Don't you just love attractive young people?

Saturday July 29th We arrive in Madrid a little after 9am local time. We have ample time to change planes and terminals and have a meal. We take a lunchtime flight to London. This turns out to be more exciting than we had planned. Just as we are about to touch down, the landing is aborted and the plane's engines scream at full power as we climb away at speed. When we are at a safe height, the captain explains that air traffic control called off the landing because the previous plane had failed to clear the runway in time. I looked up the statistics on this when I arrived home. It happens to about 1 landing in 400 at Heathrow.

The luggage comes through the excellent Terminal 5 system of belts and tubes in no time at all, and we go outside to be met by happy families. We distribute medal and participation certificates, and it is over for another year.

Thanks

Thanks to everyone who made this possible. Thanks to the the families and the Leeds Office of UKMT, and the small army of UKMT coaches and mentors and the organizers in Colombia. Thanks to James Cranch for having played such a key part in training over the past couple of years, and to my colleagues Dominic and Bev for countless kindnesses.

Finally I thank the students. Their behaviour was excellent throughout. They clearly enjoyed one another's company, and maintained an unceasing interest in working on mathematics problems before, during and after the IMO. Two are available for IMO 2014, and as for the other four, I give the University of Cambridge fair warning of what is coming.

UKMT Mentoring Schemes (Administered by BMOS)

After many years in the position of Director of the Mentoring Schemes, October 2012 saw Richard Atkins hand over the role to Vicky Neale. Our thanks go to Richard for doing such a great job. He continues to run the Intermediate Scheme.

Following another successful year, the UKMT Mentoring Schemes have again increased in size. These materials are now used in over 850 schools and with almost 200 individual students working with external mentors. We will continue to offer these free resources to all UK schools and teachers who wish to stimulate and challenge their pupils. We hope that by participating in the schemes, school pupils will be inspired to delve into the subject beyond the curriculum and develop a life-long enthusiasm for mathematics.

The schemes cater for pupils from Years 7 – 13 (in England and Wales, and the equivalent years in Scotland and Northern Ireland). Each person is linked up with a mentor who can offer help, guidance and encouragement. At the Junior and Intermediate levels we encourage teachers to mentor their own pupils because regular contact is important at this stage, although some external mentors are available at Intermediate level. At the Senior and Advanced levels, mentees are mentored by undergraduates, postgraduates and teachers who are more familiar with problem-solving techniques, but of course any teacher who is willing to act as a mentor to their own pupils is encouraged to do so. The schemes run from October through to May and anyone who is interested in either being a mentee, a mentor or using the sheets with their classes is welcome to register with Beverley at the UKMT office by emailing mentoring@ukmt.org.uk. Teachers registering on the schemes go onto a mailing list to receive the monthly materials, which they can then use in any way they like with their own students, either individually or in class.

Junior Scheme

This scheme is used by over 800 teachers and run by John Slater and Julian Gilbey. It caters for those of roughly Years 7–9 who have perhaps done well in the Junior Maths Challenge and are looking at Junior Olympiad papers. A few hints are given with the questions which aim to introduce pupils to problem-solving at an accessible level, though the later questions will usually be quite challenging. All pupils are currently mentored by their teachers and teachers are welcome to enrol in order to use the problem sheets with their classes. This is often a good way to stimulate the interest of a whole class, rather than just one or two individuals, though it is likely that only one or two will rise to producing good solutions to the later questions.

Intermediate scheme

This is used by 775 teachers and run by Richard Atkins. It is aimed at those approximately in Years 9–11 who have done well in the Intermediate Maths Challenge and are preparing for Intermediate Olympiad papers or who have attended one of the UKMT national Mathematics Summer Schools. There is quite a gradient in these problems, from some which can be approached without knowledge of any special techniques to others which require modular arithmetic, some knowledge of number theory and geometrical theorems etc. The aim is to gradually introduce these techniques through the year. As mentees come across these, we hope they will ask questions or look at the internet to find out about these methods. Most pupils are mentored by their teachers, but some external mentors are available where necessary. This year 13 external mentors worked with 34 mentees.

Senior scheme

This is used by over 380 teachers and run by Andre Rzym. It is aimed approximately at those in Years 11–13 and the questions are set at quite a challenging level, aimed at those who are tackling BMO papers or who have outgrown the Intermediate Scheme. Typically just two or three people at any school might enrol with this scheme and most of the mentors are undergraduates or postgraduates, though it is good to see that several teachers are keen to act as mentors at this level. Doing the questions is a stimulating experience for any teacher and one of the best ways to add freshness and innovation to one's regular teaching. An important role of mentors at this level is to encourage their mentees because the questions are generally more taxing than anything they confront at A-level, and each problem solved is a distinct achievement which should give huge satisfaction.

As well as being used by teachers, the senior scheme also has external mentors available to work with students and this year 46 external mentors helped 131 mentees.

Advanced Scheme

Entry to this scheme is by invitation only as the problems are extremely challenging. In 2012 this was run by a number of people, including Lex Betts, Ben Elliott and Richard Freeland. It is aimed at UK IMO squad members and others who have outgrown the Senior Scheme, the questions being very hard and mainly of interest to those who are aiming at selection for the UK team in the annual International Mathematical Olympiad (IMO). There were 24 mentees on the scheme this year, working with 13 mentors.

Sample questions from October 2012

The following were questions on the October paper in 2012 – the first paper of the year:

Junior:

How many 6-digit numbers which consist of all the digits 1, 2, 3, 4, 5, 6 are divisible by all of 1, 2, 3,4, 5 and 6?

Intermediate:

Let AD and BC be two chords of a circle that intersect inside the circle at the point X. Show that $(AX)(DX) = (BX)(CX)$.

Senior:

(a) How many numbers between 1 and 1000 (inclusive) are divisible by none of 2, 5 and 7?

(b) In how many ways can the letters of the word 'polina' be arranged such that none of the letters are in their original place (for example, we would count 'apolin' but not 'paolin', because in the latter case, the 'p' is in its original place)? What about the word 'flawless'?

Mentoring conference and dinner

The mentoring conference in October 2012 was held at Balliol College, Oxford for the first time and our thanks go to Professor Frances Kirwan for her help with this. A workshop run by Vicky Neale, and attended by the more experienced mentors, resulted in many ideas on how to develop the schemes in the future; a second workshop for new and prospective mentors was led by James Cranch and looked at the role of the mentor. Gerry Leversha gave a presentation on Mentoring in Geometry to all delegates.

Survey and feedback

In June 2013 we again sent out a survey to all mentors, mentees and teachers using the materials. The aim of this was to get their feedback on what was going well with the schemes, what could be improved and what should be introduced or changed. As usual there were some really good ideas and comments that came over, and in the coming months the Mentoring Committee will be looking at all the responses to see which can be taken further. The general comments about the scheme were positive and very encouraging:

'I have both really enjoyed and really benefited from the mentoring scheme. Thank you.' (Mentee, Senior Scheme)

'I have really enjoyed participating on the scheme this year, and hope to do so again next year.' (Mentee, Senior Scheme)

'Thank you to everyone for another excellent year of mentoring!' (Mentor, Intermediate scheme)

'THANK YOU for all you do – I really appreciate this input – it certainly makes my job easier having these wonderful enrichment schemes so available. We use it as an opportunity for older students to 'inspire and lead' younger students – so the scheme has many benefits.' (Teacher using Junior and Intermediate Scheme)

'These schemes are excellent resources to motivate and engage able mathematical students.' (Teacher using Junior, Intermediate and Senior schemes)

'Well done. Great resource and the students really love doing them. Thanks!' (Teacher using Junior and Intermediate schemes)

And also our thanks must also go to all the volunteer mentors and question setters who have freely given so much time to make the schemes work and encourage the next generation of young mathematicians. They are too numerous to name here (although they do appear later in the list of volunteers), but without them there would be no schemes at all. If you would like to find out more about becoming a mentor, contact Beverley at UKMT by email: mentoring@ukmt.org.uk

Vicky Neale, Director of Mentoring

And finally...

Thanks go to Vicky Neale for her work as Director of Mentoring during the year. Unfortunately due to other commitments she is unable to continue in the role for the coming year. So from September 2013 James Cranch has agreed to take over the position of Director of Mentoring.

UKMT Team Maths Challenge 2013

Overview

The Team Maths Challenge (TMC) is a national mathematics competition which gives pupils the opportunity to participate in a wide range of mathematical activities and compete against other pupils from schools in their region. The TMC promotes team working and, unlike the Junior, Intermediate and Senior Challenges, students work in groups and are given practical tasks as well as theoretical problems to add another dimension to mathematics.

The TMC is designed for teams of four pupils in:

- Y8 & Y9 (England and Wales)
- S1 & S2 (Scotland)
- Y9 & Y10 (Northern Ireland)

with no more than two pupils from the older year group.

Sample TMC material is available to download from the TMC section of the UKMT website (www.tmc.ukmt.org.uk) for use in school and to help teachers to select a team to represent their school at the Regional Finals.

Report on the 2013 TMC

The eleventh year of the competition saw another record number of participating schools, despite the extreme weather conditions which meant that two Regional Finals were snowed off and later rescheduled. Entries were received from 1647 teams, of which 1517 turned up to take part at one of 67 Regional Finals.

As usual, competition details and entry forms were sent to schools in early October and made available on the UKMT website, which also provided up-to-date information on Regional Final venues and availability of places, as well as past materials for schools to use in selecting and preparing their team. Schools also received a copy of the winning poster from the 2012 National Final, originally created by Ysgol Dyffryn Taf and professionally reproduced by Arbelos.

Each team signed up to participate in one of the 67 Regional Finals, held between late February and the end of April at a widely-spread set of venues. Each Regional Final comprised four rounds which encouraged the teams to think mathematically in a variety of ways. The Group Round is the only round in which the whole team work together, tackling a set of ten challenging questions. In the Crossnumber the team splits into two pairs; one pair gets the across clues and the other pair gets the down clues.

The two pairs then work independently to complete the Crossnumber using logic and deduction. For the Mini Relay, teams compete against the clock to answer a series of questions, with each pair working on different questions and the solution of each question dependent on the previous answer. The final round of the day, the Relay, is a fast and furious race involving much movement to answer a series of questions in pairs. Each Regional Final was run by a regional lead coordinator with support from an assistant coordinator and, at some venues, other local helpers. The teachers who accompanied the teams were fully occupied too – they were involved in the delivery and marking of all of the rounds.

TMC National Final

Eighty teams (the winners from each Regional Final plus a few runners-up) were invited to the National Final on 17th June, which was again held at the Lindley Hall, part of the prestigious Royal Horticultural Halls, in Westminster, London. As usual, the four rounds from the Regional Finals also featured at the National Final except that the Group Round became the Group Circus: a similar round but with the inclusion of practical materials for use in solving the questions. In addition, the day began with the Poster Competition, which is judged and scored separately from the main event. The Poster theme for 2013 was 'Packing' and the entries were exhibited down the side of the hall throughout the day for the perusal of the participants as well as the judges.

The following schools (coming from as far north as the Shetland Islands and as far south as Guernsey) participated at the National Final:

Abingdon School	Abingdon, Oxfordshire
Alcester Grammar School	Warwickshire
Anderson High School	Lerwick, Shetland
Aylesbury Grammar School	Buckinghamshire
Badminton School	Bristol
Bancroft's School	Woodford Green, Essex
Belfast Royal Academy	Belfast
Bishop Wordsworth's School	Salisbury, Wiltshire
Blue Coat School	Oldham, Lancashire
Bohunt Community School	Liphook, Hampshire
Brighton and Hove Girls' High S.	East Sussex
Cargilfield Prep School	Edinburgh
Chailey School	South Chailey, East Sussex

Cheadle Hulme School	Cheshire
Christ Church Academy	Stone, Staffordshire
Churston Ferrers Grammar School	Brixham, Devon
City of London Freemen's School	Surrey
City of London Girls' School	Barbican, London
City of London School	London
Cockermouth School	Cumbria
Colchester Royal Grammar School	Essex
Cottenham Village College	Cambridgeshire
Devonport High School for Boys	Plymouth, Devon
Dollar Academy	Clackmannanshire
Durham High School for Girls	Durham
Elizabeth College	St Peter Port, Guernsey
Forest School	Snaresbrook, London
Fulford School	York
Gillingham School	Dorset
Glasgow Academy	Glasgow
Haberdashers' Aske's S. for Boys	Elstree, Hertfordshire
Hampton School	Middlesex
Heckmondwike Grammar School	West Yorkshire
Hereford Cathedral School	Hereford
Highgate School	Highgate, London
Highworth School	Ashford, Kent
Holmfirth High School	Huddersfield, West Yorkshire
John Taylor High School	Barton-u-Needwood, Staffordshire
King Edward VI Camp Hill Boys' S.	Kings Heath, Birmingham
King Edward VII School	Broomhill, Sheffield
King Edward's School	Birmingham
King's College School	Cambridge
Kings' School	Winchester, Hampshire
Lancaster Royal Grammar School	Lancaster
Leicester Grammar School	Great Glen, Leicester
Liverpool Blue Coat School	Liverpool, Merseyside
Loughborough Grammar School	Loughborough, Leicestershire
Magdalen College School	Oxford
Malmesbury School	Wiltshire
Manchester Grammar School	Manchester

Marling School	Stroud, Gloucestershire
Monkton Combe School	Bath
Moreton Hall School	Oswestry, Shropshire
Nonsuch High School for Girls	Cheam, Surrey
Orley Farm School	Harrow, Middlesex
Penair School	Truro, Cornwall
Pocklington School	Pocklington, York
Queen Elizabeth's School	Barnet, Hertfordshire
Repton School	Repton, Derby
Royal Grammar School	Jesmond, Newcastle-upon-Tyne
Simon Langton Boys' Grammar S.	Canterbury, Kent
St Olave's Grammar School	Orpington, Kent
St Paul's School	Barnes, London
Stewart's Melville College	Edinburgh
Summer Fields School	Oxford
Taverham Hall	Norwich
The Grammar School at Leeds	Leeds, West Yorkshire
The King's (The Cathedral) School	Peterborough
The Perse School	Cambridge
The Priory Academy LSST	Lincoln
Tonbridge Grammar School	Kent
Twyford CofE High School	Acton, London
Ulverston Victoria High School	Cumbria
Warwick School	Warwick
Wellingborough School	Northamptonshire
Wells Cathedral School	Somerset
Whitchurch High School	Cardiff
Wycombe Abbey School	High Wycombe, Buckinghamshire
Wymondham High School	Norwich
Yarm School	Stockton-on-Tees

We were delighted to have in attendance Rob Eastaway, author of bestselling books such as '*Why do Buses Come in Threes?*' and '*How Many Socks Make a Pair?*', and also Elizabeth Truss, Parliamentary Under Secretary of State for Education and Childcare, both of whom addressed the teams and awarded the prizes at the end. We are also grateful to Arbelos and Hewlett-Packard for providing additional prizes for the event and to UKMT volunteer Andrew Bell for capturing the day's excitement in his additional role as official photographer. Congratulations go to the 2013 Team Maths Challenge champions City of London School and to the winners of the Poster Competition: The Perse School (Cambridge).

As usual, thanks are due to a great number of people for ensuring another successful year of the TMC: the team of volunteers (listed at the back of this book) who generously give up their time to write, check and refine materials, run Regional Finals (with a helping hand from family members in a few cases!) and readily carry out countless other jobs behind the scenes; the staff in the UKMT office in Leeds for the way in which the competition is administered (particularly Nicky Bray who has responsibility for the central coordination of the competition, assisted by Shona Raffle, with additional support from Jo Williams) and the team of packers for their efficient and precise preparation and packing of materials; the teachers who continue to support the competition and take part so willingly, some of whom also undertake the significant task of organising and hosting a Regional Final at their own school and, of course, the pupils who participate so enthusiastically in the competition at all levels. Our thanks also go to additional contacts at schools and other host venues responsible for organising and helping with Regional Finals (listed at the back of this book).

TMC Regional Finals Material

Each of the 67 Regional Finals held across the UK involved four rounds:
1. Group Round   2. Crossnumber
3. Mini Relay   4. Relay Race

Group Round

Teams are given a set of 10 questions, which they should divide up among themselves so that they can answer, individually or in pairs, as many as possible in the allotted time.

Question 1

How many times does the digit 3 appear when the whole numbers between 1 and 150 are written down?

Question 2

A car's milometer shows that the number of miles it has travelled is 15951. This number is palindromic which means it reads the same forwards as backwards. The next time a palindromic number appears on the milometer is exactly two hours later. Find the average speed of the car during these two hours.

188

Question 3

What is the value of

$$1 - 2 + 3 - 4 + 5 - 6 + \ldots + 2011 - 2012 + 2013 ?$$

Question 4

Five consecutive whole numbers add up to 162 after the middle one has been doubled. Find the smallest of these five numbers.

Question 5

How many diagonals does a regular octagon have?

Question 6

Five positive whole numbers have the following properties:

> Their mean is 4;
> Their median is 2;
> Their mode is 2;
> Their range is 6.

What is the product of these five positive integers?

Question 7

A shopkeeper paid £30 (cost price) for a coat. She wishes to place a price tag on it so that she can offer a 10% discount on the price marked on the tag and still make a profit of 20% on the cost price.

What price should she mark on the tag?

Question 8

Claire, David, Jean and Richard are queuing for the bus. In how many different ways can they line up in single file, one behind the other, without Jean being last?

Question 9

A cube is divided into 64 identical smaller cubes. Seven of these smaller cubes are removed. The resulting shape has a volume of 1539 cm^3.

What is the surface area of the original cube?

Question 10

Dean spent one fifth of the amount of money in his wallet and then one fifth of what remained. He spent a total of £72. Find the amount of money in his wallet to start with.

Crossnumber

Teams are divided into pairs, with one pair given the across clues and one pair given the down clues. Each pair answers as many questions as possible on the grid, showing their answers to the supervising teacher who either confirms or corrects them. The correct version is then shown to both pairs. Pairs only communicate through the supervisor, but they may make a request for particular clues to be solved.

Across:

1. The mean of 12 Across, 12 Down and 1 Across   (3)
3. The square of one less than 9 Down   (4)
6. A factor of 8 Down   (2)
7. The solution to $\frac{x+1}{3} + \frac{x-9}{5} = 30$ (2)
10. The remainder when 8 Down is divided by 91   (2)
12. $12^2 + 4^2 + 2^2 + 1^2$ (3)
14. The sum of 9 Down and 25 Down   (2)
15. Half of 13 Down   (3)
16. Twice 19 Down   (3)

17. An interior angle of an isosceles triangle with one angle equal to 26 Across (2)
18. A multiple of 11 (3)
20. A consecutive prime to 19 Down (2)
23. The sum of all its factors is 28 (2)
26. The sum of 4 Down and 9 Down (2)
27. The value of $(x + 1)(2x + 1)$ when $x = 49$ (4)
28. The area of a triangle with base 24 Down and height 25 Down (3)

Down:

1. The product of 5 Down and 6 Across (4)
2. The sum of the digits of this number and the other digits in this column comes to 24 Down (3)
4. A perfect number (that is, a number which is the sum of all its factors not including itself) (2)
5. A Fibonacci number (2)
8. The largest three digit square number (3)
9. A square number that is also a triangular number (2)
11. A quarter of 13 Down (3)
12. Two more than 12 Across (3)
13. A cube number (3)
14. Twenty less than double the sum of 11 Down and 15 Across (3)
17. An odd multiple of 12 Down (3)
19. A prime number (2)
21. The number of minutes in 12 Across hours (4)
22. A square whose digits sum to a square (3)
24. The value of $\frac{10 \times 8 \times 6 \times 4 \times 2}{2 \times 2 \times 2 \times 2 \times 2 \times 5}$ (2)
25. The square root of 3 Across (2)

Mini Relay

Teams are divided into pairs, with one pair given Questions 1 and 3 (along with the record sheet on which to record their answers) and the other pair given Questions 2 and 4. The first pair works on Question 1 and then passes the answer to the students in the other pair who use it to help them answer Question 2, for which they can first carry out some preparatory work. This continues with the second pair passing the answer to Question 2 back to the first pair and so on until a full set of answers is presented for marking. Bonus points are awarded to all teams which present a correct set of answers before the 6-minute whistle, then the other teams have a further 2 minutes in which to finish. Four of these mini relays are attempted in the time allowed.

A1 D is the value of $2^2 + 2^0 + 2^1 + 2^3$.

Pass on the value of the odd number D.

A2   *T is the number that you will receive.*

The area of the trapezium shown below is three times the area of the triangle.

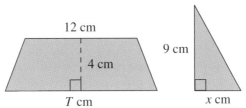

Pass on the value of the whole number x.

A3   *T is the number that you will receive.*

Inside a cuboid box of dimensions Tm × 2 m × 2 m I can fit a maximum of C cubes of side $\frac{2}{3}$ m.
Pass on the value of C.

192

A4   *T is the number that you will receive.*

The angle $x°$ is marked in the diagram below.

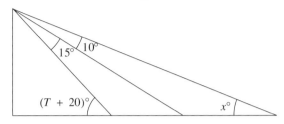

Write down the value of $x°$.

B1 U, K, M and T are different single digit numbers such that

$$U + K + M = T \text{ and } U \times T = K \times M.$$

Pass on the value of T.

B2   *T is the number that you will receive.*

$x = 10\,(T + 3) - 8\,(T + 4)$
Pass on the value of x.

B3   *T is the number that you will receive.*

£$(8T)$ is divided in the ratio $2 : 5 : 13$.
The middle share is £P.
Pass on the value of P.

B4   *T is the number that you will receive.*

The irregular pentagon below has angles as marked.

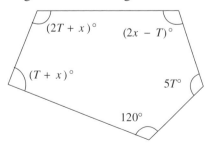

Write down the value of x.
Note: the angles in a pentagon sum to $540°$.

C1 Tania was given M mints yesterday morning, and immediately she ate $\frac{1}{3}$ of them.

Earlier today she ate $\frac{1}{3}$ of her remaining mints.

This leaves Tania 4 mints to enjoy tomorrow.

Pass on the value of M.

C2 *T is the number that you will receive.*

Pass on the mean of the numbers:

$T + 2, T + 4, T + 8, T + 16, T + 32, T + 64$

C3 *T is the number that you will receive.*

Natasha is playing a game where she starts facing North. She then turns alternately clockwise and anticlockwise, increasing the angle through which she turns by $10°$ each time.

Thus, her first 4 turns are: $10°$ clockwise, $20°$ anticlockwise, $30°$ clockwise, $40°$ anticlockwise.

When Natasha has completed T such turns, the smallest angle through which she must turn to face North again is $D°$.

Pass on the value of D.

C4 *T is the number that you will receive.*

The lowest common multiple of 105 and T is 1050.

Write down the highest common factor of 105 and T.

D1 In this question $(n)^*$ means
'the sum of the squares of the digits of n'.

For example: $(85)^* = 8^2 + 5^2 = 89$.

Let $Q = \left((2013)^*\right)^* + 1$.

Pass on the value of Q.

194

D2   *T is the number that you will receive.*

In the Martian Olympics, Team Deimos achieved
T silver medals. They achieved three times as many
gold medals as silver medals and four times as
many bronze medals as silver medals.

M is the total number of medals that Team Deimos won.

Pass on the value of *M*.

D3   *T is the number that you will receive.*

A cube of side 18 units has a surface area which is
numerically equal to the volume of a cuboid with
sides 9, *T* and *x* units.

Pass on the value of *x*. (Fully simplify your answer.)

D4   *T is the number that you will receive.*

Dominique is driving her new car. It will travel
13km per litre of petrol. Petrol costs £1.30 per litre,
and Dominique travels 8*T* km.

Write down how many pence her journey will cost her.

Relay Race

The aim here is to have a speed competition with students working in pairs
to answer alternate questions. Each team is divided into two pairs, with
each pair seated at a different desk away from the other pair and their
supervising teacher.

One member of Pair A from a team collects question A1 from the
supervising teacher and returns to his/her partner to answer the question
together. When the pair is certain that they have answered the question,
the runner returns to the front and submits their answer. If it is correct, the
runner is given question B1 to give to the other pair (Pair B) from their
team. If it is incorrect, Pair A then has another go at answering the
question, then the runner returns to the front to receive question B1 to
deliver to pair B. (Pair A can only have one extra attempt.) The runner
then returns, empty handed, to his/her partner. Pair B answers question B1
and a runner from this pair brings the answer to the front, as above, then
takes question A2 to Pair A. Pair A answers question A2, their runner
returns it to the front and collects question B2 for the other pair, and so on

until all questions are answered or time runs out. Thus the A pairs answer only A questions and the B pairs answer only B questions. Only one pair from a team should be working on a question at any time and each pair must work independently of the other.

A1   The volume of a cube is 343 cm3.
What is the surface area of the cube?

A2   Bob likes his coffee cooled and has observed that it is just right to drink seven minutes after it is made. It takes six minutes to make the coffee. Bob wants to drink his coffee at 11:03.
At what time should he start to make the coffee?

A3

How many triangles are there in this diagram?

A4   Calculate:

$$\tfrac{1}{2}\left(8^3\right) - 6^2$$

A5   What is the median of all the prime factors of 2013?

A6   What is the sum of the squares of the first three prime numbers?

A7   Thirty people go on a weekend coach trip. The ratio of men to women on the coach is 1:4. On the second day four more women join the trip.
What is the new ratio of men to women? Give your answer in its lowest terms.

A8   The diagram shows two identical circles, each of radius 4.25 cm, and a rectangle that just touches both circles. What is the area of the rectangle?

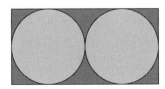

A9 At Christmas a mathematical grandmother finds that the sum of the ages of her two eldest grandsons is 24. Next Christmas the product of their ages will be 168. How old are they each now?

A10 In a class of 32 pupils, five-eighths were boys, who were all present. One quarter of the girls were absent. How many pupils were present?

A11 Celeste starts off facing north-west. She turns 120° anticlockwise, then 165° clockwise.

In which direction is she facing now?

A12 In this magic square each of the rows, columns and the two main diagonals has the same total. What number replaces n?

Give your answer in its simplest terms.

$\frac{3}{4}$	$\frac{7}{8}$	
	$\frac{5}{8}$	
n		$\frac{1}{2}$

A13 Sums United played football in a local league. The teams were given three points for a win, one for a draw and none for losing. At the end of the season, Sums United had 45 points after playing 24 games. They drew six games. How many did they lose?

A14 Below is a record of the minimum and maximum temperatures for a week in June. What is the mean daily temperature range?

	Sun	Mon	Tue	Wed	Thu	Fri	Sat
min	3	5	5	4	4	7	9
max	20	18	20	17	18	22	20

A15 Each row and column has one each of the four letters U, K, M and T. Complete the bottom line of the grid.

U		M	T
	T		
		K	M
K			

B1   Nine students were selected at random and their shoe sizes recorded:

5   6   4   6   7   4   8   3   4

What is the median shoe size?

B2   A train is carrying 42 people. When six men get on the ratio of men to women is 1:5. How many women are on board the train?

B3   When I add the squares of two positive consecutive whole numbers the answer is 145.

What is the total of the two positive consecutive numbers?

B4   When the caretaker sets up the hall for school examination week it takes an average of 15 seconds to put up a table and 10 seconds to put a chair at each table in the right place.

How many minutes will it take to set up the hall for 72 candidates?

B5   A nurse needs to give the correct amount of medicine to a patient who is going away for a fourteen-day holiday. One dose is 10 ml and the patient needs the medicine three times a day.

How much medicine will be required altogether?

B6   What is the mean of all the prime factors of 2013?

B7   Write down the answers to the following calculations, in ascending order.

$\frac{1}{3}$ of 21 $1^2 + 2^3$ $\frac{1}{3}\left(\frac{1}{4} \times 48\right)$

B8   Triangle ABC has vertices with coordinates A (2,1), B (5,1) and C (5,4).

The triangle is rotated 90° clockwise about the origin.

What are the coordinates of the image of C?

B9   This year, 2013, is written using four consecutive digits.

When was the last year that used four consecutive digits?

B10

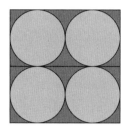

The diagram shows four circles, each of radius 3.5 cm.

What is the area of the square that just surrounds them?

B11   A children's book must have at least 20 sheets and cost no more than £2.20. A sheet with only black ink will cost 3p, and a sheet with colour will cost 25p.

What is the maximum number of coloured sheets that will be possible?

B12   A square of side 8 cm has an equilateral triangle drawn onto each of its sides to create a new shape. What is the perimeter of the new shape?

B13   Harry starts off facing south-east. He turns 135° clockwise, then 90° anticlockwise.

In which direction is he facing now?

B14   Sue's heart beats 72 times in a minute when she is sitting doing calculations.

She starts a page of problems at precisely 12:47, and finishes at precisely 13:12.

How often has her heart beaten in this time?

B15   Two different digits in this calculation are replaced by # and @.

$$36 \times 6\# = 23@4$$

What is the sum of the missing digits?

TMC National Final Material

At the National Final, the Group Round is replaced by the Group Circus.

Group Circus

Teams move around a number of stations (eight at the 2013 National Final) to tackle a variety of activities, some of which involve practical materials.

Station 1

A domino has two parts, each containing one number.

A complete set of dominoes containing the numbers 0, 1, 2, 3, 4, 5 and 6, part of which is shown, has a total of 28 dominoes.

Part A: How many dominoes does a complete set containing the numbers 0, 1, 2, 3, 4, 5, 6, 7, 8 and 9 have?

Part B: A similar complete set of dominoes containing the numbers 0, 1, 2, 3,..., n has a total of 91 dominoes. What is the value of n?

Station 2

In a certain code the vowels A, E, I, O and U represent the five smallest positive square numbers in increasing order. All the other letters in the alphabet, B, C, D, ... , X, Y, Z represent the twenty-one smallest positive even integers that are not square numbers, again in increasing order.

Thus, $A = 1, B = 2, C = 6, D = 8$ etc

When the letters in 'TEAM MATHS FINAL' are changed into numbers, using the code shown above, what is their sum?

Station 3

You are provided with 8 number cards, each bearing a prime number: 3, 5, 7, 11, 17, 19, 37 and 43

Place the eight cards, one in each square, in the grid below, such that the sums of the 3 prime numbers in 1 down and in 2 down are both equal to 53 and the sums of the 3 prime numbers in 1 across and in 3 across are equal to the same prime number.

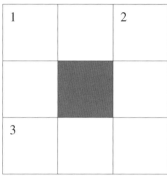

Station 4

How many regular polygons have an internal angle $\alpha°$ such that $160° \leqslant \alpha° < 170°$?

Station 5

Using the 16 cards provided (4 Aces, 4 Kings, 4 Queens and 4 Jacks), arrange the cards in four rows of four so that in each complete horizontal, vertical and diagonal line you have one of each suit and also one of each denomination.

Station 6

Draw two straight lines on the cross below (after first cutting it out) in such a way that when you cut along those lines you can rearrange the pieces of the cross into a square. No overlapping of, or gap between, the separate pieces is allowed.

Station 7

Arrange the number cards provided (1 to 8) on the grid below, one number in each square, so that no number is in contact on any side or diagonal with any number that is one greater or one less than it. So, for example, 4 cannot be next to 3 or 5.

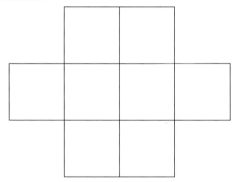

Station 8

A Harshad number is an integer that is exactly divisible by the sum of its digits. For example 1729 is a Harshad number because 1 + 7 + 2 + 9 = 19 and 1729 can be divided exactly by 19.

Find the smallest positive Harshad number with a digit sum of 13.

Crossnumber

Across:

1. A multiple of 28 Across   (4)

3. A palindromic square whose square root is not palindromic   (3)

5. Twice 6 Down plus six   (3)

7. Fourteen less than 4 Down   (2)

9. A Fibonacci number   (3)

11. The sum of 11 Down and 20 Down   (3)

13. The cube root of 8 Down   (2)

15. An angle of an isosceles triangle that has 76° as one of its angles   (2)

16. The sum of the first six triangular numbers   (2)

17. A square which is a multiple of the sum of its digits   (2)

18. The number of different ways to arrange the letters in 'MATHS' (3)

21. Product of two consecutive primes (3)

23. The hypotenuse of a triangle with two sides of 39 and 80 (2)

25. An even number (3)

27. A cube that is the sum of three cubes as well as being a square (3)

28. A twelfth power (4)

Down:

1. The product of nine and the largest two digit prime (3)

2. The square root of 3 Across (2)

3. One more than 4 Down (2)

4. One side of a right-angled triangle with other sides 15 Across and 25 Down (2)

6. A multiple of the product of its digits (3)

8. The number of cubic inches in a cubic foot (4)

10. A number which is a multiple of the sum of the digits of 1 Down (2)

11. The sum of the divisors of 81 (3)

12. Ten times a Fibonacci number (3)

14. 28 Across minus 8 Down (4)

19. A sixteenth of the difference between 28 Across and 1 Across (3)

20. The magic constant of a four by four magic square that uses the numbers from 1 to 16 (2)

22. The sum of the squares of its digits is the square of a prime (3)

24. One of a pair of consecutive primes that differ by eight (2)

25. A multiple of a factor of 21 Across (2)

26. The product of the square root of 11 Down and the sixth root of 28 Across (2)

A1
$$1\tfrac{2}{3} + 4\tfrac{5}{6} + 7\tfrac{8}{9} = a\tfrac{b}{c}$$

where $b < c$ and b and c have no common factors.

Pass on the value of $a + b + c$.

A2   *T is the number that you will receive.*

A semi-circle with radius $(T + 1)$ cm has the same area as eight circles of radius x cm.

Pass on the value of x.

A3   *T is the number that you will receive.*

The Lowest Common Multiple of T, $2T$ and 15 is x times the Highest Common Factor of $6T$, 48 and 84.

Pass on the value of x.

A4   *T is the number that you will receive.*

In *Mathstown* media store, all DVDs cost a fixed price. Each CD costs £T more than each DVD, and each book costs £$(T + 1)$ more than each CD.

On her latest shopping trip to the store, Rachel bought three books, four CDs and five DVDs, spending £125 in total.

In total, 1 book, 1 CD and 1 DVD cost £P.

Write down the value of P.

B1   The product of two whole numbers is equal to the square of a third whole number.

The first two numbers are two less, and three more, respectively, than the third number.

Pass on the sum of the three whole numbers.

B2 *T is the number that you will receive.*

The diagram below shows three interlinked pairs of parallel lines.

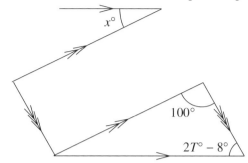

Pass on the value of *x*.

B3 *T is the number that you will receive.*

This year, Dean is doing a sponsored swim. He aims to swim *T* lengths of his local pool and is looking to raise £1200 in total.

His sponsors have agreed to give him £10 a length for the first $\frac{T}{2}$ lengths, £20 a length for the next $\frac{T}{5}$ lengths, £30 a length for the next $\frac{T}{10}$ lengths and £*x* a length for the rest.

Assuming he swims exactly *T* lengths and raises exactly £1200, pass on the value of *x*.

B4 *T is the number that you will receive.*

Steve has just returned from holiday.

On his outward flight, he noticed that the ratio of men to women to children was $\frac{T}{10}$: 5 : 3 while on his return flight the ratio was $\frac{T}{12}$: 4 : 3.

He also noticed that there were 60 children on the outward flight and 75 men on the return flight. There were *P* people on the two flights in total.

Write down the value of *P*.

C1 $K = 12 + \left(11 \times (10 \times 9 + 8 - 7 \times 6 + 5) - 4\right) \times 3 \div (2 - 1)$

Pass on the value of K.

C2 *T is the number that you will receive.*

To mix a certain horse medicine, Holly takes a fluid which is 20% water, and mixes it with another fluid which is 15% water, in the ratio 3 : 2.

When Holly makes $(T - 13)$ ml of her medicine, there is H ml of water contained within it.

Pass on the value of H.

C3 *T is the number that you will receive.*

A year ago, *Cheapo Charlie's Cafe* and *Dodgy Dave's Diner* charged exactly the same as each other for their 'Meat Surprise Pie'.

Recently, Charlie cut his prices by 20%, whereas Dave put his prices up by 20%.

Dave now charges T pence for the 'Meat Surprise Pie', and Charlie now charges C pence.

Pass on the value of C.

C4 *T is the number that you will receive.*

The diagram shows a right-angled triangle with side lengths as marked.

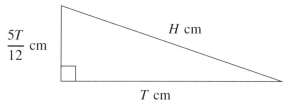

$\frac{5T}{12}$ cm

H cm

T cm

Write down the value of H.

D1
$$1 - 2(x - 3(x - 4)) = 5$$

Pass on the value of x.

D2 *T is the number that you will receive.*

Mathstown swimming pool is a cuboid with internal dimensions 25 m × 10 m × 2 m.

It is filled, from empty, by a hose which delivers T litres of water per second. Rounded to the nearest hour, this takes H hours.

Pass on the value of H.
[1 litre = 1000 cm^3.]

D3 *T is the number that you will receive.*

The Tth triangular number is added to the $(T + 1)$th triangular number, and the Tth square number is subtracted. The result is N.

Pass on the value of N.

[*The Tth triangular number is given by $\frac{1}{2}T(T + 1)$.*]

D4 *T is the number that you will receive.*

The first T even numbers are added together, and the result is divided by the $(T - 1)$th triangular number. This gives a top-heavy fraction F in its lowest terms.

Write down the value of F.
[*The Tth triangular number is given by $\frac{1}{2}T(T + 1)$.*]

Relay Race

A1 When written in DD/MM/YYYY form, 21st March 2013 (21/03/2013) uses each of the digits 0,1,2 and 3 twice. What is or was the first date this year that has this property?

A2 I pour half a litre of paint into a rectangular tray 10cm by 20cm. How deep is the paint?

A3 Eight friends go to a café for lunch. They can have one course at £6.45 or two courses at £9.95. The bill comes to £62.10. How many of the friends had two courses?

A4   Calculate the value of X:

$$8 \times X + 15 \div 5 = 11 + 6 \times 8$$

A5   Calculate the total of all the square numbers less than 40.

A6   Martha counts up all the money in her piggy bank, and finds she has £3.64. She has equal numbers of just four different coins, each worth less than 50p. How many does she have of each coin?

A7

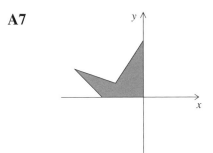

Reflect this irregular pentagon in the x-axis and name the new shape.

A8   Two of the angles of an isosceles triangle are in the ratio 2:5. What is the largest possible angle in such a triangle?

A9   A volleyball team has three strips (shorts, tee-shirts and headband) all white, all black and all red. The sponsor agrees that they can mix up the strips provided they do not wear the same colour headband as shorts. How many different outfits can they make?

A10   What is the median of ALL of the factors of 2013?

A11   A mole starts burrowing horizontally.
He goes 4 metres West, 2 metres North, 1 metre East and 6 metres South. How far is he from his start point?

A12   A rectangle 16cm wide and 25cm long has the same area as a square.
What is the ratio of the perimeter of the square to the perimeter of the rectangle?

A13   A young farmer calculates that the mean number of eggs laid by each of his five hens last week is six. He then finds Esmeralda (one of the five hens) sitting on an extra secret clutch of four eggs behind a bush. What is the mean now?

A14 Three of the vertices of a parallelogram are at the points (8,5), (5,4) and (5,8).

Give the coordinates of the three possible positions of the fourth vertex.

A15 A slug and a snail finish eating a lettuce in my garden and then set off together at their top speeds towards a cabbage 3 metres away. The speedy slug travels at 2.5 metres/hour, the slower snail at 2 metres/hour. How many minutes of cabbage-eating does the slug have before the snail joins her?

B1 Calculate the product of all the single-digit prime numbers.

B2 A rectangle 10cm long has the same perimeter as a square of side 6cm.

What is the ratio of the area of the square to the area of the rectangle?

Give your answer in lowest terms.

B3 Harry counts up all the money in his piggy bank, and finds he has £1.85. He has equal numbers of just four different coins, each worth less than 50p. How many does he have of each coin?

B4 When written in DD/MM/YYYY form, 21st March 2013 (21/03/2013) uses each of the digits 0,1,2 and 3 twice. What will be the last date this year that has this property?

B5 A mole starts burrowing horizontally.

He goes 6 metres West, 1 metre North, 3 metres East and 4 metres South. In which compass direction must he dig to return to his start point?

B6 In a mathematics class of 36 pupils the ratio with long hair (more than shoulder length) to short hair (less than shoulder length) is 8:1. When four more join the class the ratio changes to 7:1. Now how many have long hair?

B7 The pipkin is a traditional small barrel holding seven pints of beer. Approximately how many litres of beer will fill 6 pipkins?

(1 litre is approximately a pint and three-quarters.)

B8 Two of the vertices of a rectangle are at the points (8,5) and (4,1). One line of symmetry is $x = 6$. What is the equation of the other line of symmetry?

B9   Calculate the value of *X*:

$$7 \times 9 - 13 \times 2 = 5 \times X + 2$$

B10   A mathematical grandmother makes a round cake, but only has a recipe for an eight inch square cake. She has four round cake tins with diameters 7, 8, 9 and 10 inches.

Which round tin will give a cake nearest to the same height as the square tin?

B11   Three poles are tied together to make one long pole exactly 4 metres long. The three poles are 1m, 2m and 1·5m long. If the overlap is the same for each join, what is that overlap in cm?

B12   The restaurant deal was: two courses for £9.95 or three courses for £14.45. At the end of the meal six friends received a bill for £68.70.

How many had just two courses?

B13   A group of friends set out each week to complete a five-mile walk. After eight walks they calculate that their mean walk is 5·15 miles, so they plan to take it easy next week with a shorter walk to return the mean length to 5 miles. How far must they walk?

B14   What is the mean of ALL of the factors of 2013?

B15   After a Team Maths Challenge, 80 students were asked which was their favourite round. Twice as many said Group as said Relay. Five more said Crossnumber than Relay, and three fewer said Mini Relay than Crossnumber. Twelve said Mini Relay.

How many did not have a favourite?

Solutions from the Regional Finals

Group Round Answers

1.	35	6.	384
2.	55 mph	7.	£40
3.	1007	8.	18
4.	25	9.	864 (cm^2)
5.	20	10.	£200

Crossnumber

¹1	6	²6	■	³1	⁴2	2	⁵5	■
7	■	⁶3	1	■	8	■	⁷5	⁸9
0	■	1	■	⁹3	■	■	■	6
¹⁰5	¹¹1	■	¹²1	6	¹³5	■	¹⁴7	1
■	¹⁵2	5	6	■	¹⁶1	9	4	■
¹⁷5	8	■	¹⁸7	¹⁹9	2	■	²⁰8	²¹9
0	■	■	■	7	■	²²1	■	9
²³1	²⁴2	■	²⁵3	■	²⁶6	4	■	0
■	²⁷4	9	5	0	■	²⁸4	2	0

Mini Relay

A1	15
A2	4
A3	54
A4	49

B1	6
B2	10
B3	20
B4	70

C1	9
C2	30
C3	150
C4	15

D1	18
D2	144
D3	1.5 or $\frac{3}{2}$ or $1\frac{1}{2}$
D4	120p

Relay Race

A1	294 (cm^2)	B1	5
A2	10:50	B2	40
A3	6	B3	17
A4	220	B4	30 (mins)
A5	11	B5	420 (ml)
A6	38	B6	25
A7	3 : 14	B7	4, 7, 9
A8	144.5 (cm^2)	B8	(4, −5)
A9	11, 13	B9	1432
A10	29	B10	196 (cm^2)
A11	North (or N or 0°)	B11	7
A12	1	B12	64 (cm)
A13	5	B13	South (or S or 180°)
A14	14°	B14	1800
A15	Bottom line KMTU	B15	4

Solutions from the National Final

Group Circus

1. Part A: 55 ; Part B: 12
2. 246
3.

11	17	3
37	■	43
5	19	7

5	19	7
37	■	43
11	17	3

3	17	11
43	■	37
7	19	5

7	19	5
43	■	37
3	17	11

Any one of the 4 correct solutions shown is fine.

4. 18
5. Correct arrangement as viewed
   (there are many different solutions)
6. Correct square as viewed
7.

	6	4	
2	8	1	7
	5	3	

	4	6	
7	1	8	2
	3	5	

	5	3	
2	8	1	7
	6	4	

	3	5	
7	1	8	2
	4	6	

Any one correct will suffice.

8. 247

Crossnumber

¹8	1	9	²2	■	³6	7	⁴6	■
7	■		⁵6	⁶3	6	■	⁷5	⁸1
⁹3	¹⁰7	7	■	1	■	■	■	7
■	2		¹¹1	5	¹²5	■	¹³1	2
¹⁴2	■	¹⁵5	2	■	¹⁶5	6	■	8
¹⁷3	6	■	¹⁸1	¹⁹2	0	■	²⁰3	
6	■	■	■	5	■	²¹1	4	²²3
²³8	²⁴9	■	²⁵3	6	²⁶4	■		2
■	²⁷7	2	9	■	²⁸4	0	9	6

Mini Relay

A1	39
A2	10
A3	5
A4	34

B1	19
B2	50
B3	60
B4	460

C1	2013
C2	360
C3	240
C4	260

D1	7
D2	20
D3	41
D4	21/10

Relay Race

A1   23/01/2013

A2   2.5 cm

A3   3

A4   7

A5   91

A6   13

A7   Heptagon

A8   100°

A9   18

A10   47

A11   5 m

A12   40 : 41

A13   6.8 or $6\frac{4}{5}$

A14   (2, 7), (8, 9), (8, 1) any order

A15   18 mins

B1   210

B2   9 : 5

B3   5

B4   30/12/2013

B5   North East (or NE)

B6   35

B7   24 litres

B8 $y = 3$

B9   7

B10   9 inches

B11   25 cm

B12   4

B13   3.8 or $3\frac{4}{5}$ miles

B14   372

B15   23

UKMT and Further Maths Support Programme
Senior Team Maths Challenge 2013

The Senior Team Maths Challenge is now entering into its 7th year and continues to grow in size and popularity. The 2012-13 competition comprised of over 1100 schools competing in 56 Regional Finals held across the United Kingdom, three more venues than in 2011-12 and a higher number of competing teams than ever before.

Each team was made up of four students from years 11, 12 and 13 (at most two year 13 students per team) and the Regional Competition consisted of 3 Rounds; The Group Round, the Crossnumber and the Mini-Relay. For the Group Round, 10 questions were to be answered by each team in 40 minutes, while the Crossnumber involved each team solving a mathematical version of a crossword by splitting in two to work on the 'Across' and the 'Down' clues. The competition finished with the Mini-Relay round, which consisted of sets of four linked questions, answered in pairs against a timer.

The culmination of the competition was held at the National Final in February, where the top 62 teams were invited to the Camden Centre in Central London to compete once again, this time for the title of 'National Champions'. The overall winners for 2012-13 were Westminster School.

The National Final consisted of the Group Round, the Crossnumber and the Mini-Relay with the addition of a Poster Competition at the start of the day. Teams were required to answer questions on 'Sets and Logic' and set these in the form of an attractive poster. Thanks to Peter Neumann, Matthew Baker, Alexandra Hewitt, Andrew Jobbings, Richard Lissaman and Alan Slomson for their hard work in preparing the materials and judging the posters once again. The Poster Competition did not contribute to the overall result of the National Final but a poster based on the work of the winning team (The Grammar School at Leeds) has been professionally produced and printed. This will be sent to all of the schools that took part in the competition.

The National Final was an excellent event at which the high level of energy and enthusiasm throughout the day created a wonderful celebration of mathematics.

As with all UKMT competitions, thanks must be given to all of the volunteers who wrote questions, acted as checkers for the materials produced, ran Regional Finals alongside FMSP coordinators and who helped on the day at the National Final.

The checkers of the questions were: John Silvester, Jenny Ramsden and Martin Perkins.

The 4 Round Rulers, who oversaw the materials for each round, were: Karen Fogden (Group round), Peter Hall (Crossnumber), Mark Harwood (Mini Relay) and James Cranch (Starter questions).

The writers of the questions were: Kerry Burnham, Tony Cheslett, Anthony Collieu, David Crawford, Andrew Ginty, Charlie Oakley, Dennis Pinshon and Katie Ray.

As ever, many thanks to everyone involved for making 2012-13 another successful year.

Alex Crews, Lead Volunteer Senior Team Maths Challenge

Congratulations to all the schools who took part in the STMC National Final. These schools were:

Abbey College; Alton College; Aylesbury Grammar School; Beverley Grammar School; Bristol Grammar School; Bungay High School; Caistor Grammar School; City of London School; Claremont Fan Court School; Clitheroe Royal Grammar School; Colchester Royal Grammar School; Concord College; Dollar Academy; EF International Academy; Eton College; Fraserburgh Academy; Grange School; Haberdashers' Aske's School for Boys; Hampton School; Kenilworth School; King Edward VI Camp Hill Girls' School; King Edward VI Grammar School; King Edward VI School; Lancaster Royal Grammar School; Loughborough Grammar School; Magdalen College School; Malvern St James; Manchester Grammar School; Merchant Taylors' School; Norwich High School; Oakham School; Pate's Grammar School; Poole Grammar School; Prior Pursglove College; Queen Elizabeth Grammar School; Queen Margaret's School; Rainham Mark Grammar School; Repton School; Robert Smyth School; Royal Grammar School, Newcastle; Ruthin School; Sheldon School; Shrewsbury School; Simon Langton Boys' Grammar School; St Dunstan's College; St John's College; St Paul's Girls School; Stephen Perse Foundation; Stewarts Melville College; Stonyhurst College; Stover School; Taunton School (Upper School); The Grammar School at Leeds; The High School of Glasgow; Treviglas Community College; Ulverston Victoria High School; Victoria College; Warwick School; Wellington College, Belfast; Westminster School; Workington 6th Form Centre; Worthing VI Form College.

The winners were Westminster School; Eton College, Magdalen College School and City of London School were joint second.

The following pages contain much of the material which was used in both the Regional Finals and the National Final.

Regional Group Round

1   Given that $p^2 = q^2 + 4$,

calculate the value of $\dfrac{p^2 - q^2}{(p + q)^2 (p - q)^2}$.

2 | $n! = n \times (n - 1) \times (n - 2) \times \ldots \times 1$ for any positive integer, n. |

What is the last non-zero digit of 50! ?

3 | $160 = 30 + 31 + 32 + 33 + 34$ |

How many numbers between 100 and 1000 cannot be written as the sum of two or more consecutive positive integers?

4   Find the value of $x + y$, given that,

$$\frac{270}{x - 15} = \frac{y + 4}{8}, \qquad \frac{120}{x} = \frac{y}{20}, \qquad x > 0 \text{ and } x > 0.$$

5   A group of five people consists of Jacks and Jokers. Jacks always tell the truth and Jokers always lie.
Each member of the group makes a statement.
The first person says 'Exactly 1 of us is a Joker.'
The second person says 'Exactly 2 of us are Jacks.'
The third person says 'Exactly 3 of us are Jokers.'
The fourth person says 'Exactly 4 of us are Jacks.'
The fifth person says 'Exactly 5 of us are Jokers.'

How many of the group are Jacks?

6

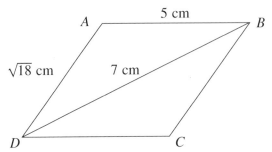

The parallelogram $ABCD$ is such that $AB = 5$ cm, $AD = \sqrt{18}$ cm and $BD = 7$ cm.

Calculate the area of the parallelogram in cm^2.

7 How many five-digit numbers can be formed, containing exactly two non-zero digits (not necessarily distinct), and such that the sum of the digits is a square number?

8 In a sale, the price of a computer is reduced by 20%. At this reduced price the shopkeeper still makes a profit of 20%. What would have been his percentage profit if the computer had been sold at full price?

9

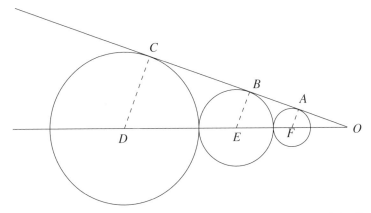

Three circles lie with their centres D, E and F on a straight line that passes through O. The common tangent to the circles touches the circles at C, B and A respectively and also passes through O. The middle circle touches the other two circles.

If $AF = 3$ cm, $OF = 5$ cm and the area of the largest circle is $k^2\pi$ cm^2, find the value of k.

10 | The German mathematician Carl Friedrich Gauss (1777-1855), is sometimes referred to as 'The Prince of Mathematicians' and has had a significant influence in a large number of fields of mathematics.

Gauss was a child prodigy and, anecdotally, amazed his teacher at the age of 7 by adding up the numbers from 1 to 100 instantly, by noticing that their were $\dfrac{100}{2}$ pairs, each equal to 101.

In 1796, amongst many other things, he discovered that every positive integer can be represented as the sum of at most three triangular numbers. He wrote in his diary the famous note,

'EYPHKA! num = Δ + Δ + Δ'

Find the smallest three-digit triangular number that can be represented both as the sum of three different triangular numbers, and as the sum of two different triangular numbers.

Regional Final Crossnumber

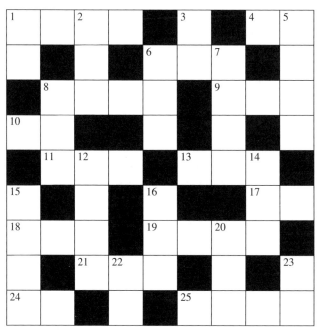

220

Across

1	The value of n^n where n is an integer
4	The value of $n!$ where n is an integer
6	Two thirds of the difference between 5 Down and 25 Across, rounded to the nearest integer
8	The value of $x + 600$, where

$$3x + 2y = 5 \text{ Down} \qquad 4x + 3y = 12 \text{ Down}$$

9	The sum of the remaining angles in a heptagon, with one known angle equal to 23 Down
10	A square number which is one eighth of a cube number
11	The cube of the largest prime factor of 14 Down
13	The interior angle of a regular 11-sided polygon, rounded to the nearest integer
17	A cube number
18	The product of 8 and a prime number
19	A rearrangement of the digits of 5 Down
21	A palindromic number
24	The square of the cube root of 2 Down
25	Larger than 1 Across, a product of a square number and the first three-digit prime number

Down

1	The result when 25 Across is divided by the first three-digit prime number
2	A cube number
3	Twelve more than 4 Across
5	The value of $20 - x$, where

$$3x + 2y = 9 \text{ Across} \qquad 4x + 3y = 25 \text{ Across}$$

6	One fifth of 1 Across
7	The value of $(x + a)(x + b)$ where a is 10 Across and b is 24 Across and x is the mean of 10 Across and 24 Across
8	An odd number
12	Two thirds of 25 Across
14	The sum of all the angles on all the faces of a tetrahedron
15	Three more than the difference between 19 Across and 5 Down
16	Larger than 6 Down, the product of 3 Down and 4 Across
20	The sum of the remaining angles in a pentagon, with one known angle equal to 10 Across
22	The sum of the digits of 1 Across, 9 Across, 24 Across and 25 Across
23	The square of the cube root of 10 Across.

Mini-Relay questions

A1 Evaluate the following:

$$\left(\frac{3}{2}\right)^{12} \times \left(\frac{8}{9}\right)^{3} \times \left(\frac{4}{27}\right)^{2}$$

Pass on your answer.

A2 *T is the number that you will receive.*

The value of a single share in UKMT Bank decreased by $10T$ % in 2010 and by a further $5T$ % in 2011.

Its current value is £54.

Pass on, in pounds, its original value.

A3 *T is the number that you will receive.*

In the diagram, *DE* is a tangent to the circle, $AB = AC$ and $\angle BCE = (T - 3)°$.

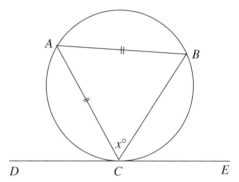

Pass on the value of *x*.

A4 *T is the number that you will receive.*

A cylinder of radius 6 cm and height $\frac{2}{3}T$ cm has a volume that is four times the volume of a cone of height 12 cm.

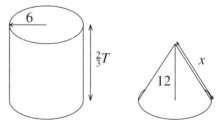

Write down the value of *x*.

222

B1   Evaluate the following:

$$\sqrt{\frac{0.36}{0.1 - 0.06}} + \frac{0.2 + 0.01}{0.03} + \frac{0.5 + 0.04}{0.06}$$

Pass on your answer.

B2   *T is the number that you will receive.*

The angles of a pentagon form a sequence that increases by a constant amount each time, where the middle angle is $\sqrt{T - 1}$ times bigger than the smallest angle.

Find the size of the smallest angle.

B3   *T is the number that you will receive.*

There are two possible integer solutions to the equation

$$\frac{Tx - 26}{x^2 - 6} + \frac{1}{x + 2} = 1$$

Pass on the sum of the two solutions.

B4   *T is the number that you will receive.*

Evaluate the following:

$$\frac{3(T^2 - 4)}{2T^2 + 9T + 4}$$

You should express your answer as a fraction in its simplest form.

Write down the difference between the denominator and the numerator.

C1   Evaluate:

$$\frac{1 + 2}{3 \times 4} \div \frac{5 + 6}{7 \times 8} \div \frac{9 + 10}{11 \times 12} \times \frac{13 + 14}{15 \times 16}$$

Express your answer as a fraction in its simplest form.

Pass on the difference between the denominator and the numerator.

C2   *T is the number that you will receive.*

Calculate the mean of the following frequency distribution.

X	5	10	15	20	25
Frequency	$T + 3$	$T + 4$	$T + 2$	$8T$	5

Pass on your answer.

C3   *T is the number that you will receive.*

Express

$$\sqrt{8T} + \sqrt{3T + 2} - \sqrt{32}$$

in the form $a\sqrt{b}$ where b is a prime number.

Pass on the value of $a + b$.

C4   *T is the number that you will receive.*

Solve the simultaneous equations

$$x + 2y + 3z = T$$

$$2x + y + 2z = T + 1$$

$$4x + 4y + 6z = 3T - 3$$

(Hint: Start by adding and subtracting sets of equations).

Write down the value of $x + y + z$.

D1   The equation below has six solutions.

$$\left(x^2 - 2\right)^{\left(15 + 4x - 3x^2\right)} - 1 = 0$$

Pass on the product of the six solutions.

D2   *T is the number that you will receive.*

Evaluate the following:

$$\frac{-2 + 6\sin 30° \times 2\sqrt{T} + 24}{2}$$

Pass on your answer.

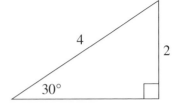

D3   *T is the number that you will receive.*
A triangle has a base of $\frac{80}{T}$ cm
and height of $\frac{40}{T}$ cm.
A square has an area equal to
that of the triangle and has a
perimeter of P cm.

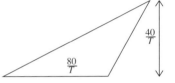

Pass on the value of P.

D4   *T is the number that you will receive.*
The radii of two touching identical
circles and two tangents form a
pentagon *ABCDE* as shown.

The radius of each circle is $T - 18$
cm and $AB = AE = 5$ cm.

Write down the area of the pentagon.

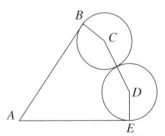

Group Round answers

1.	Value of expression	$\frac{1}{4}$
2.	Last digit	-2
3.	Number of numbers	3
4.	Value of $x + y$	107
5.	Number of Jacks	2
6.	Area of parallelogram	21 cm^2
7.	Number of five-digit numbers	56
8.	Percentage profit at full price	50%
9.	Value of k	48
10.	Smallest three-digit number	120

Crossnumber: Completed grid

¹3	1	²2	5	■	³3	■	⁴2	⁵4
6	■	1	■	⁶6	6	⁷9	■	6
■	⁸9	6	7	2	■	⁹8	8	4
¹⁰6	4	■	■	5	■	0	■	0
■	¹¹1	¹²2	5	■	¹³1	4	¹⁴7	■
¹⁵1	■	4	■	¹⁶8	■	■	¹⁷2	7
¹⁸8	7	2	■	¹⁹6	4	²⁰4	0	■
0	■	²¹4	²²5	4	■	7	■	²³1
²⁴3	6	■	8	■	²⁵3	6	3	6

Mini-Relay answers

	1	2	3	4
A	2	75	54	15
B	5	9	10	1
C	1	16	11	7
D	-15	8	20	20

1 If all of the integers from 1 to 99999 are written down in a list, how many zeros will have been used?

2 The positive integers m, n and p satisfy the equation

$$mnp + mn + np + pm + m + n + p = 1000$$

What is the value of $m + n + p$?

3 One integer is removed from a set of integers 1 to n.
The mean of the remaining numbers is $20\frac{1}{3}$.
Which number was removed?

4 The region R is the intersection of the interiors of the two circles given by

$$x^2 + y^2 = a^2 \qquad \text{and} \qquad x^2 + y^2 = a^2$$

where $a \geqslant 0$.
Find the value of a, such that the area of R equals $\pi - 2$ units^2.

5 Three circles lie on a line so that each circle touches the other two. The smallest circle has radius r and the larger two circles each have radius R.

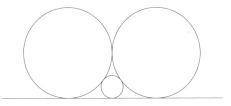

What is the ratio of the radii $r : R$?

6 An equilateral triangle *ABC* is placed on top of a trapezium *ACDE* to form a pentagon *ABCDE*.
BE intersects *AC* at *P*.
BD intersects *AC* at *Q*.
$AP : PQ : QC = 1 : 1 : 1$ and $ED : AC = 2 : 3$.

If *ED* = 1 unit, what is the exact value of the perimeter of the pentagon *ABCDE* in its simplest form?

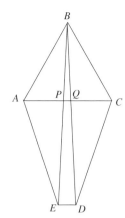

7 The quadratic curve $y = x^2 - x - 1980$ cuts the *x*-axis at *P* and *R*. It has a minimum point at *Q*.
The area of triangle *PQR* is units^3. What is the value of *k*?

8 The first term of a sequence is 1. The median of the first *n* terms is $3n - 2$.
What is the value of the 100 th term of the sequence?

9 The centres of adjacent faces of a cube are joined to form the edges of another regular polyhedron.
If the surface area of the cube is 6 units^2, what is the value of the surface area of the smaller polyhedron in units^2?

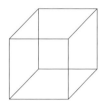

10 Eight of the digits from 1 to 9 are placed in the cross-number grid according to the clues given. The clues are in no particular order.

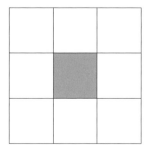

Across
Two times a prime number
The digits of a Pythagorean triple in ascending order

Down
A triangular number
A cube

National Final Crossnumber

Across

1. The value of 5^7 (5)
4. One more than a power of 7 (3)
6. The value of *y* in: $11x + 7y = 3786$; $5x + 3y = 1658$ (3)
8. A square (2)
11. Double a Fibonacci number (2)
12. A multiple of 3, of 7, of 37, of 2 Down and of 19 Down (6)
13. One less than 16 Across (2)
14. A square (2)
15. 1001 multiplied by the sum of 9 Down, 3 Down and 4 Down (6)
16. One more than 13 Across (2)
17. ab^2 where *a* and *b* are prime numbers (2)
19. A solution of $x^2 - 194x + 2013 = 0$ (3)
22. A prime number close to the square root of a quarter of 5 Down (3)
23. The square of the remaining side of a right angled triangle with hypotenuse 19 Across and shortest side 9 Down (5)

Down

1. A multiple of 14 Down (3)
2. A factor of 18 Down (2)
3. A prime number (2)
4. A square (2)
5. The square of the length of the hypotenuse of a right-angled triangle with sides 9 Down and 19 Across (5)
7. The product of 14 Across and 23 Across (6)
9. The value of x in: $11x + 7y = 3786$; $5x + 3y = 1658$ (3)
10. 10200 less than a cube (6)
13. One more than the difference between 1 Across and 5 down (5)
14. A factor of 1 Down (3)
18. Two more than a square, where each digit of the square is a triangular number (3)
19. The value of $\dfrac{19 \text{ Down} + 65}{6}$ (2)
20. An odd number (2)
21. The largest two-digit prime number ending in 1 (2)

National Final Mini-Relay

A1 Evaluate the following:

$$1 - (-2)^{-5} + (-4)^{-3} - (-8)^{-1}$$

Your answer should be expressed as an improper fraction $\frac{a}{b}$, where a and b have no common factors.

Pass on the value of $a + b$.

A2 *T is the number that you will receive.*

In the diagram, *A*, *B* and *C* lie on a circle, centre *O*, and *DE* is a tangent to the circle at *A*.
Angle $CAB = 80°$.
Angle $AOC = (T + 3)°$.

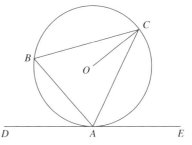

Pass on the value, in degrees, of angle *BCO*.

A3 *T is the number that you will receive.*

The diagram shows two similar cylinders, closed at both ends. The larger cylinder has volume 320 cm³ and total surface area 20*T* cm². The smaller cylinder has a total surface area of 50 cm².

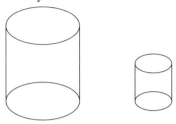

Pass on the value, in cm3, of the volume of the smaller cylinder.

A4 *T is the number that you will receive.*

Solve the simultaneous equations

$$xy = \frac{T}{5} \qquad x^2 + y^2 = \frac{T}{2}.$$

Write down the value of $x + y$, where x and y are positive integers.

B1 x and y are single-digit prime numbers.

The value of $10x + y$ is also a prime number and is equal to the sum of two other prime numbers.

Pass on the value of $x + y$.

B2 *T is the number that you will receive.*

How many positive factors does the number 50*T* have?

Pass on the number of factors.

B3 *T is the number that you will receive.*

Simplify the following:

$$\sqrt{T} + \sqrt{4T} + \sqrt{9T} + \sqrt{16T}$$

Your answer should be put in the form $\sqrt{x}$, where the surd is not simplified.

Pass on the value of x.

B4 *T is the number that you will receive.*

$$T = 2^w + 2^x + 2^y + 2^z$$

where w, x, y and z are all positive integers.

Write down the value of $w + x + y + z$.

C1 The quadratic equation

$$x^2 - 7x + a = 0,$$

where $a > 0$, has two integer roots.

Pass on one seventh of the sum of all the possible values of a.

C2 *T is the number that you will receive.*

Four identical circles are touching such that their centres form a square. A smaller circle is drawn, with radius T, such that it touches all four of the larger circles as shown in the diagram.

Write down the radius of the large circles.

Your answer should be expressed in the form $x + \sqrt{y}$.

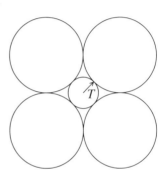

Pass on the value of $\dfrac{y}{x}$.

C3 *T is the number that you will receive.*

In the diagram, a sector of a circle has been removed from a trapezium. Find the area of the remaining part of the trapezium.

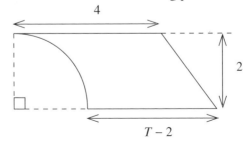

Your answer can be expressed in the form $a - b\pi$.

Pass on the value of a.

232

C4 *T is the number that you will receive.*

Solve the equation

$$3^{3x+9} = \frac{1}{27^{2x+7}}$$

Write down the value of x.

D1 The individual letters of the word BANANA are written on six counters, which are placed in a bag.

Carl removes three counters from the bag, one at a time without replacement.

The probability that the three counters show different letters and were drawn in alphabetical order is $\frac{1}{b}$.

Pass on the value of b.

D2 *T is the number that you will receive.*

The diagram shows two right-angled triangles joined along a common side.

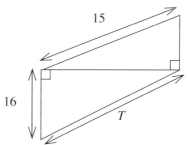

Pass on the value of one fiftieth of the area of the shape.

D3 *T is the number that you will receive.*

Solve the following equation:

$$\frac{9}{x+9} \div \frac{6x-T}{x+9} - \frac{4}{Tx-1} = 1$$

Pass on the sum of the solutions you obtain.

D4 *T is the number that you will receive.*

The diagram shows a solid cube with edges of length 5 units with a hemisphere of radius T units removed from each face.

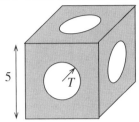

Write down the surface area of the resulting solid, in the form $a + b\pi$.

Group Round answers

1.	Number of zeros	38889
2.	Value of $m + n + p$	28
3.	Number that has been removed	27
4.	Value of a	$\sqrt{2}$
5.	Ratio $R : r$	$1 : 4$
6.	Perimeter of the pentagon $ABCDE$	$4 + \sqrt{7}$ units
7.	Value of k	44.5 or $44\frac{1}{2}$ or $\frac{89}{2}$
8.	100 th term of the sequence	595
9.	Surface area	$\sqrt{3}$ units
10.	Missing digit	9

Crossnumber: Completed grid

¹7	8	²1	2	³5	■	⁴3	4	⁵4
0	■	1	■	⁶3	4	⁷5	■	8
⁸8	⁹1	■	¹⁰2	■	5	■	¹¹6	8
■	¹²2	2	2	2	2	2	■	6
¹³2	4	■	8	■	8	■	¹⁴2	5
9	■	¹⁵2	1	3	2	1	3	■
¹⁶2	5	■	2	■	5	■	¹⁷6	¹⁸3
6	■	¹⁹1	8	²⁰3	■	²¹7	■	6
²²1	1	3	■	²³1	8	1	1	3

Mini-Relay answers

	1	2	3	4
A	137	10	40 cm³	6
B	10	12	1200	26
C	4	8	12	−5
D	20	3	1	150 + 6π

Other aspects of the UKMT

As well as the Maths Challenges, the UKMT is involved in other events and activities.

Enriching Mathematical Thinking
UKMT Teacher Meetings 2013

Eight meetings were held this year: Cambridge (University of Cambridge), Cardiff (Cardiff University), Glasgow (University of the West of Scotland), Liverpool (University of Liverpool), London (University of Greenwich), Southampton (University of Southampton), Warwick (University of Warwick) and York (York St John University).

Around 500 teachers attended the one-day events. Each meeting featured three plenary sessions with lunch and refreshment breaks, with an optional session at the end of the day on the topic of tackling mentoring questions, and delegates received a resource pack to take back to the classroom.

NRICH (www.nrich.maths.org.uk) gave sessions at all eight meetings and we are grateful to Charlie Gilderdale, Alison Kiddle and Lynne McLure for the quality of these sessions and the accompanying resources.

Rob Eastaway, author and Director of Maths Inspiration, gave inspiring and entertaining talks on the subject of Mathematical Modelling at London and Southampton, and Vinay Kathotia (Nuffield Foundation) engaged delegates at Cardiff and Liverpool with his interactive session on Mathematics and Story Telling. Richard Lissaman, Programme Leader of the Further Mathematics Support Programme, spoke about promoting problem solving in the classroom and maths promotion at Warwick, and in York, Professor Ian VanderBurgh (Director of the Centre for Education in Mathematics and Computing (CEMC) at the University of Waterloo, Canada) gave a hugely engaging talk on the CEMC and current outreach activities in Canada. At Glasgow, Professor Adam McBride discussed some of his favourite mathematical problems and got the delegates fully involved in the solutions. Finally, Peter Ransom entertained us by dressing up at Cambridge and gave the audience lots of opportunities to discover more about arithmetic, algebra, probability, geometry and statistics in his talk 'Yo Ho Ho-ratio: mathematics of Trafalgar'.

UKMT volunteers led a session at each event demonstrating the mathematical thinking behind the questions used in the UK Maths Challenges and the Team Maths Challenges, and how UKMT materials can be used to stimulate classroom interest. The 2013 speakers were David Crawford, Mary Teresa Fyfe, Howard Groves, Vesna Kadelburg, Alexandra Neville and Stephen Power.

We are also grateful to our volunteers James Cranch, Gerry Leversha and John Slater, who ran the optional mentoring sessions.

The delegate fee was £60, which included refreshments, lunch and a resources pack full of materials to take back to the classroom. Feedback was once again overwhelmingly positive.

Mathematical Circles

The Mathematical Circles are a new UKMT enrichment event. We trialled two events in spring 2012, and following on from the success of these, a further two events were run in early 2013 in Glasgow and Leeds.

Thanks to a grant from the Department for Education, we expanded these from April 2013 and ran a further five Mathematical Circles in Gloucestershire, Teesside, Wakefield, Warwick, and Watford. Local schools were able to select which two students from Year 10 they wished to send to the two-day events which were comprised of mathematically demanding work through topics such as geometry, proof and modular arithmetic. Students had the opportunity to discuss mathematics and make new friends from other schools around their region.

Our thanks go to the following people who ran the events, and to the schools who supported these:

Conyers School, Teesside (Anne Baker),
Queen Elizabeth Grammar School, Wakefield (Dean Bunnell),
Hutchesons' Grammar School, Glasgow (Mary Teresa Fyfe),
Watford Grammar School for Girls, Watford (Julian Gilbey),
Warwick School, Warwick (Karl Hayward-Bradley),
The Grammar School at Leeds, Leeds (Alan Slomson),
Wycliffe School, Gloucester (James Welham).

Thanks are also given to those people who ran sessions (a list of which is given in the Volunteers section of the Yearbook).

A further ten Mathematical Circles will be run throughout the next academic year. If you would like to find out more about how you can become involved in the Mathematical Circles, either through your school hosting an event or by supporting us in running a session, please do contact us at: enquiry@ukmt.org.uk.

Primary Team Maths Resources

In recognition and support of the growing number of secondary schools organising and hosting local team maths events for their feeder schools, UKMT developed a set of Primary Team Maths Resources (PTMR) intended for use at such events, which was launched in Spring 2012. A further set of materials was made available in January 2013.

Schools may choose to use the materials in other ways, e.g. a primary school may use the materials to run a competition for their own Year 5 and 6 pupils, or a secondary school may use the materials as an end of term activity for their Year 7 pupils.

The PTMR included more materials than would be needed for any one competition, allowing schools to pick and choose those most appropriate for their purposes. Some of the rounds are familiar from the UKMT Team Challenges (the Group Round, Crossnumber, Relay and Mini Relay) and the material included some new rounds (the Logic Round, Make a Number, Open Ended Questions, and Speed Test).

The 2013 PTMR and full instructions for suggested use is available by contacting the UKMT via email at enquiry@ukmt.org.uk. Further details including sample materials can be found on our website at www.tmc.ukmt.org.uk.

Website – www.ukmt.org.uk

Visit the UKMT's website for information about all the UKMT's activities, including the Maths Challenges, latest UKMT news, contact details, the team competitions and how to buy past papers. There are online resources featuring past questions from the Challenges, and links to sponsors, supporters and other mathematical organisations providing resources for young mathematicians.

Other similar bodies overseas

The UKMT has links of varying degrees of formality with several similar organisations in other countries. It is also a member of the World Federation of National Mathematics Competitions (WFNMC). What follows is a brief description of some of these other organisations. Some of the information is taken from the organisations' web sites but a UK slant has been applied.

"Kangourou des Mathématiques"

The European Kangaroo Competition

http://www.math-ksf.org/

The obvious question is: why Kangaroo? The name was given in tribute to the pioneering efforts of the Australian Mathematics Trust. The Kangaroo contest is run by local organisers in each country under the auspices of the 'Association Kangourou sans Frontières', which was founded by a small group of countries in 1991. There are now around 50 countries involved and more than five million participants throughout Europe and beyond, from the UK to Mongolia and from Norway to Cyprus.

In the UK in 2013, around 7000 children in the years equivalent to English Years 9, 10 and 11 took part in the 'Cadet' and 'Junior' levels of the Kangaroo competition, as a follow-up to the Intermediate Maths Challenge. Four representatives of the UK Mathematics Trust, Andrew Jobbings, Paul Murray, David Crawford and Rachel Greenhalgh, attended the meeting in Cyprus, at which the 2013 Kangaroo papers were constructed.

The main objective of the Kangaroo, like all the competitions described in this section, is to stimulate and motivate large numbers of pupils, as well as to contribute to the development of a mathematical culture which will be accessible to, and enjoyed by, many children and young people. The Association also encourages cross-cultural activities; in some countries, for example, prize-winners are invited to attend a mathematics 'camp' with similar participants from other nations.

The Australian Mathematics Trust

www.amt.canberra.edu.au

For over twenty-five years, the Australian Mathematics Competition has been one of the major events on the Australian Education Calendar, with about one in three Australian secondary students entering each year to test their skills. That's over half a million participants a year.

The Competition commenced in 1978 under the leadership of the late Professor Peter O'Halloran, of the University of Canberra, after a successful pilot scheme had run in Canberra for two years.

The questions are multiple-choice and students have 75 minutes in which to answer 30 questions. There are follow-up rounds for high scorers.

In common with the other organisations described here, the AMC also extends its mathematical enrichment activities by publishing high quality material which can be used in the classroom.

Whilst the AMC provides students all over Australia with an opportunity to solve the same problems on the same day, it is also an international event, with most of the countries of the Pacific and South-East Asia participating, as well as a few schools from further afield. New Zealand and Singapore each enter a further 30,000 students to help give the Competition an international flavour.

World Federation of National Mathematics Competitions – WFNMC

www.amt.canberra.edu.au/wfnmc.html

The Federation was created in 1984 during the Fifth International Congress for Mathematical Education.

The Federation aims to provide a focal point for those interested in, and concerned with, conducting national mathematics competitions for the purpose of stimulating the learning of mathematics. Its objectives include:

- Serving as a resource for the exchange of information and ideas on mathematics competitions through publications and conferences.

- Assisting with the development and improvement of mathematics competitions.
- Increasing public awareness of the role of mathematics competitions in the education of all students and ensuring that the importance of that role is properly recognised in academic circles.
- Creating and enhancing professional links between mathematicians involved in competitions around the world.

The World Federation of National Mathematics Competitions is an organisation of national mathematics competitions affiliated as a Special Interest Group of the International Commission for Mathematical Instruction (ICMI).

It administers a number of activities, including

- The Journal *Mathematics Competitions*
- An international conference every four years. Previous conferences were held in Waterloo, Canada (1990), Pravets, Bulgaria (1994), Zhong Shan, China (1998). In 2002, the WFNMC met in Melbourne, Australia. In 2006, the conference was in the UK and in 2010 in Riga, Latvia.
- David Hilbert and Paul Erdős Awards for mathematicians prominent on an international or national scale in mathematical enrichment activities.

The UKMT sent two delegates, Tony Gardiner and Bill Richardson, to the WFNMC conference in Zhong Shan in 1998 and provided support for several delegates who attended ICME 9 in Tokyo in August 2000, at which the WFNMC provided a strand.

In August 2002, the WFNMC held another conference, similar to the one in 1998. The venue for this was Melbourne, Victoria. On this occasion, the UKMT provided support for two delegates: Howard Groves and Bill Richardson.

In July 2006, WFNMC 5 was held in the UK at Robinson College, Cambridge. This event was a tremendous success with around 100 delegates from many parts of the world.

In July 2007, WFNMC had a strand at ICME 11 in Mexico. UKMT was represented by Bill Richardson.

In July 2010, WFNMC 6 was held in Riga. The UKMT was represented by Howard Groves, Dean Bunnell, David Crawford and James Welham.

Lists of volunteers involved in the UKMT's activities

UKMT officer bearers

Chair:	Professor Frances Kirwan
Secretary:	Dr Alan Slomson (to July 2013)
	Dr Alan Eames-Jones (from July 2013)
Treasurer:	Prof. Adam McBride

The Council

Professor Frances Kirwan

Mr Richard Atkins	Mrs Anne Baker
Professor John Brindley	Professor Chris Budd
Dr Colin Campbell	Dr Katie Chicot
Dr James Cranch	Dr Diane Crann
Mr Alex Crews (from April 2013)	Dr Ceri Fiddes
Mr Karl Hayward-Bradley (from April 2013)	
Professor Adam McBride	Mr Steve Mulligan (to April 2013)
Miss Jenny Ramsden	Mr Bill Richardson (Vice-Chair)
Prof. Alastair Rucklidge	Dr John Silvester
Dr Geoff Smith (Vice-Chair)	Mr James Welham (to April 2013)

Members of the Trust who are not on the Council or members of a Subtrust

The Mathematical Association	The Royal Institution	Mr Dennis Archer
Dr Roger Bray	Mr Dean Bunnell	Mrs Mary Teresa Fyfe
Dr Tony Gardiner	Mr Terry Heard	Mrs Margaret Jackson
Mrs Susie Jameson-Petvin	Dr Andrew Jobbings	Dr Vinay Kathotia
Mrs Patricia King	Professor Tom Körner	Dr Gerry Leversha
Mr Nick Lord	Mr Tony Mann	Mr Dennis Orton
Mrs Mary Read	Dr Adrian Sanders	Dr Sara Santos
Professor Bernard Silverman	Mr Robert Smart	Dr Brian Stewart
Mr Peter Thomas	Mr Brian Wilson	Ms Mary Wimbury

The Subtrusts

British Mathematical Olympiad Subtrust

Dr Geoff Smith (Chair)	Dr Don Collins (Treasurer)	
Mr Richard Atkins	Dr James Cranch	Dr Ceri Fiddes
Dr Vesna Kadelberg (Secretary)	Professor Imre Leader	

Team Maths Challenge Subtrust

Mr Steve Mulligan (Chair)	Mr Alex Crews	Mr Dusty de Sainte Croix
Dr Peter Neumann (Secretary)	Mr Martin Perkins (Treasurer)	
Miss Pam Hunt (Statistician)	Mr Karl Hayward-Bradley	

242

Peter Neumann (Queen's Coll., Oxford)　　Alan Pears (ex King's College, London)
Adrian Sanders (ex Trinity College, Camb.)　Zhivko Stoyanov (University of Bath)
Alan West (ex Leeds University)　　　　Brian Wilson (ex Royal Holloway, London)

BMOS Markers

Richard Atkins (Oundle School, Leader)　James Aaronson (Trinity Coll, Cambridge)
Ben Barrett (Trinity Coll, Cambridge)　　Natalie Behague (Trinity Coll, Cambridge)
Alexander Betts (Trinity Coll, Cambridge)　Robin Bhattacharyya (Loughborough GS)
Ilya Chevyrev (University of Oxford)　　Philip Coggins (ex Bedford School)
James Cranch (University of Sheffield)　　Tim Cross (KES, Birmingham)
Richard Freeland (Trinity Coll, Cambridge) Adam Goucher (Trinity Coll, Cambridge)
Karl Hayward-Bradley (Warwick School)　Tim Hennock (Trinity Coll, Cambridge)
Ina Hughes (University of Leeds)　　　Ian Jackson (Tonbridge School)
Andrew Jobbings (Arbelos)　　　　　Jeremy King (Tonbridge Sch)
Josh Lam (Trinity Coll, Cambridge)　　Gerry Leversha (formerly St Paul's School)
Sam Maltby (New Vision)　　　　　David Mestel (Trinity Coll, Cambridge)
Jordan Miller (Trinity Coll, Cambridge)　Joseph Myers (CodeSourcery, Inc)
Vicky Neale (Murray Edwards Coll., Cam.)　Peter Neumann (Queen's College, Oxford)
Sylvia Neumann (Oxford)　　　　　Craig Newbold (Trinity Coll, Cambridge)
Preeyan Parmar (Trinity Coll, Cambridge)　David Phillips (Trinity Coll, Cambridge)
Hannah Roberts (Trinity Coll, Cambridge)　Paul Russell (Churchill Coll, Cambridge)
Jack Shotton (Imperial College, London)　Geoff Smith (Uni. of Bath)
Aled Walker (Trinity Coll, Cambridge)　　Dominic Yeo (University of Oxford)

Markers for IMOK and JMO

Natalie Behague	(Trinity College, Cambridge)	IMOK
Dean Bunnell	(Queen Elizabeth GS, Wakefield)	IMOK / JMO
Valerie Chapman	(Northwich)	IMOK
Philip Coggins	(ex Bedford School)	IMOK / JMO
James Cranch	(University of Sheffield)	IMOK / JMO
David Crawford	(Leicester Grammar School)	IMOK / JMO
Tim Cross	(KES, Birmingham)	IMOK
Sue Cubbon	(St Albans, Herts)	IMOK
Wendy Dersley	(Southwold)	IMOK
David Forster	(Oratory School)	IMOK
Mary Teresa Fyfe	(Hutchesons' Grammar School, Glasgow)	IMOK / JMO
Carol Gainlall	(Park House School, Newbury)	IMOK
Tony Gardiner	(Birmingham)	IMOK
James Gazet	(Eton College)	IMOK
Nick Geere	(Kelly College)	JMO
Michael Griffiths	(Warrington)	IMOK

Howard Groves	(ex RGS, Worcester)	JMO
Peter Hall	(East Sussex)	IMOK
Jo Harbour	(Wolvercote Primary School)	JMO
Hugh Hill	(Winchester College)	IMOK
Sally E. Howe	(Leeds Grammar School)	IMOK
Magdalena Jasicova	(Cambridge)	JMO
Andrew Jobbings	(Arbelos)	IMOK / JMO
David Knipe	(Cambridge)	IMOK
Gerry Leversha	(formerly St Paul's School)	IMOK
Aleksandar Lishkov	(Oxford)	IMOK
Nick Lord	(Tonbridge School)	IMOK
Sam Maltby	(Sheffield)	IMOK
Matthew Miller	(Sacred Heart High School, Newcastle)	JMO
Linda Moon	(Glasgow Academy)	IMOK
Philip Moon	(The High School of Glasgow)	IMOK
Joseph Myers	(CodeSourcery)	IMOK
Peter Neumann	(Queen's College, Oxford)	IMOK / JMO
Sylvia Neumann	(Oxford)	IMOK / JMO
Alexandra Neville	(North London Collegiate School)	IMOK
Stephen O'Hagan	(Hutchesons' Grammar School, Glasgow)	IMOK / JMO
Andy Parkinson	(Brockhill Park Performing Arts College)	IMOK
Jenny Perkins	(Torbridge High School, Plymouth)	IMOK
Steven Power	(St Swithuns School, Winchester)	IMOK / JMO
Jenny Ramsden	(High Wycombe)	IMOK
Christine Randall	(Southampton)	IMOK
Peter Ransom	(Southampton)	JMO
Lionel Richard	(Germany)	JMO / IMOK
Chris Robson	(ex Leeds University)	IMOK
Paul Russell	(Churchill College, Cambridge)	JMO
Jenni Sambrook	(Uckfield)	IMOK
John Slater	(Market Rasen)	IMOK / JMO
Alan Slomson	(University of Leeds)	JMO
Jon Stone	(St Paul's School, London)	IMOK
Karthik Tadinada	(St Paul's School, London)	IMOK
Ian VanderBurgh	(CEMC)	JMO
Alex Voice	(Westminster Abbey Choir School, London)	JMO
Paul Walter	(Highgate School, London)	IMOK
Jerome Watson	(Bedford School)	IMOK
David Webber	(University of Glasgow)	IMOK / JMO
Brian Wilson	(University of London)	IMOK
Rosie Wiltshire	(Wootton Bassett School)	JMO

Problems Groups

There are currently five groups. The first being the BMO Setting Committee.

Jeremy King	(Chair) (Tonbridge School)
Paul Jefferys	(ex Trinity College, Cambridge)
Gerry Leversha	(formerly St Paul's School)
Jack Shotton	(Imperial College, London)
Geoff Smith	(University of Bath)
Julian Gilbey	(London)

The other four groups have overlapping membership. There is one group for each and the chair is shown in []: the Senior Mathematical Challenge (S) [Howard Groves]; the Junior and Intermediate Mathematical Challenges (I&J) [Howard Groves]; the Junior Mathematical Olympiad (JMO) [Jo Harbour]; the IMOK Olympiad papers [Andrew Jobbings]. Those involved are listed below.

Steve Barge	(Sacred Heart Catholic College)	S
Dean Bunnell	(Queen Elizabeth GS, Wakefield)	S / IMOK / JMO
Kerry Burnham	(Torquay Boys' Grammar School)	I&J
James Cranch	(University of Sheffield)	IMOK
Karen Fogden	(Henry Box School, Witney)	S / I&J / JMO
Mary Teresa Fyfe	(Hutchesons' GS, Glasgow)	S / IMOK / JMO
Carol Gainlall	(Park House School, Newbury)	I&J
Tony Gardiner	(Birmingham)	I&J / IMOK / JMO
Nick Geere	(Kelly College)	S
Michael Griffiths	(Warrington)	S
Howard Groves	(ex RGS, Worcester)	S / I&J / IMOK / JMO
Jo Harbour	(Wolvercote Primary School)	JMO
Andrew Jobbings	(Arbelos, Shipley)	S / I&J / IMOK / JMO
Gerry Leversha	(formerly St Paul's School)	IMOK
Paul Murray	(Lord Williams School, Thame)	I&J / JMO
Steven O'Hagan	(Hutchesons' GS, Glasgow)	JMO
Andy Parkinson	(Beckfoot School, Bingley)	IMOK
Stephen Power	(St. Swithun's School, Winchester)	I&J
Peter Ransom	(Southampton)	I&J
Mary Read	(Haberdashers' Aske's Hatcham C.)	I&J / IMOK
Lionel Richard	(Hutchesons' GS, Glasgow)	S
Alan Slomson	(University of Leeds)	S / I&J
Alex Voice	(Westminster Abbey Choir School)	I&J / JMO

The Kangaroo Papers were assembled by David Crawford and Paul Murray and the Senior Kangaroo Paper came from Stephen Power and David Crawford.

It is appropriate at this stage to acknowledge and thank those who helped at various stages with the moderation and checking of these papers: Adam McBride, Peter Neumann, Stephen Power, Jenny Ramsden and Chris Robson.

TMC coordinators and regional helpers
[also involved in the writing (W) and checking (C) of materials where indicated]

Anne Andrews	Patricia Andrews	Beth Ashfield (C)
Ann Ault (W)	Martin Bailey	Anne Baker
Bridget Ballantyne	Andrew Bell	Elizabeth Bull
Dean Bunnell (W)	Kerry Burnham	Keith Cadman (W)
Madeleine Copin (C)	James Cranch	David Crawford (W)
Rosie Cretney	Alex Crews	Dusty de Sainte Croix (C)
Geoffrey Dolamore	Sue Essex (W)	Sally-Jane Fell
Sheldon Fernandes	Jackie Fox	Roy Fraser
Mary Teresa Fyfe	Helen Gauld	Peter Hall (W)
Karl Hayward-Bradley (W)	Terry Heard	Fraser Heywood (W)
Rita Holland	Sue Hughes	Sally Anne Huk
Pam Hunt	Andrina Inglis	Andrew Jobbings (W)
Nathan Keeling	Tricia Lunel	Pat Lyden
Matthew Miller	Hilary Monaghan	Steve Mulligan (C)
Helen Mumby	Paul Murray	Peter Neumann (W)
Pauline Noble	Andy Parkinson	Martin Perkins (C)
Dennis Pinshon	Vivian Pinto	Stephen Power
Jenny Ramsden (C)	Peter Ransom (W)	Syra Saddique
Nikki Shepherd	John Slater	Alan Slomson
Graeme Spurr	Anne Strong	Penny Thompson (W)
James Welham	Ian Wiltshire	Rosie Wiltshire
Anthea Wright		

Additional local helpers and contacts at TMC host venues

Anthony Alonzi	Morag Anderson	Emma Atkins	Sharon Austin
Ralph Barlow	Catherine Beater	David Bedford	Helena Benzinski
Rachel Blewett	Rhiannon Bourke	Duncan Bradshaw	Nigel Brookes
Paul Bruten	Helen Burton	Amanda Clayton	Nicki Cologne-Brookes
Kath Conway	Tom Copeland	Kevin Coxshall	Andy Crabtree
David Cranch	Elin Dupasquier	Ceri Fiddes	Nishma Gohil
Tracey Greenaway	Fiona Harding	Laura Harvey	Gary Higham
Adam Jones	Martin Kemp	Neil Maltman	Helen Martin
Lin McIntosh	Iain Mitchell	Marijke Molenaar	Heather Morgan
David Morrissey	Julie Mundy	Damian Murphy	Gareth O'Reilly
Paul Pearce	Colin Reid	John Rimmer	Lois Rollings
Ann Rush	Amanda Smallwood	Gerard Telfer	Paul Thomas
Aaron Treagus	Sam Twinam	Jo Walker	Liz Ward
Dave Widdowson	Jake Wright		

STMC coordinators and regional helpers
[also involved in the writing (W) and checking (C) of materials where indicated]

Anne Andrews	Pat Andrews	Ann Ault
Matthew Baker	Andrew Bell	Kerry Burnham (W)
Tony Cheslett (W)	Anthony Collieu (W)	James Cranch
David Crawford (W)	Alex Crews (C)	Laura Daniels
Beverley Detoeuf	Geoffrey Dolamore	Sue Essex
Karen Fogden (W)	Mary Teresa Fyfe	Helen Gauld
Andrew Ginty (W)	Peter Hall (W)	Mark Harwood (W)
Karl Hayward-Bradley	Terry Heard	Alexandra Hewitt (W)
Peter Holland	Sue Hughes	Pam Hunt
Magdelena Jasicova	Andrew Jobbings (W)	Nathan Keeling
John Lardner	Richard Lissaman	Pat Lyden
Jamie McLean	James Munro (W)	Peter Neumann
Charlie Oakley (W)	Martin Perkins (C)	Dennis Pinshon (W)
Stephen Power	Jenny Ramsden (C)	John Silvester (C)
John Slater	Alan Slomson	James Welham
Anthea Wright		

BMOS Mentoring Schemes
Vicky Neale (Director)

Junior Scheme Coordinator: John Slater (assisted by Julian Gilbey)

Intermediate Scheme Coordinator: Richard Atkins

Intermediate external mentors:

Alice Ahn	Sally Anne Bennett	Neill Cooper
Yi Feng	Vesna Kadelburg	Zoe Kelly
James Munro	David Phillips	Andrew Rogers
Ian Slater	Pavel Stroev	

Senior Scheme Coordinators: Andre Rzym (assisted by James Cranch)

Senior external mentors:

Anne Andrews	Benjamin Barrett	Natalie Behague
Don Berry	Sam Cappleman-Lynes	Andrea Chlebikova
Graham Cook	James Cranch	Konrad Dabrowski
Janet Dangerfield	Chris Ellingham	Robin Elliott
Ben Fairbairn	Mary Teresa Fyfe	James Gazet
Julian Gilbey	Ed Godfrey	Fraser Heywood
Ina Hughes	Michael Illing	Robert Lasenby

Jonathan Lee	Gerry Leversha	Daniel Low
Chris Luke	Freddie Manners	Gareth McCaugham
David Mestel	Vicky Neale	Peter Neumann
Samuel Porritt	Jerome Ripp	Julia Robson
Florence Salter	Peter Scott	Jack Shotton
Balazs Szendroi	Stephen Tate	Oliver Thomas
Philip Toothill	Paul Walter	Mark Wildon
Dorothy Winn	Dominic Yeo	Alison Zhu

Advanced Scheme Coordinators: Lex Betts, Ben Elliott, Richard Freeland

Advanced external mentors:

James Aaronson	Richard Freeland	Adam Goucher	Tim Hennock
Paul Jefferys	Henry Liu	Max Menzies	Jordan Millar
Joseph Myers	Craig Newbold	Preeyan Parmar	

Mathematical Circles

The following are those who assisted at these events:

Pat Andrews	Michael Broadwith	Katie Chicot	James Cranch
Julia Collins	Sue Cubbon	Geoff Curwen	Mark Fitzsimons
Nick Geere	E Hall	Sue Harris	Ina Hughes
Zoe Kelly	Gerry Leversha	Richard Lissaman	Peter Neumann
Steven O'Hagan	Peter Ransom	Lionel Richard	Alistair Rucklidge
John Slater	Mark Thornber	Pip Waugh	Mark Webber
A Wilson	Dominic Yeo	All staff at Hutchesons' School	

In Memoriam

Christopher Bradley died on July 11th. In our community he is well-known for his books written for UKMT, his role as deputy leader of the IMO team some time ago, and for the large number of problems which he created to support the British Mathematical Olympiad and international mathematics competitions.

Ben Elliott, a young man of exceptional talent, died on 21 September 2013, following complications associated with medical treatment. He represented the UK at the Balkan Mathematical Olympiad in Moldova (2010), the Romanian Master of Mathematics (2011) and the International Mathematical Olympiad in the Netherlands (2011). He was the top scorer at BMO2 in 2011, when he was a student at Godalming College. Since October 2011, he was reading mathematics at Trinity College, Cambridge, where he rapidly became an enthusiastic volunteer for Olympiad activities.

UKMT Publications

The books published by the UK Mathematics Trust are grouped into series.

The *YEARBOOKS* series documents all the UKMT activities, including details of all the challenge papers and solutions, lists of high scorers, accounts of the IMO and Olympiad training camps, and other information about the Trust's work during each year.

1. 2012-2013 Yearbook

This is our 15th Yearbook, having published one a year since 1998-1999. Edited by Bill Richardson, the Yearbook documents all the UKMT activities from that particular year. They include all the challenge papers and solutions at every level; list of high scorers; tales from the IMO and Olympiad training camps; details of the UKMT's other activities; and a round-up of global mathematical associations.

Previous Yearbooks are available to purchase. Please contact the UKMT for further details.

PAST PAPERS

1. *Ten Years of Mathematical Challenges 1997 to 2006*

Edited by Bill Richardson, this book was published to celebrate the tenth anniversary of the founding of UKMT. This 188-page book contains question papers and solutions for nine Senior Challenges, ten Intermediate Challenges, and ten Junior Challenges.

2. *Past Paper Booklets and electronic pdfs – Junior, Intermediate, Senior Challenges and follow-on rounds.*

We sell Junior, Intermediate and Senior past paper booklets and electronic pdfs. These contain the Mathematics Challenge question papers, solutions, and a summary chart of all the answers.

The JMO booklet contains four years' papers and solutions for the Junior Mathematical Olympiad, the follow up to the JMC.

The 2013 IMOK booklet contains the papers and solutions for the suite of Intermediate follow-on rounds – the Kangaroo Grey, the Kangaroo Pink, Cayley, Hamilton and Maclaurin. Electronic versions of the IMOK Olympiad rounds and the JMO are also available.

BMO booklets containing material for the British Mathematical Olympiad Round 1 or 2 are also available.

The *HANDBOOK* series is aimed particularly at students at secondary school who are interested in acquiring the knowledge and skills which are useful for tackling challenging problems, such as those posed in the competitions administered by the UKMT.

1. *Plane Euclidean Geometry: Theory and Problems*,
    AD Gardiner and CJ Bradley

An excellent book for students aged 15-18 and teachers who want to learn how to solve problems in elementary Euclidean geometry. The book follows the development of Euclid; contents include Pythagoras, trigonometry, circle theorems, and Ceva and Menelaus. The book contains hundreds of problems, many with hints and solutions.

2. *Introduction to Inequalities*, CJ Bradley

Introduction to Inequalities is a thoroughly revised and extended edition of a book which was initially published as part of the composite volume 'Introductions to Number Theory and Inequalities'. This accessible text aims to show students how to select and apply the correct sort of inequality to solve a given problem.

3. *A Mathematical Olympiad Primer*, Geoff C Smith

This UKMT publication provides an excellent guide for young mathematicians preparing for competitions such as the British Mathematical Olympiad. The book has recently been updated and extended and contains theory including algebra, combinatorics and geometry, and BMO1 problems and solutions from 1996 onwards.

4. *Introduction to Number Theory*, CJ Bradley

This book for students aged 15 upwards aims to show how to tackle the sort of problems on number theory which are set in mathematics competitions. Topics include primes and divisibility, congruence arithmetic and the representation of real numbers by decimals.

5. *A Problem Solver's Handbook*, Andrew Jobbings

This recently published book is an informal guide to Intermediate Olympiads, not only for potential candidates, but for anyone wishing to tackle more challenging problems. The discussions of sample questions aim to show how to attack a problem which may be quite unlike anything seen before.

The *EXCURSIONS IN MATHEMATICS* series consists of monographs which focus on a particular topic of interest and investigate it in some detail, using a wide range of ideas and techniques. They are aimed at high school students, undergraduates, and others who are prepared to pursue a subject in some depth, but do not require specialised knowledge.

1. *The Backbone of Pascal's Triangle*, Martin Griffiths

Everything covered in this book is connected to the sequence of numbers: 2, 6, 20, 70, 252, 924, 3432, ... Some readers might recognize this list straight away, while others will not have seen it before. Either way, students and teachers alike may well be astounded at both the variety and the depth of mathematical ideas that it can lead to.

2. *A Prime Puzzle*, Martin Griffiths

The prime numbers 2, 3, 5, 7, ... are the building blocks of our number system. Under certain conditions, any arithmetic progression of positive integers contains infinitely many primes, as proved by Gustave Dirichlet. This book seeks to provide a complete proof which is accessible to school students possessing post-16 mathematical knowledge. All the techniques needed are carefully developed and explained.

The *PATHWAYS* series aims to provide classroom teaching material for use in secondary school. Each title develops a subject in more depth and detail than is normally required by public examinations or national curricula.

1. *Crossing the Bridge*, Gerry Leversha

This book provides a course on geometry for use in the classroom, re-emphasising some traditional features of geometrical education. The bulk of the text is devoted to carefully constructed exercises for classroom discussion or individual study. It is suitable for students aged 13 and upwards.

2. *The Geometry of the Triangle*, Gerry Leversha

The basic geometry of the triangle is widely known, but readers of this book will find that there are many more delights to discover. The book is full of stimulating results and careful exposition, and thus forms a trustworthy guide. Recommended for ages 16+.

The *PROBLEMS* series consists of collections of high-quality and original problems of Olympiad standard.

1. *New Problems in Euclidean Geometry*, David Monk
This book should appeal to anyone aged 16+ who enjoys solving the kind of challenging and attractive geometry problems that have virtually vanished from the school curriculum, but which still play a central role in national and international mathematics competitions. It is a treasure trove of wonderful geometrical problems, with hints for their solutions.

The UKMT is the European agent for a large number of books published by the Art of Problem Solving (http://www.artofproblemsolving.com/). We also sell:

1. *The First 25 Years of the Superbrain*, Diarmuid Early & Des MacHale
This is an extraordinary collection of mathematical problems laced with some puzzles. This book will be of interest to those preparing for senior Olympiad examinations, to teachers of mathematics, and to all those who enjoy solving problems in mathematics.

2. *The Algebra of Geometry*, Christopher J Bradley
In the 19th century, the algebra of the plane was part of the armoury of every serious mathematician. In recent times the major fronts of research mathematics have moved elsewhere. However, those skills and methods are alive and well, and can be found in this book. The Algebra of Geometry deserves a place on the shelf of every enthusiast for Euclidean Geometry, amateur or professional, and is certainly valuable reading for students wishing to compete in senior Mathematical Olympiads. For age 16+ mathematicians.

To find out more about these publications and to order copies, please go to the UKMT website at www.publications.ukmt.org.uk.

In addition to the books above, UKMT continues to publish its termly Newsletter, giving the latest news from the Trust, mathematical articles, examples from Challenge papers and occasional posters for the classroom wall. This is sent free to all schools participating in the UKMT Maths Challenges.